The Complete Book of Cat Care

LEON F. WHITNEY, D.V.M.

The Complete Book

OTHER BOOKS BY LEON F. WHITNEY, D.V.M.

THE COMPLETE BOOK OF DOG CARE
THE COMPLETE BOOK OF HOME PET CARE
FEEDING OUR DOGS
HOW TO BREED DOGS
BLOODHOUNDS AND HOW TO TRAIN THEM
BASIS OF BREEDING

# of Cat Care

DOUBLEDAY & COMPANY, INC.

GARDEN CITY, NEW YORK

To Ida Mellen

Author's Note:

*I*N THIS BOOK I should like to propose a new word for our language—a single word which cat owners have long felt the need of, a word not in the dictionary as yet. The female animal of almost every species has a name. You don't have to say a female equine, you say mare. You say cow for female ox.

To designate the female cat, many rather silly words with human significance have been used: Queen, matron, maiden. However, when any one of them is used, it could designate a human being.

I propose the word *catta* for the female cat. We already have *tomcat* for the male, with an abbreviation of *tom*. *Catta* is the Latin word for the female of an unknown species of animal. Why not apply it to the cat? Why has some word not been used in our language long ago? I propose to use it throughout this book.

Author's Note

Contents

DIAGNOSTIC TABLE   13

Part One

1. **YOU AND YOUR CAT** What you should know about your cat. Your obligations as a cat owner. How to choose a house cat. How to choose a veterinarian.   19

2. **THE CAT'S BODY AND HOW IT FUNCTIONS** The body's covering. The body's framework. Circulatory system. Respiratory system. Excretory system. Digestive system. Glandular system and regulation of body functions. Nervous system and organs of perception. Reproductive system.   29

3. **WHAT YOU SHOULD KNOW ABOUT FOOD AND FEEDING** Food and skin disease. Water. Minerals. Proteins and amino acids. Carbohydrates. Fats and fatty acids. Laxation. Vitamins. How much to feed.   53

4. **DISEASES AND HOW YOUR CAT CATCHES THEM** Bacteria. Rickettsiae. Fungi. Viruses. Disease transmission. Immunity. Parasitic diseases, external and internal. Protozoa. Tumors and cancer. Deficiency diseases.   74

5. **DRUGS AND THEIR USES** General anesthetics and sedatives. Local anesthetics. Topical anesthetics. Painkillers. Stimulants. Diuretics. Heart stimulants. Secre-

tory gland depressants. Drugs acting on the organs of
reproduction. Drugs to kill internal parasites. Drugs
to kill external parasites. Drugs applied to the skin.
Skin disease remedies. Burn remedies. Drugs for cuts
and scratches. Liniments. Sulfa drugs. Antibiotics.
Emetics. Cathartics. Vaccines and serums.   96

Part Two

6. **WHAT YOU SHOULD KNOW ABOUT RESTRAINT
   AND FIRST AID** How to restrain a cat. Shock.
   Heat strokes. Accidents. Cuts. Bites. Foreign bodies.
   Drowning. Electric shock. Burns. Fits. Bruises.
   Broken bones. Poisoning. Household antidotes for
   common poisons. General advice in treating poison-
   ing.   125

7. **MINOR OPERATIONS AND HOME SURGERY** Restraint. Anesthesia. Wound cleaning. Tissue joining.
   Sutures. Stopping hemorrhage. Tying off vessels.
   Stretching arteries. Devices to prevent self-injury.
   Minor operations. Tapping. Growth removal. Castration. Spaying. Teeth extractions. Hernias. Fractures
   and dislocations.   139

8. **HOW TO GIVE MEDICINES AND APPLY ACCES-
   SORIES** Methods for giving medicine to animals.
   Liquids. Pills and capsules. Bandages and their uses.
   Using thermometers.   153

9. **PROBLEMS OF REPRODUCTION** Mating characteristics. Copulation. Sterility. Birth. Spaying. Castration. How to tell the sex of a cat.   159

10. **SANITATION AND HYGIENE** Coat care. Nails.
    Shedding. Bathing. Removal of road tar and paint.
    Animal odors. Parasite control. The mouth and teeth.
    The eyes. The ears. Collars and harnesses. Beds and
    bedding. Sanitary provisions for cats. Disinfectants.
    Periodic health examination.   170

11. **HEALTH   HAZARDS   IN   HOSPITALIZATION,
    BOARDING, AND SHOWS**   181

12. WHEN THE END COMES Life expectancy. Methods of euthanasia. Care of the remains. Post-mortems.   186

Part Three

13. CATS AND THEIR FOOD   191

14. BREEDING AND RAISING KITTENS How to diagnose pregnancy. The whelping bed. Birth of the kittens. Feeding.   197

15. GENERAL DISEASES OF CATS Virus diseases. Feline distemper. Rabies. Virus pneumonia. Bacterial diseases. Coryza. Leptospirosis. Tetanus. Tuberculosis. Bacterial pneumonia.   203

16. THE REPRODUCTIVE AND URINARY SYSTEMS Kidney disease. Bladder troubles. Urinary incontinence. Uterine infections. Neutering.   212

17. THE DIGESTIVE TRACT The mouth. Lips. Stomatitis. Diseases of the teeth and gums. The gullet. The stomach. Inflammation of the stomach. Hair balls. Foreign bodies in the stomach. Ulcers. The intestines. Diseases of the intestines. The liver. Leptospirosis. Bile duct obstruction. Poisons.   215

18. OTHER AILMENTS OF CATS Parasites. Roundworms. Hookworms. Whipworms. Tapeworms. Coccidiosis. Fleas. Lice. Ticks. Mange. Ear mites. Ailments affecting the nervous system. Convulsions. Hereditary anomalies. Nutritional deficiencies. Heart ailments. Enlargement. Heart infections. Respiratory ailments. Edema of the lungs. Emphysema. Pleurisy. Hydrothorax. Tumors. Eye ailments. Enlargement of the nictitating membrane. Corneal diseases. Inflammation of the eyeball. Glaucoma. Protruding eyes. Cross eyes. Eyelid maladies. Ear ailments. Skin ailments. Growths.   222

19. WHAT YOU CAN AND CANNOT CATCH FROM YOUR CAT   241

20. HEREDITY IN CATS Fallacies. Birthmarking. Prenatal influence. Telegony. Blooded inheritance. Germ plasm. Genes and chromosomes. What determines sex. Color classifications. Genetic symbols. Color inheritance. Inbreeding and line breeding. Selective breeding. 245

21. FIFTY QUESTIONS FREQUENTLY ASKED BY CAT OWNERS 261

ACKNOWLEDGMENTS 267

INDEX 269

Diagnostic Table

$\mathcal{T}$ HE following table is designed to help you use this book easily and well. It will make it possible for you to identify many of the common diseases of cats and it will tell you where to look for information about them.

If your cat is sick it will exhibit certain symptoms—probably several. These symptoms are shown in the table in boldface, and under each of them there is a list of diseases or conditions with which they are most commonly associated. You will find in the book a detailed discussion of the symptoms, causes, prevention, and treatment of each of these diseases.

Here is an example of the way the table should be used: You notice that your cat is excessively thirsty, seems to be bloated about the abdomen, and shows signs of a soft swelling in his legs. *Excessive thirst, abdominal enlargement,* and *swellings* are all shown in the table as symptoms. The diseases listed under each of these symptoms vary greatly, but *dropsy* appears under all of them. By reading the discussion of dropsy, you will be able to determine whether your cat has the disease and, if he has, what you can do about it.

This table is *not* a cure-all chart. It will *not* make you a veterinarian. It *will* help you to recognize the signs of disease in your cat and show you where to get the information you need in order to decide whether you can treat the condition yourself or whether your pet needs expert veterinary attention.

ABDOMINAL ENLARGEMENT

Anemia (in young)
Bladder ailments
Bloat
Dropsy
Excessive thirst
Fat
Metritis
Organ enlargement
    (spleen, liver)
Overfeeding
Parasites (in young)
Pregnancy
Tumors

ABDOMINAL TENDERNESS

Colon impaction
Enteritis
Foreign bodies
Intussusception
Peritonitis
Poisoning
Porcupine quills
Stomach inflammation
Tumors
Ulcers

ANEMIA (Pale gums)

Hemorrhage
Iron deficiency
Lice
Parasites
Piroplasmosis
Poisoning
Tumors

APPETITE
Difficulty in Eating

Foreign bodies in mouth
    or throat
Insect stings
Lead poisoning
Mouth ailments
Teeth loose
Tongue injuries
Tumors in mouth
Ulcers

Loss of Appetite

Change of diet
Overfeeding

Parasites
Poisoning
Toxins
Tumors

Ravenous Appetite

Diabetes insipidus
Diabetes mellitus
Heat, onset of
Lactation
Pregnancy
Undernourishment

BLINDNESS

Cataract
Cornea, opacity of
Eye ailments
Glaucoma
Vitamins

BREATH BAD

Cancer
Constipation
Foreign bodies in or on
    teeth
Gum diseases
Kidney disease
Lip ailments
Poisoning, caustic or acid
Tartar
Teeth
Tongue injuries
Ulcers in mouth

BREATHING ABNORMAL
(Loss of breath from exertion)

Anemia
Emphysema
Heart ailments
Hernia of diaphragm
Hydrothorax
Pleurisy
Pneumonia

CONVULSIONS

Calcium-arsenate poison-
    ing
Diabetes mellitus
Eclampsia
Encephalitis

Foreign bodies in stom-
    ach
Strychnine poisoning
Uremia
Worms

COUGHING

Bronchitis
Distemper
Emphysema
Laryngitis
Pharyngitis
Pleurisy
Pneumonia
Worms

DIARRHEA

Enteritis
Exercise
Fiber, excessive
Parasites
Poisoning
Skim milk

DIZZINESS

Accidents
Cerebral hemorrhage
Ear canker
Ear mites
Middle-ear infection

EMACIATION

Diabetes
Diarrhea
Kidney disease
Liver disease
Tuberculosis
Tumors
Undernourishment

GAGGING

Foreign body in throat
Tonsillitis
Worms

HEAD SHAKING

Canker in ear
Ear, ailments of
Ear flap torn
Ear mites
Fleas
Hematoma in ear flap

Lice
Middle-ear infection

HOARSENESS

Asthma
Foreign body in throat
Injuries to throat
Laryngitis
Paralysis
Throat ailments

LUMPS

Abscesses
Bone tumors
Dropsy
Goiter
Hematoma
Hernia, inguinal
Leukemia
Salivary fistula
Tumors

MOANING OR CRYING

Anal-gland abscess
Constipation
Ear ailments
Encephalitis
Fleas
Foreign bodies
Poisoning
Skin disease
Tooth abscess

NOSE, RUNNING

Distemper
Nasal discharge
Nasal tumors
Pneumonia

PARALYSIS

Back broken or injured
Chastek paralysis
Rabies
Stroke
Toxins

SHEDDING, ABNORMAL

Burns
Diabetes insipidus
Mange
Periodic shedding
Skin diseases

SHIVERING, TREMBLING

Cold
Eclampsia
Poisoning
  Caffeine
  Calcium arsenate
  Food
  Nicotine
  Strychnine
  Theobromine

SKIN AILMENTS

Acne
Alopecia
Burns
Dandruff
Fleas
Mange
  Demodectic
  Notodectic
  Sarcoptic

SLOBBERING

Convulsions
Encephalitis
Foreign bodies in mouth
Insect stings
Lip ailments
Poison
Teeth loose or broken
Tongue injuries

SNEEZING, SNORTING

Coryza
Distemper
Nose, ailments of
Pneumonia
Tumors

SWELLINGS THAT LEAVE PITS WHEN SQUEEZED

Dropsy
Edema
Heart ailments
Insect stings
Kidney diseases
Snake bites

THIRST, EXCESSIVE

Diabetes, incipient or
  sugar
Dropsy
Food too dry
Food too salty
Kidney disease

URINARY TROUBLES

Cloudy urine: bladder
Excessive urine: kidney
  disease, diabetes
Inability to urinate: blad-
  der, urethra
Leaks (urinary inconti-
  nence): kidney disease,
  diabetes
Odor evil: bladder, blood,
  kidney
Over-yellow: jaundice
Sand in urine: bladder

VOMITING

Foreign body in stomach
Hair in stomach
Hernia, strangulated
Intussusception
Kidney disease
Parasites in stomach
Peritonitis
Poisoning
Tapeworms
Tumors, brain or other
Urinary ailments

YELLOWING TISSUE

Jaundice
Liver ailments
Poisoning

The Complete Book of Cat Care

Part One

1. You and Your Cat

*Y*EARS AGO, when I began veterinary practice, I often wondered why it was that some people seemed to get so much more pleasure than others out of owning and handling cats. As I talked with them, listened to their problems, and tried to answer their questions, it seemed to me that the difference lay largely in their general attitude toward animals, in their understanding of the nature of their cats and their relationships with them. All of these things were important factors in the choice of their cats, in the way they handled them, and in the care they were able to give them. Having worked with thousands of cat owners, I am now more than ever convinced that a proper understanding of the nature of animals is the first and greatest need of most cat owners.

WHAT YOU SHOULD KNOW ABOUT YOUR CAT

The capacity to feel love for animals is a gift—to many people a gift as rewarding as any we have. There are those unfortunates—comparatively few, I think—who lack the ability to feel affection for animals just as surely as there are those who cannot distinguish red from green. They will never understand the pleasure and the gratification which every cat owner experiences, for the love of animals can never be truly taught. But most people—even those who have never owned a cat—do not have the sympathy and warmth and patience that it takes to get the most enjoyment from the care of a cat. What they lack more than anything else, I think, is a realistic conception of what they are to the cat and what their cat should be to them.

Just as so many humans feel the need of some higher power or individual and look to it or to him for support or guidance, so your cats look to you, their provider, for their support. To them you are a god, you are Providence.

If you are to get the most fun out of owning a cat, perhaps nothing is more important than that you learn to accept your cat for what it is, to cultivate the proper attitude of mind toward it. A dog is a dog; a cat, a cat; a pigeon, a pigeon; and a fish, a fish. Glorifying your cat in your own mind, thinking of it or treating it as a human being, is a basic source of many of the difficulties some people encounter in cat owning. You must learn to refrain from the natural tendency of projecting yourself into the cat. It is poor logic; it will make your cat unhappy and you dissatisfied.

Here is an example of what I mean. A woman I once knew had an outdoor frog pond. In it she had frogs and turtles. Every winter she spent a great deal of time feeling sorry for the frogs hibernating down in the cold. I have known others who think it cruel to leave pet raccoons in outdoor pens in the winter; instead they bring them into the cellars of their houses. Still others go out into the woods to feed animals and birds so that they will not have to prey on each other. They simply cannot accept the way of nature. They cannot believe what Charles Darwin said: "The war of nature is not incessant, no fear is felt, death is generally prompt, and the happy and the healthy survive and multiply."

Not all cat owners are as misguided as these people. Some recognize these natural processes and are not foolishly disturbed because nature seems to them needlessly cruel when judged by human standards. They realize that each species of animal has gradually adapted itself to its particular environment through a series of hereditary changes which have enabled it to live happily and without suffering. They do not feel sorry for the frog hibernating down in the mud. They understand that for a raccoon it is perfectly right to eat like a glutton because of some drive he cannot resist and then den up and become quiescent in a deep sleep for several months. He has been provided with wonderful equipment to protect him against intense cold and has stored so much food in the form of fat on his body that he semihibernates most happily indeed. The animal lover who is aware of this is more likely to be envious of the animal which has so perfectly adapted itself to its environment than to be unduly concerned about its welfare.

Though most people are willing to accept the laws of nature as they apply to wild animals, some of them are still reluctant to extend the same reasoning to the animals they keep as intimate pets. In principle, there is no difference. You should always try first to understand the nature of the species you are interested in, not just that of a particular animal. A pet's background in nature is still our most reliable guide to proper care. We learn our best lessons, particularly about food and feeding, from nature, and we would all be much better providers if we could bring ourselves to rely more on such guidance.

Take feeding, for example. Because we have learned to enjoy a great variety in food, we are inclined to project our tastes on pets. A horse will quite contentedly eat hay, oats, and a little salt for a whole lifetime. Wild dogs can live by eating what appears to be a single item, animal bodies. Even today, when cats become wild, they exist primarily on rodents. From a study of the natural habits of animals we can and should learn a great deal about the kind of food that is best for them. It would, of course, be foolish to suggest that we slavishly follow the natural diet of animals. Cats will thrive on mixed diets all their lives—boiled kidneys, oatmeal and milk, fish—and on almost as great a variety of foods as dogs. No one with any sense at all would ever spend his time catching rodents for his cat, but he might well spend a little time considering that the rodent which the wild cat eats is full of vegetable matter which the cat devours. Do we always see to it that household cats have vegetable matter in their diets? Not the person who feeds them only boiled kidneys day after day. The principle applies equally to all species.

YOUR OBLIGATIONS AS A CAT OWNER

The obligations of cat owning are few, but you must fulfill them. All that the animal asks of you is *food, water, comfort, exercise, health,* and *protection.* If you can't fulfill these simple requirements, it would be better for you not to have cats, for they will only be a burden.

One of the first requirements implicit in the list is that you know the kind of cat that is best for you. You should know enough about the species you select—and about your own needs—so that it will never become a liability. You should never obligate yourself to care for a pet that demands more attention than you can freely give it.

It is difficult to believe that thousands of human beings have been enslaved by pet ownership—by white mice, by goldfish, by parrots, by cats. In addition to the people who have foolishly allowed themselves to become merely servants to their pets, there are those who are convinced that it is impossible to keep a pet without being prepared to spend most of their time in looking after it. One man believes, quite wrongly, that he can't indulge his desire for tropical fishes because they must be fed five times a day. Others believe that dogs and cats require elaborately prepared meals, which in 99 per cent of the cases is entirely unnecessary.

It is true, however, that some cats require more attention than others; that some breeds, in fact, are more difficult to care for than other members of the species. In choosing a cat you will be wise to get one of a breed which from long years of selection is best adapted to the purpose for which you want it. If you need a cat for a ratter, get a short-haired ordinary cat or a Maine coon cat, not a fancy, long-haired, ornamental variety. If you want a beautiful, ornamental creature to decorate your living room, and if you have time and patience to care for it as it deserves and demands, buy a lovely Persian or long-haired cat. But be sure to buy one from parents with dispositions which allow their owner to comb them. I see many long-haired cats which are such spitfires that no one can comb them properly. They must be anesthetized occasionally to be cared for. Their owners may even consider them "cute," but such cats should never be bred to perpetuate such temperaments. You should inquire to be as sure as you can be that the long-haired litter comes from particularly docile parents.

Veterinarians often have people bring cats to them with their coats solidly matted and fleas having a regular Old Home Week beneath the mat's protection. No one could possibly comb them. The owners lament, "Oh, why didn't somebody tell me what he would be like when he grew up!" A cat allowed to get in such a condition is a medical problem and a nuisance to the owner as well. When the cat has been clipped all over, deflead, and the owner made to understand that from then on he must spend some time on the cat's grooming, he is likely to say, "But that's so expensive!" The owner should have known before he bought the cat that one with a shorter nap is cheaper to keep.

Beyond the few simple obligations which a cat owner assumes, there are a few things he learns to avoid. He soon finds that it doesn't pay to let his cats roam any more than he can help. It costs less to feed a cat on neighbor's garbage—but not for long does it cost less. Sooner or later the animal gets some tainted swill, sickens, and perhaps dies. Animals that are turned loose are in constant danger of being injured in accidents or hurt in fights.

HOW TO CHOOSE A HOUSE CAT

Every day several hundred, or perhaps a thousand, persons acquire a new cat. This must be so, since there are somewhere between 20,000,000 and 50,000,000 cats in America which live anywhere from one day to twenty years. If you are considering the acquisition of a kitten or grown cat I would like to help you make a choice which will be satisfactory after your kitten is grown. Every kitten is entrancing when it is tiny, but that animate fluff ball can and does change. My strong recommendation is that you regard the appearance of the kitten in the light of what that kitten will grow into. Once the choice has been made, your generous nature will make it impossible for you to dispose of an unfortunate selection and obtain the cat of your dreams. Therefore, choose wisely.

Here are some of the facts I have learned about the more popular breeds—points to be considered in deciding upon the most nearly perfect cat for your requirements. Knowing these facts, you can decide on the best breed.

If you obtain a cat magazine, remember that cat fanciers have special names for each of the colors, coat characteristics, sexes, and so forth. For example, a female cat which has had kittens is a *queen*.

The Domestic Short-Haired Cat. (You may know it by the name of alley, barn, common, or just plain *cat*.) Fanciers consider it a definite breed, but when you see all the variations of size, form, color, and temperament, it becomes evident that just about any combinations of cat characteristics are included. I have seen full-grown cats which weigh four pounds and others which weigh fifteen. They can have huge ears, tiny ears, long tails, short tails, bushy tails, or no tails at all.

There are a few breeders who specialize in distinct types. Cat show catalogues list Blue-eyed Whites, Silver Tabbies, Smokes, Blacks, Red Tabbies, and Tortoiseshells. Whether a show-type Domestic Short Hair will delight you more than a kitten from the grocer's cat depends on your special desires. The show cats are bred for sleek coats, distinct marking, and carriage, and are indeed lovely creatures, but, as a famous cat authority once remarked to me, "There are hundreds of cats who never saw a show which could win over the best now being shown."

There is no need to choose a Domestic Short Hair on the basis of any standards, but I do suggest that, if possible, you see the parents. You can expect the kitten to become more or less like them. If they satisfy you, your choice is simple.

The show standard calls for a powerfully built cobby animal with large eyes and a short face and nose. They are much like the long-haired cat to be described later, and of the same colors.

Your color choice is wide, but you will notice that aside from all-white cats, there is only one type among those in any breed standard which shows white—the tortoise and white. At cat shows you never see black and white, blue and white, or tabby and white cats. Yet some of the most beautiful common cats I know are liberally marked with white.

Among the short-haired cats the two which have been set apart as distinct and well-known breeds are the Siamese (and Burmese) and Manx. The Abyssinian and Russian Blue constitute two rare short-haired breeds in America.

The Siamese Cat.   This cat is a lovely, lithe, agile, svelte, pantherlike, fawn-colored feline, with blue and seal points. Although you may have seen large, powerful Siamese cats, the show Siamese is a small, dainty, sleek, long-bodied creature. The head presents a pointed or wedge-shaped effect because of the rather large ears and the face tapering to a point at the nose. The slant eyes are often slightly crossed. The show standard permits cross eyes, but contrary to much popular opinion, does not require it, nor does it require a kink near the end of the tail. A good Siamese is intelligent, affectionate, aristocratic.

No breed has the unique voice changes of the Siamese, and few—if any —such loud voices. One tone, disliked by some people, is eerie. About the only criticism of the breed I have ever heard concerns this quality of voice.

Kittens are born nearly white in color with dark-shaded tails, ears, facial masks, and feet. The body color gradually darkens as they grow older. Their greatest beauty—the contrast of dark points and fawn body—comes around nine months of age.

The Burmese Cat.   This breed is much like the Siamese but the body, instead of being a mauve shade, is nearer chocolate in color. Burmese is distinct from its cousin, as you will see in Chapter 20 when we look into the inheritance. The show standard calls for a coat of a seal-brown color. This does not produce the same lovely contrast of dark points against a light body as in the case of the Siamese. The darker points are much less conspicuous in the Burmese. They have yellow eyes in contrast to the blue of the Siamese.

The Russian Blue Cat. A rather average-looking short-haired cat of dilute black color. A color which is usually called "Maltese" in America.

The Abyssinian Cat. This is also a short-haired breed and is characterized chiefly by its color—tabby with narrow pencil stripes. The feet are black and the black hair extends conspicuously up the back of the hind legs. The body hairs are banded as in all tabbies. The Abyssinians have a considerable amount of orange hair which gives them a brownish cast over their slender bodies. Some are pepper-and-salt-colored without tabby stripes.

Their heads are long and pointed, their ears sharp, and the tail is long and tapering.

The Manx Cat. A pure Manx is short-bodied, has a rounded rump and long hind legs, and moves with an almost rabbitlike hopping gait. A genuine Manx does not have a tail. A distinct depression can be felt where the tail—if the cat had one—would normally join with the spine. (Caution: a cat with no tail is not necessarily a Manx. Many a litter of long-tailed kittens is "manxed" by unscrupulous persons and sold as the real thing.) Manx cats have large heads with pointed noses. The coat does not lie flat like that of the Siamese, but has a warm thick feeling which is produced by medium-length guard hairs and a dense fine undercoat. You can find almost any color of Manx except white-spotted.

The Long-Haired Cat. At one time cat shows registered two distinct breeds of long-haired cats—Persian and Angora. Today we find only one breed—the Long Hair—divided into sixty-two classes (according to a recent cat show catalogue), based on color and sex. You will find them in any color you wish: blue-eyed white, orange-eyed white, odd-eyed white, silver, blue, smoke, cream, black, red, tabby, and tortoiseshell. The variety is as wide as in the domestic cat.

In form the Long Hairs hew closely to a single standard, with the exception of the Peke-faced group. These are cats whose faces are so retrorse, or "pushed in," that they resemble a Pekingese dog.

The Long Hairs are more inclined towards a lazy disposition and a carefree life than the Domestic. This is probably the result of so many generations of being bred primarily for beauty. They drape over furniture and add a touch of luxury to any room. Their soft woolly coat with dense undercoat requires frequent deep combing. Anyone who dislikes giving painstaking care to a pet should not choose a Long Hair. They are very impractical for farm life since the coat picks up burrs and mats easily. During the shedding season the Long Hair may also become sick from accumulation of hair in the stomach.

There are definite seasons when these lovely creatures are at their best. If you chance to buy a kitten when the mother is out of coat, you cannot judge her fairly because the mother may lack the finesse her new coat will give her. In such a case the breeder can show you photographs of the mother that will show you what you can expect from the kitten.

The Maine Coon Cat.   These long-haired cats of unusual beauty generally have the temperament of the Domestic. The animal got its name from the mistaken belief that it was half raccoon and half cat. It differs from the show type of Long Hair in having far less undercoat, although it has enough to enable it to withstand cold weather. It makes an excellent ratter, is less inclined to a matted coat, and is unusually well-equipped to fend for itself. Many are among the most beautiful cats I have ever seen. Coon cats come in all colors and in combinations with white. Usually they have less ruff about the neck, and generally the tail is long and bushy. Few persons breed them but many Maine farms have a number to hold the rodent population in check. No one shows them at cat shows but they are wonderful cats just the same.

The Hairless Cat.   This cat is not hairless in the same way as the Mexican hairless dog, but it is hairless none the less. One strain which breeds true is a Siamese hairless. In some no hair ever develops; in others there is a downy fuzz which comes and goes with seasonal changes.

In Mexico a different hairless cat was bred which experts believe came from an Uruguayan ancestor. Some of the Mexican cats of this strain were partially hairless and others were entirely bald.

Surely no one today would want such illy protected felines as human companions, yet someone must have wanted them enough to have continued their propagation.

Where does one go to buy a fancy cat of a particular type? A trip to the cat show will bring you in contact with breeders. A telephone call to the local veterinarian may help you. A glance through one of the several cat or pet magazines will show you what is being offered. Nobody need have trouble in locating a Domestic unless his requirements are unusually specific—just put out the word that you want one and you will soon be turning them away.

HOW TO CHOOSE A VETERINARIAN

The failure to understand the simple processes of life, such as healing, bone knitting, and body functions, is to blame, I think, for those myriads of people who—possibly because of the habit acquired in taking their cars to a mechanic and ordering a new transmission or universal joint—take a cat to the veterinarian and say, "Kidneys out of order, Doc, fix her up." Or, "He's got kind of wobbly in the back end, sort of paralyzed. He's the only cat we have. We don't want anything to happen to him. Fix him up. When'll we call for him?"

A body just isn't like an automobile. You don't replace parts by taking something out and putting something else back. You remove causes and supply adequate nutrition; you may remove growths, but you must wait for the body itself to do the regenerating. Though it may disturb you to think of it, physiologically a cat is no different from Grandpa. You don't take *him* to the hospital and leave him with the admonition, "Fix him up, Doc. He's the only grandpa we have and we don't want anything to happen to him."

People are inclined to expect either too little or too much of their veterinarian. Perhaps they have been misled in part by seeing too many movies in which the "vet" is depicted as a dirty, mussed, careless drunk, with a large cigar in his mouth, spilling ashes over his patient. This old gent is perfectly content to sleep in the bedding beside a sick horse, and his boon companion is always Dickie, the stableboy.

Most people today know, I think, that veterinarians neither look nor act like this caricature. They are men who have spent a good many years of their lives in rigorous study in order to be able to help you and your cat as well as all other animals kept by us human beings. Their skills and their abilities are of the utmost importance to the welfare of your cat and to your own comfort and enjoyment. It is well worth spending some little time and thought in selecting the one who can best help you with your problems.

What is the most important factor in your choice of a veterinarian? What makes you select one man, and only one, to take care of the health of your cat? It is *confidence*.

Before you place your confidence in a veterinarian the main thing you want to decide is: How much does he know? In addition it is often wise to inquire into how he got that information, because what a person appears to know is not always the truth. When the veterinarian talks about a "slight cold in the kidneys" or a "cold in the intestine," when he advises cutting a cat's skin in order to eradicate mange, or tells you to change the diet when the cat starts to itch, or operates to remove the cat's tonsils when it has a cough, an occasional client may be deeply impressed. Conscientious and up-to-date veterinarians are ashamed that members of their profession can be so ill-informed or unscrupulous.

When a client visits two veterinarians and is given two diametrically opposite diets for her cat, how is the client to know which man to trust? In the first place she should try to decide which of the two is a conscientious student. That man is the one to trust. Why? Because much education is thirty years behind the times. What veterinarians were taught in college is sometimes almost the sum total of what they know about veterinary **medicine** today *unless they have studied diligently since they left school.*

What a man knows about the discoveries which have been made in recent years is the difference between a horse doctor of thirty years ago and a competent, modern veterinarian. Assuming that you know two men of equal educational background, one of whom has studied diligently since he finished his course while the other has not, you will have no difficulty in knowing where you can safely place your confidence. After you have read this book you will be able to tell without question whether or not your veterinarian talks in contemporary veterinary medical terms.

There are certain indications which you will look for immediately in choosing a veterinarian. You cannot fail to notice the cleanliness and efficiency of his office or of his hospital. You will probably see on his walls his credentials, which must include study at an accredited college of veterinary medicine and a state license to practice.

But the cat owner is looking for something more. She wants to know that her doctor lives up to the ethics of his profession. She will consult the man who is guided by the code of ethics of the American Veterinary Medical Association. Here are my ideas of what that kind of veterinarian should be.

He should be completely honest. There are many opportunities to dodge around the truth. The ethical veterinarian will avoid them conscientiously. He will not give unnecessary injections at exorbitant prices, using five cents' worth of vitamin concentrates. He will not exaggerate the seriousness of an illness. He will try to effect a cure in a single visit. Not only does he do what he can for the patient in his office, but he respects the owner by instructing her in the care of the patient. If repeated visits to the office will give you added confidence, that is a matter for you to decide. The wise veterinarian, however, knows that the pet which costs the owner too much is a burden rather than a pleasure.

The ethical veterinarian charges moderate fees. There are, unfortunately, a few who callously feel that "it's not unethical to charge all the traffic will bear." It is. To be ethical, the veterinarian should consider all the factors involved. If a bill must be too large for the value of the animal, or if it is beyond the owner's ability to pay without hardship, that person should be advised that the very purpose of owning a cat—namely, to have something to enjoy—is gone. Veterinarians who overcharge do infinite damage to their profession by reducing the number of cat owners.

The ethical veterinarian is democratic. He does not exclude from his attention the laborer in work clothes, or the man or woman with a dark skin. Yet there are doctors who do exclude the poor, the laboring man, and the colored man. They should be reminded that when a cat needs care, *it* is the patient, not the owner.

The ethical man thinks first of the service he may render. He does not ask to be paid before treating his patient. Prepayment is not only unethical, it is unprofessional as well. Money is not and cannot be the veterinarian's first consideration.

The modern veterinarian shares his discoveries freely with the members of his profession. Through the presentation of studies at association meetings and in the proper veterinary journals, he makes his observations available to others so that they can be used to relieve suffering.

Finally, the ethical veterinarian does not advertise. Neon signs are frowned upon as are blatant window advertisements. Claims of unusual ability to effect cures by secret methods are not used. The veterinarian does not allow his picture to be displayed in undignified ways. He does not issue circulars advertising his low fees. However, if he operates a hospital on a standard fee basis, he may upon request give you a card stating those fees.

The man in whom you can place your confidence may not wear all these qualifications like shining armor. They represent an ideal, but more and more the conscientious veterinarian is approaching this ideal. The veterinary profession today is distinguished by many truly magnificent characters—men who have the most unselfish attitudes, who sacrifice themselves for their patients just as willingly and unstintingly as ever the family physician gave of his strength and knowledge. That should not be surprising to anyone. A veterinarian must of necessity love animals, and the man who truly loves animals must also love his fellow man.

2. The Cat's Body and How It Functions

So MANY high-school and college graduates have managed to escape courses in even human physiology and anatomy that I have long ceased to be surprised that few cat owners have any conception at all of animal physiology. If you are to get the most out of this book, it will be necessary to review briefly both structure and function as they are related to our pets. Even though the study of the mechanism of the living body is to me one of the most fascinating in the world, the general attitude toward the subject is such that I feel I must warn you that you are not in for an "organ recital." All that will be necessary here is to learn enough about your cats' bodies so that you may treat them sensibly.

The science which treats of the functions of living things or of their parts is called physiology. That which treats of the structure of the body and the relationships of its parts is called anatomy. Let us combine the two and see how the body is formed and how its parts function.

The body of every animal grew from a single cell. What is a cell? It is a unit of life smaller than our eyes can see. The whole body of some tiny animals is a single cell: the amoeba and paramecium, for example. Other animals consist of whole colonies of cells. All the visible animate creatures we see are immense colonies of cells, and each cell has some special function. Every one of these cells is composed of a covering within which is some protoplasm, a substance not unlike egg white, and a nucleus, which is its business part.

The first cell, which resulted from the uniting of a male cell (sperm) and a female cell (ovum), and thus started an animal, is complete in every detail. It is a favorite academic paradox to say that a cell multiplies by dividing, and quite true, of course. If one cell divides into two cells, it has divided, but because it is two, it has multiplied. The two become four; the four, eight. As they go on dividing and thus increasing, different cells become specialized at certain stages. Some may become skin, some liver, some heart, some germ plasm, some tonsils, and so forth. There are cells which never renew themselves; brain cells, for example. Then there are other very much specialized cells, like those in the hair and nails, which constantly renew themselves. They all live together in a happy community or colony, doing their work unless hindered by improper nourishment or crowding (from overfatness), or disease. That's what our cats are—big colonies of cells.

THE BODY'S COVERING

The skin is composed of several layers, each made up of innumerable cells. Two main layers are recognized: the outer layer, *epidermis;* the lower layer or true skin, the *dermis.* Sometimes we hear the epidermis called the cuticle or the scarfskin and, colloquially, the scurfskin. The true skin, in turn, consists of two layers. The skin is constantly shedding and renewing itself, a fact that has an important bearing on the treatment of skin diseases.

Under the skin we find subcutaneous connective tissue, an interesting

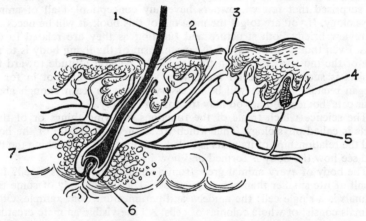

(*1*) *Hair growing out of follicle.* (*2*) *Erector muscle.* (*3*) *Sweat duct.* (*4*) *Nerve end organ.* (*5*) *Blood vessels.* (*6*)*Bottom of hair follicle or papilla.* (*7*) *Subcutaneous fatty tissue.*

part of the body. It is made up of very elastic cells. Through it run nerves, lymph vessels, blood vessels, and fat is often deposited in it.

Out of the skin grow the appendages we call hairs in mammals. Even the finest fuzz is composed of myriads of thin hairs each having the same general construction of the coarser. Hair grows out of the skin from follicles. In the follicles (sacs or sheaths) are little muscles which, for example, cause a cat's hair to stand on end.

In some places on the bodies of pets sweat glands are found, and everywhere in some pets there are sebaceous glands which usually discharge their waxy secretion into the follicles. As the hair grows, it comes out coated with this sebum, a substance with an acrid smell, which, in dogs, partly accounts for the doggy odor. In cats the amount is so small that the coat is never gummy nor does it have any obnoxious odor. This helps to make cats the desirable pets they are. Other glands secrete oil, which helps the cat to shed water.

These protective coats, plus its natural resistance to water, make the skin waterproof. It is not, however, resistant to all oils, some of which can soak through it. In fact, the skin can absorb a good many drugs and substances which can be toxic (poisonous) to the pet.

In addition to its function as a protective covering, skin is also an organ of touch. Some parts are extremely sensitive. Through it, too, the pet responds to variations in heat and cold outside.

The skin heals by growing outward from the lower layers if it is not wholly destroyed by a gash, scald, or other injury. (Blisters usually are pockets of fluid between layers of skin.) When all the layers are destroyed, growth occurs from the sides. It is for this reason that your veterinarian, in case of injury to your cat, will want to bring the sides of the destroyed area as closely together as possible, so that the space to be covered over will be as narrow as he can make it. Moreover, if left open, the newly generated skin will be devoid of glands and hair. Great scalded areas become covered with skin, but not skin with the usual accessories.

THE BODY'S FRAMEWORK

The Skeleton. The skeleton is the framework of the body and protection for the organs. The ribs cover the lungs, heart, liver, stomach and kidneys, pancreas; the skull covers the brain and such delicate organs as the hearing mechanism and the organs of scent. These services which bones perform are not always fully appreciated, because we think of them primarily in their role of support.

Each species differs from the next in form; breeds within species differ from other breeds, and individuals vary in some respects. The skeleton on which the soft tissue of the body hangs is the basic cause of these form differences. In some animals, for example, the mere absence of certain bones can cause a startling difference in appearance—compare the normal long-tailed cat with the Manx whose lack of tail is one of its breed's characteristics.

Some bones are solid, others hollow or filled with marrow in which red blood cells may be generated. Some are mere beads and others long and strong. The way they are joined is an interesting study in itself. There are ball-and-socket joints (hips), hinge joints (knees), others made by one bone abutting another with a cushion between (vertebrae), and modifications of all three kinds. Some animals are more agile than others; some have difficulty turning around in a short radius, while others, because of their skeletal construction, can "turn on a dime."

The skeleton is a marvelous framework, replete with strength where strength is needed, rigidity where rigidity is needed, flexibility, swivels, and hinges where stretching, bending, and rotating are required.

Each long bone is made up of a shaft of hard, brittle material with a soft center of marrow and ends of spongy material with a covering of dense, hard bone. Around the whole is a sort of skin called the *periosteum*. On top or on the bottom of the spongy end—if the bone terminates at a joint—is a springy, cartilaginous pad, called the *epiphyseal cartilage*, which takes the shocks. All through the bone small spaces form tunnels which carry blood and nerves; nourishment is also furnished by the periosteum.

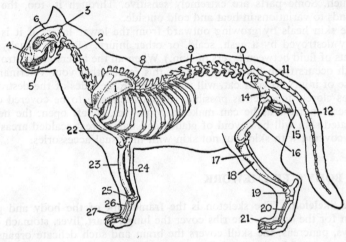

Skeleton of a cat. (*1*) *Shoulder blade.* (*2*) *Neck vertebra.* (*3*) *Occiput.* (*4*) *Nasal bone.* (*5*) *Mandible.* (*6*) *Cranium.* (*7*) *Ribs.* (*8*) *Cervical vertebra.* (*9*) *Lumbar vertebra.* (*10*) *Lumbar vertebra.* (*11*) *Sacrum.* (*12*) *Tail vertebra.* (*13*) *Ilium.* (*14*) *Ischium.* (*15*) *Pubis.* (*16*) *Femur.* (*17*) *Fibula.* (*18*) *Tibia.* (*19*) *Tarsus.* (*20*) *Metatarsus.* (*21*) *Rear toes.* (*22*) *Humerus.* (*23*) *Radius.* (*24*) *Ulna.* (*25*) *Carpus.* (*26*) *Metacarpus.* (*27*) *Front toes.*

Some bones are flat; ribs, head bones, and shoulder blades are examples. They are not so solid as they seem, but are well fortified with nourishment. The ribs join at the lower extremities with cartilages. These look like true ribs but are only extensions upward from a flat "bone"—the *sternum* or breastbone—to which all but one or two of the last ribs in some species are joined. The sternum is not actually a bone, but is composed of cartilage of a springy, tough nature, which is fortunate as the breastbone needs to be flexible, considering all the strains it undergoes

At the points where ribs and these cartilaginous extensions of the breastbone meet, one sometimes finds enlargements which may stay throughout life. These enlargements are an indication of rickets, or, in other words, evidence that the pet was inadequately fed or was sick for a considerable part of his growing period. Coupled with these one generally finds abnormal enlargements on the lower end of the *radius,* a large bone of the forearm, where it joins the wrist joint. The spongy end may be so abnormal as to turn the leg, making it crooked (bandy leg), or weak, so that the leg from the wrist down bends out sideways. Some cats are born with hereditary "bench" legs which are characterized by front feet which turn out sideways and which are not due to rickets or other dietary deficiencies.

The process of bone healing is most interesting, and it is worth while to understand it in case you have to manage a pet, one or more of whose bones are fractured.

Let us suppose that a fairly simple break occurs in the bones of the forearm of a cat. The break is a simple one, and when our cat returns home after his accident the broken leg is obviously shorter than the others. He holds it up, cries with pain. Your veterinarian waits until the cat has recovered from shock, then makes a splint from a round aluminum rod, well padded with cotton where it passes under the leg, or he may pin the bone or apply other devices, such as a cast. The cat is anesthetized and the splint or cast applied. Considerable traction—force in drawing—is required to pull the leg out so that the ends of the bone may be brought together; *in apposition,* your doctor calls it.

Now the ends of the bone must knit. Here is where it is worth while for the owner to know exactly what happens, so that he can give the pet all the attention and care required.

For several days the body decalcifies or withdraws lime and other minerals from the bone ends. Gradually they become soft, like cartilage. Up to the end of this period it doesn't make much difference if the bones are not perfectly matched at the break. The second step, after the softening process, is the growth from each end of connective fibers which join the bone ends together, whereupon it shrinks, pulling the ends closer. This process is completed in fourteen or fifteen days. Up to this time it doesn't make much difference how straight the bone is kept, so long as the ends are in apposition. At any time during this interval it is possible to bend it at the break.

Next comes a stage when the junction or callus becomes impregnated with mineral salts of calcium and phosphorus—in other words, it hardens. From this point on it is essential that the bone be kept straight, and meticulous care must be given to seeing that it is. If the splint slips or the tapes loosen, your veterinarian will want to see the cat at once. Remember that a crooked leg he has set is a poor advertisement for him—to say nothing of its effect on the cat's future, with which both you and the veterinarian are concerned. You owe both your pet and your doctor the co-operation of careful attention at this point. Once the callus is strong enough so that the bone will not bend, the splint or cast can be removed.

The last period involves the shrinking of the callus. Some bones will set with what appears to be a disfiguring bulge about the break, but in time this largely disappears, leaving a strong repaired bone even stronger than the adjacent unbroken parts.

Many injured bones can't be set properly. Some are so badly shattered that chips must be removed and nature be trusted to pull the pieces together. The *pelvis,* that girdle of bones forming a framework for the rear part of the abdomen, is often broken into many pieces which, without any attention, set by themselves without too much constriction of the passage.

There are breaks of such a nature that the bone breaks but stays in place; others where part of the bone breaks and part does not. These are called *greenstick fractures. Compound fractures* are those in which the broken bone protrudes through the skin.

Muscles. Skeletal muscles help hold the framework together and co-operate with it in locomotion. But there are two kinds of muscles, the skeletal being obvious. The others, not seen outside of the body, are called the *smooth muscles.* Under a microscope, fibers of a skeletal muscle appear to have bands or striations, which do not exist on the smooth muscles. The striated muscles are under voluntary control. The duties of the smooth muscles are generally restricted to the functioning of organs and digestive tract. The gullet, intestines, bladder, blood vessels, and sphincter muscles, which act more or less involuntarily, are all smooth.

THE CIRCULATORY SYSTEM

Heart and Vessels. The body is nourished by the blood. It delivers to the cells the substances they need, picks up the bad and useless, and delivers waste to the organs of excretion. At the center of this marvelous system is a pump, the heart, an organ situated in the chest, as we know, and which for efficiency is not excelled by any man-made device.

The heart receives blood into two sides, then squeezes or contracts, so that the blood is driven into two large tubes (vessels). One leads to the lungs; the other divides and carries blood fore and aft into smaller vessels which, in turn, carry it about the body. In the lungs the blood liberates a gas, carbon dioxide, takes up another gas, oxygen, and is hustled back to the heart to be pumped around the body to distribute the oxygen and pick up cell wastes.

The great arteries which carry the blood from the heart start dividing into smaller arteries, these into other smaller and smaller ones, called *arterioles,* and thence into capillaries. From the capillaries the blood returns to the heart via *venules,* veins, and finally large veins. It also returns in lymph tubes or vessels. (The lymph is blood without red cells.) So blood leaves by arteries and returns by veins and lymph vessels.

The pump keeps up its contracting squeezes and relaxations rhythmically for the life of the animal. It says *lubb, dubb, lubb, dubb,* and, in a forty-pound animal, pumps about a gallon of blood every minute. Everything about it is wonderful: the delicate *valves*, the strength, its four *chambers*, the skin around it, called the *pericardium*, the nervous mechanism which causes it to beat.

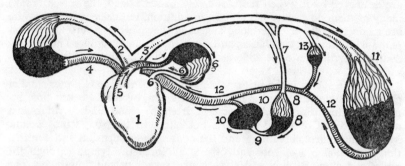

Heart and circulatory system. (1) Heart. (2) Anterior aorta, supplying front end of body. (3) Posterior aorta, supplying rear of body and organs. (4) Anterior vena cava returning blood from front of body. (5) Pulmonary artery, carrying blood to lungs. (6) Pulmonary vein, carrying blood from lungs. (7) Celiac and mesenteric arteries carrying blood to (8), (9), and (10) stomach spleen, intestines, liver, and other organs. (11) Blood supply to rear of body. (12) Posterior vena cava returning blood from rear of body. (13) Kidney circulation.

The Blood. The blood is an organ. Even though it is fluid, it is a colony of specialized cells in a specialized fluid which, as we have seen, discharges carbon dioxide and picks up oxygen and nourishment, which it transports.

The liquid part is called *plasma*. In the plasma float red cells, disks concave on two sides. These contain a chemical called hemoglobin, whose job it is to handle the oxygen, as mentioned above. When arterial blood gushes from a cut it is bright red, the hemoglobin being rich in oxygen; when it runs from a vein it is darker and almost bluish, because the hemoglobin has given up its oxygen.

Then there are white blood corpuscles of various sizes. Usually they appear spherical, but because of their softness and elasticity they can move through small openings, changing shape to do so. Moreover, they can engulf impurities and germs.

Platelets, oval or circular disks which help blood to coagulate or to clot, are another tiny component of blood.

Besides these visible entities there are chemicals, such as *fibrin*. Fibrin stays in solution until an injury allows blood to escape; then a ferment called *thrombin* causes the fibrin to clot.

Spleen and Lymph Nodes. All along the path of the blood and lymph are filter organs, chief of which is the spleen. This varies in size with the size of the animal. A cat's spleen is small, three or four inches long, and three sixteenths of an inch thick. It is a flat, long, narrow organ, more purplish than red, which lies close to the stomach. The spleen's function is chiefly that of an organ of blood purification. Great numbers of bacteria are destroyed by it. When red blood cells become aged, the spleen breaks many of them down into liquid; but, in addition, red cells as well as white are made in its tissue. The blood spaces in the spleen are very large compared with ordinary capillaries; and when the organ is ruptured in an accident, hemorrhage into the abdomen may result in death, though not necessarily.

While the spleen is the principal filter organ of the blood, other smaller glands are situated along the lymph vessels and, by their construction, remove solid impurities, such as bacteria, from the blood fluids. Lymph does not move about by blood pressure, but rather by the body's movements. Muscle movement, breathing and the consequent expansion and contraction, intestinal movements and others, all force the lymph through the nodes and along its course. Valves in the vessels permit flow in but one direction, which is also true of veins.

THE RESPIRATORY SYSTEM

A pair of organs situated in the chest, one on each side, the lungs function in co-operation with the blood in the oxygen-carbon-dioxide transfer and, to a certain extent, in body temperature control as well.

In all mammals a partition—strong in some and almost gossamer in others—divides the chest cavity so that the lungs are separated. In the cat the membrane is extremely thin, and if the chest cavity is broken open on one side, so that air can enter, not only does the lung on that side collapse but the other as well. In humans, where the partition is stronger, if one lung collapses the other may not.

From the throat a tube made up of many rings of tough cartilage runs down into the chest and branches into two bronchial tubes, one for each lung. (Bronchitis is inflammation in these tubes.) They, in turn, branch and subdivide into bronchioles, and finally into air sacs, each of which is surrounded by a network of blood capillaries so thin that gases can be absorbed or escape through them.

THE EXCRETORY SYSTEM

The Kidneys. Blood disposes of certain chemical substances, other than gases, through the kidneys. All the blood travels through their intricate mechanism, disposing of waste. These wastes are principally urea, sugar, poisons, and substances such as carbonates, which can be got rid of in no other way.

Urea is the end product of the breakdown of the proteins in the body.

The nitrogen, which is the principal constituent of protein, is also the principal component of urea. Everyone knows how urine gives off ammonia when hot. Ammonia also contains nitrogen.

In most animals the kidneys are located under the protection of the ribs and on either side of the body close to the backbone. They constitute one of the most delicate and ingenious filter plants possible to imagine. Everyone who has eaten kidneys or fed them to animals knows in general what they look like. But few have observed, microscopically, the minute inner workings, or even wondered at their marvelous construction. If one slices a kidney lengthwise, one sees a *"pelvis,"* so called, which constitutes a pocket for collecting urine, from whence it is conducted via a tube—the ureter—to the bladder. That is about all one does see of the mechanism with the naked eye. The microscope reveals the most interesting features: the blood vessels, which divide to become capillaries, in tiny containers called *glomeruli,* and minute collecting *tubules* into which the urine filters and is conveyed to the pelvis. There are beautiful and ingenious arrangements to effect the transfer and reabsorption into the blood of certain useful substances and rejection of the useless—all of which is accomplished while the blood is passing through the kidney, entering under high pressure and coming out under much lower pressure.

Diseases can easily upset the normal function of the kidneys so that they cannot retain the useful nitrogenous substances like albumin or may lack absorptive capacity, so that too much water is secreted from the blood, causing great thirst. Albumin found in urine and excessive thirst are both indications of kidney disease or dysfunction.

Kidneys that function properly regulate the amounts of blood ingredients in considerable degree. If too much sugar is present, some will be found in the urine. The same may be said of salt. Urine is composed mostly of water (95 per cent). Urea constitutes about 2.3 per cent, salt 1.1 per cent, and the balance, 1.6 per cent, is composed of other solids.

The bladder is a storage reservoir with elastic walls. It is amazing how it can stretch: to almost the size of a baseball in a large cat and the size of a tennis ball in almost any cat.

Other Excretory Means. Other impurities and surpluses from the blood —some mineral salts, for instance—are also excreted into the intestines; some gases are excreted by the lungs, and still other substances by the skin in sweat. The excretory system actually is composed of four parts, and not of the kidneys alone, as the average layman thinks.

THE DIGESTIVE SYSTEM

As we have seen, one of the functions of the blood is to transport nourishment to the body's cells. The nutrients are made ready for the blood by the digestive system.

The Mouth and Teeth. A cat's mouth is one of the most interesting parts of its anatomy and most important to health. The lips are the portal of the mouth. They are also remarkably sensitive organs of touch for some animals. The horse is an excellent example of this point. If he can, with his coarse lips, feel among a lot of debris in a manger for a single oat grain, think what our cats can do with their more delicate lips! Monkeys use their lips with singular effectiveness. Watch one eat and you will see. Cats, on the other hand, instead of feeling dexterously with their lips, as monkeys do, seem to use their lips almost entirely for their primary purpose—to retain the food, as it is chewed, and the mouth juices or secretions.

Whereas humans frequently need dental care for cavities in their teeth, cats develop very few such painful defects. Nearly all their tooth troubles are either germ infections or are due to defective diet. Our pets almost never have their teeth cleaned, so this care does not account for their sound teeth. Nor can chewing hard foods be the reason, because many pets are fed on soft, mushy food all their lives, and their teeth, while becoming covered with tartar, do not decay; the difference is to be found in the structure.

The cat has two sets. The first, or milk teeth, fall out after their roots are partially resorbed by the body at about halfway through the growing period. The eruption of the new teeth takes place so rapidly that it often causes loss of weight in growing animals and fever may sometimes accompany the teething.

Anatomists and students of natural history have a method of representing the number and arrangement of teeth of a species which tells the story, graphically, at a glance.

The front "biting-off" teeth are called the incisors. A cat has three on each side of the mid-line of the upper jaw and three on the lower. Observed from the front, there appear to be in the upper and lower jaws six nice teeth in a row. So the formula for these incisors is I $\frac{3-3}{3-3}$. Behind the incisors on each side is a long, strong canine tooth in both upper and lower jaw: C $\frac{1-1}{1-1}$.

Next we find premolars: P $\frac{2-2}{2-2}$. Finally there are the molars: M $\frac{1-1}{1-1}$. We write the whole formula:

$$I \frac{3-3}{3-3} \quad C \frac{1-1}{1-1} \quad P \frac{2-2}{2-2} \quad M \frac{1-1}{1-1} = 28.$$

The part of the tooth above the gum is called the crown, and that part between the crown and root is called the neck. The part embedded in the socket is called the root. Some teeth have one straight root, some several.

At least half the length of each canine tooth is embedded inside the gums; their roots are strong and exceedingly difficult to extract.

The tooth structure is interesting because of its toughness. When one sees a cat become angry and shear the end off a hardwood stick with its small, sharp teeth, as I have seen one do, our respect for animal teeth deepens.

Enamel adds to the hardness and strength and covers a softer substance called dentine. The root has no enamel covering. Inside each tooth we find the pulp, a structure with nerves and blood vessels. These structures seldom give way, but cats can and do have tooth and gum troubles even though they are only rarely of the cavity sort.

The teeth of no two species are exactly alike. It has been said that the natural diet of any species of animal can be told by examination of the teeth. This is probably true. With long, sharp tusks like those of cats or raccoons, it is logical to suppose that the animal's natural prey was some small animal easily killed and eaten.

Into the mouths of all animals is poured a fluid (saliva) from glands below or behind the mouth. Some animals have a starch-digesting substance in the saliva. Cats have very little. This explains in part why it is so important to cook such foods as potatoes before feeding them to these pets—to break up the starchy granules.

The roof of the mouth has a hard surface, the hard palate, going as far back as the last teeth and made up of ripples or bars extending across the mouth. Behind the teeth, the roof (soft palate) is flabby. By the time a pet's food is chewed and reaches the soft palate, it is practically in the throat.

The Tongue.   The tongue is the principal organ for moving food into the mouth and for taste. Taste is experienced by the reaction to chemical stimuli of "buds," or sensitive areas, which stud this organ and produce the sensations of saltiness, sweetness, bitterness, and acidity. The taste buds are situated all over the tongue but are more abundant in the tip and at the back, in the throat proper.

The Throat.   In the throat the delicate business of getting food properly started down the gullet instead of down the windpipe is accomplished by the pharynx and larynx (pronounced larinks, not larnicks). The gullet and windpipe are located one above the other, with the gullet above. An arrangement called the epiglottis, which is part of the larynx, kicks the food over the windpipe and down the gullet, then drops down to allow the passage of air.

Peristalsis.   In order to understand how food moves along through the body, one must realize that those smooth muscles we mentioned earlier are at work carrying out this function. The only so-called voluntary muscles concerned are in the lips, the throat, and the anus, and these are partly involuntary. Physiologists regard the inside of the alimentary tract as continuous with the skin on the outside of the body. Actually the lining is of the same origin as the skin. The tract constitutes a tube with valves and enlargements. The food is swallowed. At once a constriction in the gullet starts behind it and, as it progresses, forces the bolus (lump) of food into the stomach. The progress may be upward. A cat drinks with his head downward, and the water is moved upward for some distance before it goes downward into the stomach. The contraction which passes along the tube is called peristalsis.

In the stomach this wavelike movement continues. It mixes the stomach juices with the food. The exit valve of the stomach, the *pylorus,* opens and lets the food out into the intestine in sausagelike gobs into which constrictions have divided it. Soon other constrictions may start which cut the sausages in half, but all the while this marvelous process pushes the intestinal contents along through the whole length of the intestine as digestion continues.

The Stomach.   Down the gullet goes the swallowed food and into the stomach, which has walls sufficiently elastic to accommodate the varying amounts of food swallowed. Here in the stomach some digestion of food takes place, for it is a reservoir into which glands pour an acid liquid that helps digest proteins and fats. Starch digestion stops when the food in the stomach becomes acid, but few animals rely on such digestion.

The Intestines.   The *duodenum* is a thickened area of intestine between the stomach and *small intestine.* It is important because into it two *ducts* or tubes discharge their contents. One is *bile,* which is made in the liver and stored in the *gall bladder.* Bile splits fat up into tiny globules so small they are invisible and at the same time affords a laxative effect to the food. When an animal vomits a yellow substance, it is stomach secretion together with bile which has been pumped backward into the stomach by the regurgitation.

The second duct conducts from the *pancreas* more starch-digesting substance, which the pancreas, as one of its duties, manufactures. Starches are turned into dextrin, and then, as the food is pushed along, it is broken down into glucose by another substance excreted by the small intestine and thence absorbed through the intestine. Glucose is blood sugar. It is also the sugar of grapes and an article of commerce as corn syrup. And so in this way digestion transforms the carbohydrates in the food into a form in which they may be transported by the blood. Proteins and fats are also reduced to their component parts, amino acids and fatty acids—forms in which they, too, can pass through the intestinal walls and into the lymph and blood.

Absorption of materials from the intestine is increased by a unique arrangement. The inner surface feels—and indeed is—almost like velvet, being studded with microscopic, short, hairlike projections called *villi.* Each one, while minute in itself, increases the surface of the intestine by a little, and in the aggregate these tiny projections increase the area of the intestines immensely.

This efficient "factory" of the digestive system is like an automobile assembly line running backward, with the cars being taken to pieces bit by bit, instead of being built up. As it passes through the digestive system

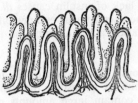

How the inside of a cat's intestine appears when magnified to show the villi. This arrangement enormously increases the absorbing surface of the intestine.

the whole mass of food which entered the mouth is reduced to its essential parts—fatty acids, glucose, and amino acids—and these disassembled products are absorbed into the blood.

The Liver. The liver is the largest organ of the body. It lies in front of the stomach and just behind the diaphragm, and is constantly massaged by the regular inhalations and exhalations caused by breathing. In color the healthy liver is a dark red with a glistening surface and several lobes, the number differing among the species.

All its activities are not concerned with digestion. Besides turning old red blood cells into bile pigment, it is a prime organ of regulation and manufacture. Bile, as we have said, comes from the liver. Urea is made in the liver by converting ammonia left over from protein metabolism (chemical changes). Bacteria are destroyed in the liver to some extent, too, as they are in the lymphatic system and spleen.

As a sugar regulator for the body, the liver is essential. Suppose glucose is absorbed from the intestine in greater quantities than the body can use. The liver then changes it into glycogen (actually animal starch) and stores it. When the blood sugar level gets too low, the liver obliges by releasing glucose from the conversion of the glycogen.

When the gall duct or gall bladder becomes plugged or the bile cannot escape, the pigment gets into the blood, producing a yellow color known as jaundice. Jaundice is not a disease but a condition.

Fats are absorbed and not acted upon by the liver. Fat is deposited in the tissues of the body to be used when called upon, or it may be used at once for energy if needed.

The Pancreas. We cannot leave the subject of digestion without mentioning an important function of the pancreas, besides that of furnishing enzymes (digestive ferments). That is the regulation of the power of the body to handle blood sugar. In this task it functions with the liver, which, as we have seen, stores up or liberates the sugar (glucose). In the pancreas are tiny islands that manufacture *insulin,* and it is insulin which in some way regulates the percentage of glucose in the blood. If there is too much, it sees that the liver stores it; if too little, the pancreas sees that glucose is called out. A lack of insulin causes *diabetes mellitus,* or sugar (or honey) diabetes. The excess sugar escapes into the urine and may be measured. The disease also causes an increase in thirst and amount of urine excreted.

Final Steps in Digestion. What is left of the food after it has traveled through the small intestine is deposited through a valve into the large intestine, where it may contain large amounts of water. Here water is absorbed, and here a huge growth of bacteria takes place. In some species it has been estimated that over half of the feces is living and dead bacteria. The more unassimilated food ends up in the colon, the more there is for bacteria to work on and the more products of bacteria there are to be absorbed by the body along with the surplus water. This is another good reason for not overfeeding and underexercising pets.

THE GLANDULAR SYSTEM
AND REGULATION OF BODY FUNCTIONS

Ductless Glands. The blood acts also as a vehicle for transporting the products of the body regulators, only one of which has thus far been considered—the pancreas. The spleen and lymph glands are also ductless glands but, so far as we know, do not secrete regulators. A ductless gland is one which does not have an outlet except back into the blood.

Some glands, like the pancreas, are mixed ductless and ordinary glands. Salivary glands are good examples of ordinary glands because they have ducts which lead their products away from the glands, secreting saliva in the mouth. The important, strictly ductless glands are the pituitary, the adrenal, thyroid, and parathyroid. The important mixed ductless and ordinary glands are pancreas, ovaries, and testicles.

The Pituitary. Probably most important as a body regulator is the pituitary gland, located at the base of the brain, to which it is attached by a stalk. It has a front and a rear lobe. It seems incredible that such a tiny organ could be capable of performing such feats as it performs. Yet its direct and indirect chemical influence on other glands and organs persuades them to extraordinary accomplishments. Here are a few of its capacities; it can:

Cause an animal to come in heat.
Make an unmaternal animal become maternal.

Affect the shedding of the coat.
Cause a pregnant female to commence labor.
Stimulate growth and cause giantism, if overactive.
Cause stunted growth if underactive.
Cause sexual development.
Help regulate metabolism of carbohydrates.
Cause overfatness if underactive.
Raise blood pressure.

Because it is so potent, the amount of chemical required for these tasks is very small.

The Adrenal Glands. These glands, situated near the kidneys, are also known as the suprarenal glands. They produce epinephrine—also called adrenalin—a potent chemical concerned with blood pressure by its effect on the heart and vessels right down to the capillaries. They also determine in some manner the amount of salt in the urine and affect the use of fat and sugar. Their outer layers secrete a substance now being used in the treatment of arthritis.

The Thyroid. This gland lies in the neck on either side of the windpipe, the two parts being connected by an "isthmus." It is attached to the larynx, so that with every swallowing movement the thyroid is moved too. An important chemical regulator, thyroxin, is secreted by it, and this is known to contain about 60 per cent iodine. Animals whose diets are low in iodine content become sick, and some young animals grow into cretins—peculiar abnormalities not often seen among pets. A cretin is a dwarf, stupid, slow, dull, gross in appearance.
Thyroxin regulates the speed of living in any animal. Slow, poky animals, overweight and phlegmatic, respond by quicker actions, more rapid pulse, restlessness and sleeplessness when given the drug. When the gland secretes too much of its regulating substance, the animal becomes nervous, develops a ravenous appetite, wastes away, exhibits protruding eyeballs and usually an increase in the size of the gland itself. Any such increase is called goiter in man or in animals.

Parathyroids. Located beside the two parts of the thyroid are two small glands whose concern is with the regulation of calcium metabolism. If they are removed, a condition known as tetany, involving violent trembling, is established and death ensues. It has been thought that they are also concerned with eclampsia, characterized by trembling and rigidity in nursing mothers. Injections of parathyroid extract increase the percentage of calcium in the blood, even when none is fed, by forcing the body processes to draw it from the bones.

The Ovaries. Located behind the catta's kidneys are the ovaries. They have several functions. Their first and most important task, of course, is that of perpetuating the animal, but that function we shall deal with later. Here we are interested in the secretions which regulate the animal's behavior.

That the ovaries, even before reproductive functions begin, are concerned with body development no one can doubt. Even such a thing as mental interest is controlled by them. If the ovaries are removed before puberty (sexual maturity), the animal grows somewhat ungainly and tends to put on fat more than a twin whose ovaries have not been removed. This propensity continues through life. The pet tends to become an intersex. A female kitten grows larger and lazier than her whole sisters; not a bad fault. In fact it may be considered an advantage when the owner has no thought of raising kittens.

Working in co-operation with the pituitary, the ovaries initiate the sex cycle, but there is some question as to which gland is of the greater importance. Once started, the actions of the female, as we know them during the sex cycle, are produced by an ovarian-secreted hormone in the blood known as the follicular hormone. It is also called estrone and is known by trade names, such as Theelin, Amniotin, and others. This hormone produces the swelling of the vulva, and, after several days, the desire for mating.

If we could observe an ovary through a window in the female animal's side, we would see some interesting changes take place. Take the ovary of a catta as an example. At times it might appear about the shape of a yellow-eye bean. The visible surface would seem smooth and glistening. A week after commencement of bleeding from the vulva, we would see small bumps protruding from the ovary's surface. These would continue to grow. Eventually, at about the eleventh to the eighteenth day of the period (counting from the first faint showing of blood), they would look like peas in size and shape. The time of this ripening varies in different cattas. Perhaps we would see half a dozen of these pea-shaped bumps completely distorting the shape of the ovary. Each one of these is called a follicle, and it is they which secrete the follicular hormone (estrone). At first they were tiny, almost invisible bubbles growing within the ovary, secreting their hormone. It took them several days to become large enough to push up a bump on the ovary's surface. But when they reach their maximum size, their internal pressure causes the surface, which has grown thin, to rupture. All during the growing period an egg (ovum) has been contained in each follicle, so that the rupturing sets the egg free. In dogs the rupturing (ovulation) occurs spontaneously, but cats have to copulate (mate with a male) to ovulate. Usually, if the animal has been mated, there are male sperm waiting to fertilize the eggs.

As soon as the rupture (ovulation) occurs, a blood clot forms in the follicle and then the growth of yellowish cells begins. These grow until they have filled the follicles with a solid mass. We call them luteal bodies. This mass secretes a hormone. It puts a brake on the mating behavior, not suddenly, but in the space of a few days. The female is no longer receptive, nor does she attract the male. It is my theory that her attraction is lost because of a positive odor which the luteal bodies secrete. Males lose interest in her often after no more than a single sniff.

Whether or not the aging of the ovary is responsible to some extent for the aging of the animal was partially settled by the author in an ovarian transplanting experiment. Ovaries from aged bitches were transplanted in place of those of young bitches. These caused no premature aging in the recipients. Instead the ovaries themselves became rejuvenated and have functioned for six years as this is written.

The Testicles. Besides producing sperm, the testicles secrete the male hormone, testosterone, which functions in connection with the pituitary gland. Some grave errors were made in the use of testosterone in the mistaken notion that it stimulated the testicles to greater activity. Much was administered until it was learned that its use actually lessened testicle activity and caused the deterioration of the testicles. It was the pituitary gland whose secretions caused testicle activity and production of testosterone, which in turn affected the maleness of the animal. Some good stud animals have been temporarily sterilized by the indiscriminate use of testosterone, some possibly permanently. The natural secretion does affect the male animal profoundly, and without it he would be little good as a sire.

THE NERVOUS SYSTEM AND ORGANS OF PERCEPTION

The nerves are the telegraph wires of the body. Thousands of miles of these fibers control the body's activities. They stimulate the muscles to contract, and each of even the tiniest muscles has its nerve supply. The brain is the central station from which the nerves radiate through several pathways, the principal one being the spinal cord. Most of the conscious body movements are regulated by the brain and cord. These two wonderful organs are exceedingly well protected, entirely enclosed in bone—the skull and spine.

Nerves carry impulses to the brain from distant parts of the body. Organs of sense, such as the delicate nerves in the skin, may telegraph to the brain. For example, feeling is a function of these nerves of the skin—sensitivity to temperature, to electrical stimuli, to wetness or dryness, to sharpness, as in the case of a pin prick. Some disease—rabies, for example—may destroy the skin's sensitivity, so that a rabid animal may not even feel the bites of another animal.

Whereas telegraph wires carry messages both ways, nerves conduct impulses in only one direction, some *to* the brain and some *away from* it. Suppose a cat touches a hot electric-light bulb. Her sense organs tell the brain with the speed of electricity, and instantly the muscles are given an impulse which pulls them away from the hot object.

We used to talk about the five senses, but today, besides the ordinary five, psychologists recognize many more: the kinesthetic sense, or muscle sense, the sense of balance, which can be demonstrated even while animals are embryos, the sex sense, to mention only a few.

The Brain and Cord. The nerves are unlike other cells in that they are long, thin fibers. Many fibers may be associated in bundles, and the largest bundle of all is the spinal cord, which gives out and takes in pairs of nerves between every vertebra of the backbone. The bundles of fibers branch here and there (the trunk divides into branches) until the final divisions are tiny individual fibers innervating some small area of the body.

Besides the cord there are other nerves which leave the brain, running to organs and other parts of the body. All of the body—organs, muscles, glands, intestine—is controlled by the cord and by these "cranial" nerves.

For every sensitive area in the body there is a corresponding center in the brain. Sometimes when a cat has a paralyzed leg it is difficult to realize that the origin of the ailment is a part of the brain or spinal cord. Nor, when we see a pet scratch, do we think that a nerve somewhere in the skin telegraphed the brain which set in motion the pet's hind leg. Nerves control the reflex actions of cats. Everyone knows about the human knee jerk—how tapping a definite area just under the kneecap produces an involuntary forward kick of the foot. Cats have many similar reflexes. Anyone who has grasped a big handful of skin at the cat's neck and shoulders knows how she tends to curl up like a kitten being carried by its mother. Some persons misinterpret this action as being due to early training; it's not—it's a reflex action. Everyone who has scratched a cat on the back close to the tail knows that the cat will stretch the hind legs as high as possible, hold the tail straight up, and move about. This is not only because the cat enjoys being scratched, but is also due to an involuntary reflex.

When compared with our own, the brain itself is small in pets, chiefly because the fore part, called the *cerebrum,* is so much smaller in lower animals. The positive, willing, conscious actions are evolved in this portion of the brain. Ordinary living is a concern of the lower part, called the *cerebellum*. There are other parts, most of which, like the two mentioned, are in pairs.

Animals can function mechanically without the cerebrum, but have no memory, can't learn or will to do anything. Their existence is almost like that of a vegetable. They can breathe, eat if their faces are held over the pan, defecate, urinate, sleep, wander aimlessly around, bite or growl when hurt. But by the way some of our pets are trained (or not trained) one might conclude that all they had were cerebellums.

The cerebrum is the part of the brain which responds most to training. Let no one think a cat can have its brain "cluttered up" by the training. Once a pet learns what is wanted of it and is properly rewarded, each succeeding act or trick taught it is easier to teach than the acts before. Those most highly educated of all cats find learning easier and easier. Unfortunately our pets do not live long enough. Just as they become "almost human" mentally, they break down physically and die or must be destroyed.

The Eye. Many misconceptions exist about the eye. It is not so complicated as many think and is much tougher than most people believe it to be. From the front of an animal one sees a big, round, transparent part of a globe, the *cornea*. Surrounding it we see a ring of clear white glistening tissue, the *sclera*. In the lower part of the eye some animals have a third eyelid, the *nictitating membrane*. Cats are no exception. This thin membrane acts as a protection to the eye. It is a small detail which observing cat owners watch because, in some unknown manner, intestinal upsets and intestinal parasites cause it to stand up across the inner side of the eye.

In the middle of the eye we see the *pupil*. This really is only a name for an opening between the two chambers of the eye. The pupils get larger or smaller, depending on the amount of light the eye needs for vision, or on drug action, or on brain disease. An animal looking at a bright light shows a very small pupil; the cat, an up-and-down slit; the dog shows a round spot. When it gets dark, the pupil enlarges. The colored tissue we see around the pupil is called the *iris*. It ranges from pearl in some pets, yellow, green, blue in others, to blood color in albinos and dark brown in still others; cats and dogs often have each eye of a different color.

Behind the pupil lies the *lens*. It is tough, crystalline, and fibrous. Through it light rays are bent so that the image comes to rest on a sensitive area behind the lens, known as the *retina*.

People so often think that scratches on the cornea constitute a cataract

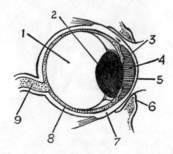

Cross section of the eye. (1) Vitreous humor. (2) Lens. (3) Iris. (4) Aqueous humor. (5) Cornea. (6) Lids. (7) Sclera. (8) Retina. (9) Optic nerve.

that it should be stated a cataract is an *opacity in the lens*. When you look through the pupil and see a white spot it is a cataract. The spot should enlarge and contract because the iris will react to light, but the pupil appears white no matter how dilated or contracted the iris is. Really all we see is the white lens, since, as we have said, the pupil is actually an opening in front of it.

Sometimes a cat's eye is pierced with a sharp instrument. If the hole is in the cornea and no deeper, the fore part of the eye will collapse as the aqueous humor escapes. The opening will promptly heal and, if no infection has entered, the fluid will be renewed and the eye will regain its normal shape. The white cells, in healing, may produce a temporary milky effect in the cornea, and a scar may be formed which does not always show. If it is not in the line of vision, it does not interfere with sight.

The *retina* is the part of the eye which receives the light impressions on nerves imbedded in it, which in turn transmit those impressions via the optic nerve to the brain. Cats, so far as scientists have been able to discover, are color blind (see colors as shades of gray).

The Ear.   Though the eye is a marvelous organ, the ear excites even more wonder. Here is a truly marvelous device for catching sounds and carrying the impressions to the brain on nerves. The natural four-legged animal has the cupped erect ear to enable it to pick up distant or faint sounds. By turning the head, the sounds can be captured as by a trumpet or radar antenna. The sounds are conducted downward through the external canal. Every cat owner has looked down into his pet's ear, probably cleaned it, and knows the projections to be found there. And that is all of the ear most people do know about. They often wonder if they might

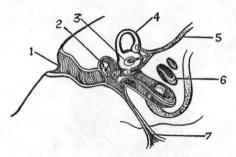

Cross section of the ear. (1) Auditory opening and canal. (2) Middle ear with mechanism for feeling vibrations. (3) Tympanum. (4) Semicircular canal. (5) Auditory nerve. (6) Cochlea (a spiral represented in sections). (7) Eustachian tube.

not pierce the drum when they are cleaning the canal. So long as they clean downward, they do no harm. The tube becomes smaller at the bottom, then turns upward slightly and terminates in a very delicate membrane, the *drum*. All the rest of the ear is within the solid bone of the skull.

Behind the drum are three tiny delicate bones. A delicate mechanism via the *semicircular canal* communicates the impressions of vibration registered by these bones to the nerves, which carry impressions or stimuli to the brain via the auditory nerve. From the small cavity in which they are found, the *middle ear*, a tube called the *Eustachian*, runs into the throat. By means of it, pressure on the drum is equalized. If we go up a high hill or mountain or under a river in a subway, we feel a sensation in our middle ear. If we swallow, the pressure is relieved or, in other words, equalized. If it were not for this provision, the delicate drum might be broken from the changes of atmospheric pressure.

Suppose some ear medicine is dropped into the ear canal of a cat. The canal is rubbed and squeezed by the fingers, to mix the wax with the medicine. While that is being done, the pet sticks out his tongue as if he has experienced an unpleasant taste. Perhaps we open his mouth and smell his breath. There is the odor of the medicine. This is a certain indication that the eardrum is broken. Some of the worst cases of ear disease, and hardest to cure are due to infections in the middle ear. When the drum is broken, special medicines are required to effect a cure.

The Nose. That part of the animal's face which we call the nose is only a small part of his smelling apparatus; all the important parts are out of sight. These consist of a complicated pair of cavities with a partition or *septum* between. The front part is called the *anterior nares;* the back part, the *posterior nares.* The bones of the face cover the anterior nares. This part of the cavity is called the *vestibule.*

In warm-blooded pets the inspired air passes through the vestibule and thence through a remarkable shelflike arrangement made up of *turbinate bones* covered with erectile tissue which can become engorged with blood. A mucous membrane overlies this tissue.

When the air is cold, the erectile tissue fills with extra blood which helps to warm the air before it passes to the lungs. The arrangement of bones and erectile tissue also filters the air at all times, removing dust and bacteria from it.

Before animals can smell odors, the odors, which are gases, must be dissolved in the watery secretion which is present in the olfactory organs. A chemical stimulus received by large numbers of nerve fibers terminating in olfactory hairs in the mucous membrane goes to the brain via the olfactory nerve. At the first stimulus or acknowledgment of the new odor, most animals begin to sniff, which, of course, brings more of the odor into contact with the mucous membrane where it dissolves. The stimulation is thereby increased. It is difficult for us to realize how minute an amount of odor is required to effect this remarkable recognition by cats and other pets.

THE REPRODUCTIVE SYSTEM

The sex organs exist as a means of producing the next generation. Eggs are produced by the female; sperm by the male. An *egg* and a *sperm* unite and the plans for a new individual are completed. The architectural scheme awaits unfolding. Mammals are arranged so the egg or eggs develop within the female.

Female Organs. The female's ovaries contain her heritage—the germ plasm of which she is the custodian and which created her. At certain times, as we saw when we discussed glands of internal secretion, the ovaries produce eggs in blisterlike follicles. The eggs are conducted to a resting place, but before they arrive they are generally fertilized by the sperm—a tiny tadpolelike cell containing the male's heredity. Yes, all the heredity from the male is in a "package" so small we would have to multiply one a hundred times to be able to see even its crudest details.

The female mammal has a *uterus* in which the fertilized eggs rest. This organ is of various shapes in the different species. In the catta it is like a letter Y, but the stem is short and the two horns long and capable of growing much longer. At the lower end of the uterus is a muscular ring which constitutes its mouth and is known as the *cervix*. And the cervix is at the upper end of the *vagina,* that part of the reproductive tract into which the penis of the male is inserted during copulation. Close to the opening of the vagina (the vulva) is the *clitoris,* a small glandular organ known to be the equivalent of the penis of the male. If a female kitten is regularly injected with enough of the male sex hormone, this clitoris will grow to be almost as large as the penis of a male of the same species. The function of the clitoris in mammals is not known. Being of erectile tissue, it becomes somewhat enlarged at times. Probably it assists in making the sexual act pleasant for the animals and, if so, is helpful in stimulating procreation.

The *vulva,* which one sees below the anus, is the termination of the reproductive system of the female. Into it, urine is discharged, so that it serves two functions. During the mating cycle it enlarges considerably.

The *breasts* of the female mammal are glands of the skin. Richly supplied with blood, they make milk. Many people have an entirely erroneous idea about the process of milk production (*lactation*). The young take hold of the teats and suck. Milk may not come at first, or if it does, not more than a few drops at best. Then it begins to come so fast in some animals that it may actually run out of teats to which no young are attached. This is because the mother exerts a positive pressure which forces the milk out easily. Milk is made by glands, from blood *while* the young are nursing and not made up in advance and then drained out. The breasts could not possibly hold such amounts.

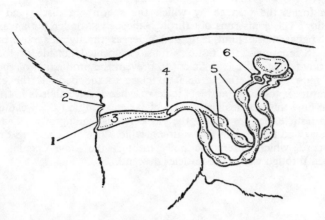

Reproductive system of a catta. (1) Vulva. (2) Anus. (3) Vagina. (4) Cervix. (5) Developing embryos in uterus. (6) Ovary. (7) Kidney.

Male Organs. The male organs are pairs of the following: the *testicle*, in which the sperm are produced, an *epididymis*, in which they are stored and which is connected directly on the outside of the testicle, a *vas deferens*, through which the sperm are transported to a common duct. Anyone with a knowledge of human organs may wonder why the seminal vesicle is not mentioned. Most male pet animals have none. The vas deferens from one testicle joins the one from the other side, and the

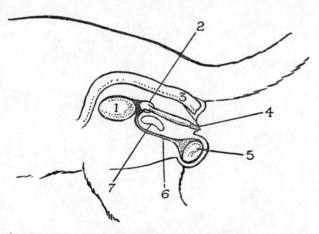

Reproductive system and neighboring organs of a tomcat. (1) Bladder. (2) Prostate. (3) Rectum. (4) Penis. (5) Testicle. (6) Vas deferens. (7) Cross section of part of pelvic bone.

urethra forms the passage by which the sperm are discharged during copulation. The penis runs out through the pelvis, under the anus, bends around between the hind legs, and emerges through its covering, the sheath. In mammals, the testicles must be located outside of the body since body temperature is sufficient to prevent the production of sperm. A strong muscle draws the testicle up close to the body if the external temperature is too cold, and lets it down when the weather is hot. Notice in a cat how the testicles are low or high depending on the weather.

Each testicle, besides having the vas deferens leading away, has a vein and artery and the muscle (*cremaster*), which together compose the spermatic cord, which enters the body through the same opening in the abdomen through which the testicles descend.

3. What You Should Know about Food and Feeding

ANIMALS are usually divided into three classes—flesh-eating (carnivorous), plant- and seed-eating (herbivorous), and those which eat both plant and animal matter (omnivorous). These classifications are made not only on the basis of the food which the animal eats, but also on such characteristics as teeth and digestive apparatus as well.

The distinction between these three general types of animals is not so sharp and clear as most people think. There can be no doubt, of course, about the group to which some animals belong. Having observed large numbers of rabbits and cavies without finding a single instance in which they ate food of animal origin—even crickets—the scientist can be certain that they are as herbivorous as the cow or deer. But the classification of most household pets is not so simple. The layman is likely to think of dogs, cats, rats, and raccoons, for example, as carnivorous animals. The zoologist, however, very properly considers them omnivores, because he has observed that they eat *all* of the animals they catch—including the partially digested vegetable matter in the intestines. Despite the fact that their teeth are typical of carnivorous animals, well adapted to tearing the flesh and puncturing the skull and vital organs of the smaller animals on which they prey, studies have shown that most of the mammals we keep as pets are nearly as omnivorous as we are. With one notable exception, there is practically nothing that we eat which these animals cannot digest as well as humans. This one exception is, as we have seen in Chapter 2, that they must have certain starchy foods crushed for them. When wild cats consume the stomach and intestinal contents of their prey, they are getting the benefit of the chewing and mastication which has already been done.

Today we are beginning to doubt whether any of our pets, in fact, can live for very long on flesh alone without deficiency diseases developing sooner or later. It is fortunate that this is so—fortunate that our pets can assimilate foods of vegetable origin. It may well become increasingly so in the years to come, when the earth has more people and less to feed them.

Nearly all the information we have about nutrition has been provided by the great laboratories of the world since 1900. And much of our knowledge of food values and human nutritional needs has come through feeding experiments with pets. Yet we have been extremely slow in applying this knowledge in the care of household animals. Recently, as I was reading through a volume on dogs published in 1872, I found that the directions given in the section on feeding are just about what the average owner today thinks is the proper way to feed his dog! Cat feeding, too, is just as old-fashioned. We have put into daily practice innumerable scientific findings with regard to our own food requirements, but we still cling stubbornly to outdated ideas in feeding our pets.

No one should assume, of course, that because we are interested in adopting scientific methods in the feeding of animals that we intend to depart from their natural habits and tendencies. In Chapter 2 we stressed the point that if we want to keep pets healthy and happy, it is essential that we understand and consider their native inclinations. A cat is a cat, we said, not a human being. In choosing or preparing our cats' food, we might well consider their natural propensities in choosing their own food. We, partly because of our training, enjoy our meat cooked, but Eskimos eat much of theirs raw. Even the raw intestinal contents of their food animals are eaten raw. How often do we provide our cats with well-chopped raw leafy vegetable matter? While it is true that we should interfere as little as possible with an animal's natural mode of life, it is also true that when we refuse to use what knowledge we have of their care we are being foolish and wasteful.

We know that cats differ from their remote ancestors because human selection of certain odd characteristics has made them most unnatural in many respects. Their mildness and ease of domestication are the most interesting illustrations of that fact. Few similar forms of animal can be domesticated to such a degree of dependability as the cat. Many of what we consider the finest characteristics of cats and many of those most useful to us are the very ones which would make them less able to survive if they were suddenly dropped back into a wild existence. And yet cats of all breeds have such marvelous qualities of adapting themselves to wide environmental changes that they rate among the most adaptable animals known to man.

Cats have been evolved to be useful to man, and while they were being developed they lived closely enough to man to share his food. They became accustomed to it as time went on, and those which could not manage it died off, while those which could lived and reproduced. Partially as a result of that selection, we find that cats today thrive on a variety of diets that is almost unbelievable—such a wide variety of diets, indeed, that we may safely say they can digest anything a human can digest. So the problem boils down to how to feed our cats *best* and most *completely* with the foods we have available, rather than to consider what they *must* be fed.

Let us see first how cats' digestive apparatus differs from ours. Starting at the mouth, we find that the teeth are different. The teeth useful for ripping an animal apart and cutting the tissue off are longer and sharper than the equivalent teeth in our mouths. Our back teeth (molars) are flatter and more useful for grinding grain into powder. The cats' habits of eating consist of tearing their food apart, cutting off pieces with the back teeth, and gulping them with only sufficient chewing to make them small enough to swallow.

The next difference is in the saliva. We have a starch-digesting enzyme —*ptyalin,* now called *salivary amylase*—which does something toward splitting the starch we eat into one step nearer sugar. The cat has very little of that enzyme. It was this discovery that caused the early students of cats to say that they couldn't digest starch. Probably such students never saw a human eat a huge mouthful of doughnut and wash it down with a gulp of coffee—and stopped to think that that too is digested.

Let's see how starch digestion works for man and for cats. Our pets' stomachs secrete somewhat stronger juice than do ours. When cats eat bones, they are acted upon by this juice which is rich in hydrochloric acid and pepsin, and actually dissolved in the stomach. A bone in a healthy cat's stomach becomes soft and pliable in less than an hour. Actually the same thing might happen in the human stomach, but it would take much longer.

Upon emerging from the stomach the food is mixed with the same kind of juices—pancreatic and bile—which affect our food. Here, then, is where most of the digestion of starch takes place. The boy who washes down the half-chewed doughnut and the cat who gulps his starchy meal both live and thrive because digestion takes place in the small intestine. But here is the important difference to remember: we usually chew our foods, so that we crack the starchy grains and nuts into a fine paste, but the cat doesn't. When the pancreatic enzyme (amylase) works on these starches, in our case, they are so fine that the enzyme has little trouble. In the cat, when the starchy foods are in too large lumps, the enzyme cannot do its work effectively. To some degree the same thing happens in the human digestive tract if a person fails to chew a nut or a kernel of sweet corn—neither is digested any more than it would be by a cat. A cat will usually regurgitate any such indigestible material, as he often does hair or mouse tails.

In feeding of cats, it has been found that it pays well to feed either very finely ground raw starch or precooked starches. Corn meal fed raw is an inefficient food, but corn meal which has been boiled until the starch granules have been cracked open, so that they are vulnerable to the attack of the amylase, is an efficient, if incomplete food. Another point of difference between the human and the cat is the length of the small intestine. Cats' food travels through more quickly and there is less time for absorption—another reason for feeding easily digested foods. Cooking makes for this ease in digestion, especially with those foods which pets do not chew—raw cereals, vegetables, fruits. Meats are digested as easily raw.

FOOD AND SKIN DISEASE

It is often said that certain foods are too "heating to the blood," that they cause skin disease. There is very little truth in that idea. We used to be (and still, alas, are) advised too often that we must never feed fat or starches in hot weather because they cause eczema. Remember that the fungus spores which are everywhere in nature float around in the air, are found in dust, in grass and hay, and that they grow best during warm, moist weather. It has been found that many of the skin diseases of cats, except those of insect origin, are caused by these fungi. Many kinds have been isolated from cats' skins. Let us suppose that an infection gets started on your cat's skin close to the tail. You had not noticed it during its incubation. Then suddenly your cat starts to chew at the infected area. He furnishes saliva to add moisture needed for rapid growth of the fungi. The infection seems to you almost to have boiled out of the skin. You might very logically conclude, as did early students, that it was moist eczema. Eczema means "boiling out." Something had to boil. Blood is liquid. Something must have made it boil. Food! That's what caused it. Some foods must be "heating to the blood"—not an unreasonable conclusion for those who didn't know better.

In time students began to inquire and reason further. If we can cure this disease by external applications, while at the same time feeding the same food, the problem cannot be a dietary one. I was one of those who tried such treatment. I have never yet found a single food that causes this breaking out on cats, although I have read studies which seem to show that cats in rare cases are allergic to certain proteins. I believe that nearly all cat skin diseases are caused by external infections. I have cured thousands and have yet to find one that I couldn't cure by external applications of a skin remedy, of which several excellent ones are available to every pet owner.

So don't worry that what you feed, if it is a complete diet, is going to cause breaking out, itching, eczema, or mange.

Now, there are certain known requirements which must be fulfilled in the diet of every kitten or cat. These are the essentials without which our pets develop nutritional deficiencies. First of all, it is obvious that each must have *enough* food. This is another way of saying that there must be sufficient food to furnish energy for his day's living. We measure this energy in the food by burning it in calorimeters to see how many heat units it holds. The heat units are *calories*. It is now known how many calories any resting animal of a given size requires. He needs more, of course, as he exercises or works more. Living, exercise, or work all require energy, and this energy is extracted from the food. If he gets too few calories he will live on his fat; he'll get thin. If he gets too many, he may discard the surplus in the feces or he may use some to make fat to store for a time when his food will be scanty. In other words, he puts it away for a rainy day. Laymen often forget that the pet doesn't have to consume food to obtain nourishment when he is carrying it around in the form of fat. But more about this when we take up the very common problem of how to reduce a pet.

Besides having enough food, our pets need these essentials: water, minerals, amino acids, fatty acids, vitamins. Some species can live without consuming certain essentials which other species must have. (Cavies need vitamin C; dogs and probably, cats make their own.) Some animals require vitamin E (rats, for example). Kittens need it but probably adult cats do not.

WATER

That water is essential to living is obvious. Everybody who observes at all has seen what its absence produces in the way of dehydration, knows the sensation of thirst, the dry mouth, the way some sick, dehydrated cats develop a coat which stands in folds when it is squeezed together, the sunken eyes. And since blood, the very vehicle of transportation of nutrition to the cells, consists mostly of water, the need for water is patent. Besides its internal uses, its evaporation regulates temperature.

Water carries out waste products; it bathes the cells and totes off their excreta as it carries useful substances to them, to mention only a few of its uses. But supplying water is so easy that it is not a problem. A pan from which the pet can drink at will is all he asks. Then if there is enough water in his food so he needs no more, he is satisfied, and if his food is of such a type that he must have additional water, he drinks.

Seventy per cent of our cats' bodies is water. Here are the percentages for the separate parts:

Teeth	10%	Brain	79%
Cartilages	55%	Blood	88%
Bones	60%	Urine	93%
Skin	72%	Lymph	96%
Muscles	75%	Gastric Juice	97%
Ligaments	77%	Saliva	99%

Nearly all the water drunk is absorbed. Normally about 20 per cent passes out with the breath, and in hot weather more is thrown off in this manner. Almost all the rest is passed in the urine. Very little water is used in combination with other substances. It acts as a solvent or vehicle. As water it enters the body; as water it leaves.

In foods, water content varies greatly. The juiciest meat contains about 75 per cent water. So do many brands of canned animal food. Dehydrated meals and baked biscuits contain about 7 per cent water. If they are dried below that, they often absorb enough water from the air to build up to 7 per cent. It is important that these facts be known because, when they are, the pet owner understands that some feeding schedules require that more water be fed. High water consumption need not be indicative of kidney disease or diabetes, as some pet owners surmise; perhaps the diet is too dry.

On the other hand, inferior canned foods contain so much water and so little actual nourishment that a growing kitten, to get enough calories, has to consume so much water that it may seem to use its pan all too frequently. This predicament may be overcome by adding more dry food to the canned.

MINERALS

Some uncombined chemical elements are called minerals. You learned about the elements in your high-school chemistry course. A chemical element is a substance, made up of atoms, which cannot be decomposed by chemical means. Some of these elements are minerals, some gases. Most of the pets' nutrition is in combinations of elements, very complicated combinations, chemically.

Minerals compose about 6 per cent of the animal's body in the following proportions:

Calcium	40
Phosphorus	22
Potassium	5
Sulphur	4
Chlorine	3
Sodium	2
Magnesium	0.7

with many minerals in lesser amounts. Among these are: iron, manganese, copper, iodine, zinc, cobalt, fluorine, boron.

Table I—Minerals: Their Functions and Sources

MINERALS	FUNCTIONS IN BODY	PRINCIPAL SOURCES
Calcium		
90% of body calcium is in the bones; 1% in circulation Stored in body	Bone building. Rickets preventive Blood component Reproduction Lactation Muscle function Nerve function Heart function Tooth component	Bones and bone meal Alfalfa-leaf meal Milk

MINERALS	FUNCTIONS IN BODY	PRINCIPAL SOURCES
Phosphorus		
Bones, blood, muscles, and teeth	Bone building Tooth component Carbohydrate metabolism Fat metabolism Blood component Rickets preventive Liquid content of tissues	Cereals Meat Fish Bones Milk So abundant in pet diets it is of little concern to owners
Iron		
Composes only 4/1000ths of the body weight Needed in minute quantities Is stored in body	Component of red blood cells Transports oxygen in blood 65% is found in blood 30% is found in liver, bone marrow, and spleen 5% is found in muscle tissue	Egg yolk Liver Kidney Gizzard Heart Bone marrow
Potassium		
	Body-fluid regulator Helps regulate blood Muscular function	Blood Potatoes Vegetables
Sodium		
Found in body in combination with phosphorus, chlorine, and sulphur	Regulates body fluids Blood regulator Component of gastric juice Component of urine	Table salt Blood
Chlorine		
Found combined with sodium and hydrogen	Component of gastric juice Blood regulator Regulates body fluids Component of urine	Table salt Blood
Iodine		
Most of iodine in body is found in thyroid gland	Thyroid health and normal growth Regulates metabolism Prevents goiter and cretinism In formation of thyroxine	Foods grown in iodine-rich soils Iodized salt Fish meal made from salt-water fish Shellfish

MINERALS	FUNCTIONS IN BODY	PRINCIPAL SOURCES
Magnesium		
Needed only in minute amounts	Muscle activity Bone building Normal growth Nerve function Blood function	Bones Vegetables Epsom salts
Copper		
Needed only in minute amounts	Forms hemoglobin with iron	Blood Copper sulfate
Sulphur		
Minute amounts required but needed regularly	Body regulation Combination in salts as sulfates	Meat Egg yolk Any food which, when decomposed, smells like bad eggs

You can refer to Table I for information on the functions of the minerals in the body, the daily requirements, and the best sources of them.

PROTEINS AND AMINO ACIDS

A second general group of essentials for every diet is proteins. These complex chemicals always have the element nitrogen as a component. Every protein is composed of amino acids, which contain the NH_2 group as chemistry students know it. Proteins differ in that they contain different amino acids.

There are twenty-two amino acids, each of which has been studied both for its composition and its essentiality. There are ten without which life cannot go on. They must be part of the diet of all cats so far as is known. These are: arginine, histidine, isoleucine, leucine, lysine, methionine, phenylalanine, threonine, tryptophane valine. In Table II you will find some of the commoner proteins listed, but no breakdowns into amino acids.

Two of the amino acids, cystine and methionine, contain sulphur. The most satisfactory way to feed sulphur is not as the element, because as such it is not absorbed, but as one of these two amino acids, for with them ample sulphur is available. Wheat, meat, fish, milk, yeast, egg are excellent sources of both cystine and methionine.

In Chapter 2 we saw some interesting properties of protoplasm—the principal ingredient of protein. The same may be said of the amino acids which compose it. There is so much sulphur sold to pet owners—little sulphur cats to go in drinking water, or sulphur tonics to be added to food

—that it is necessary to say here that practically all of it is wasted. The way to feed sulphur—more than cats can use—is to feed foods containing amino acids which have sulphur in their composition. Chances are you are feeding them anyway.

The proteins found in various foods have unequal properties. Milk proteins possess all of the essential amino acids, and all are digestible. But corn, with its protein called zein, is not complete and is less valuable in feeding. Here, taking milk as a standard, are relative values of the proteins found in some common animal foods:

Beef	104	Yeast	71
Milk	100	Casein	70
Fish	95	Peas	56
Rice	88	Wheat flour	40
		Corn meal	30

Most proteins contain more than one amino acid. Some have one complete and others incomplete. Proteins, with their different assortments of amino acids, can be mixed to produce complete rations of amino acids. Corn meal and horse meat, milk and cereals, alfalfa with wheat or oat flour—all are compatible mixtures. Even meat protein can be supplemented to advantage. It is the mixtures of proteins which produce the almost limitless variety in diets, varying flavors, aromas, and appearances.

Protein Requirements.   If we could feed just the minimum of complete proteins, the average full-grown cat could, in all probability, get along on a diet which included 4 to 6 per cent of protein and the growing animal on 15 per cent. Nearly all pet foods and rations contain over 20 per cent of protein mixtures, some complete, some incomplete, some supplementing others so the results are excellent.

Protein is used primarily in building the body. Some is burned as energy, the nitrogen passing out in the urine, but protein foods, such as meat, are not primarily energy foods. And yet cat owners often make the grave mistake of feeding their cats only liver, kidneys, chicken, horse meat, etc., thus contributing to their ill health.

Table II lists the most important proteins together with their most common sources and some of their properties. It will be useful to those interested in checking the protein content of diets.

Table II—Some Common Proteins and Sources

PROTEIN	RICH SOURCES	PROPERTIES
Albumin	Egg white	Soluble in water
	Milk	Does not precipitate by
	Meat	dilute acids or salts
	Blood	Coagulates when boiled

PROTEIN	RICH SOURCES	PROPERTIES
Casein	Milk Cheese Cottage cheese	Does not coagulate when boiled Coagulated by renin Coagulated by pepsin Coagulated by acids
Fibrinogen	Blood	Soluble in weak salt solutions Coagulated by heat Forms scabs Elastic Dissolved by weak acids
Myesin	Muscle meat	Dissolved by weak acids Flexible only while alive Semifluid consistency Coagulated by heat Shrinks Easily digested
Syntonin	Muscles and organs End product of digestion of other proteins by gastric juice	Dissolved by weak acids Next step in digestion is to a peptone
Peptone	An end product of protein digestion by gastric juice	Leaves stomach and enters intestines after protein digestion Can diffuse through intestinal walls Has more hydrogen and oxygen than proteins
Gelatine	Well distributed throughout animal body	Becomes solid on boiling Three per cent or more in a batch of food will solidify it Trick ingredient often used in cat food to give appearance of solid goodness Precipitated by tannic acid and alcohol
Chondrin	Ligaments, cartilage	Similar to gelatine in properties Requires longer boiling of the tissues which contain it to bring it out

PROTEIN	RICH SOURCES	PROPERTIES
Keratin	Horns, hair, nails, hoofs	Tough fibrinous indigestible, useless in pet feeding but sometimes found in foods Manufactured in hair follicles, etc. Contains much sulphur
Vegetable Proteins	All vegetable matter Richest in seeds, especially legumes	Very similar to animal proteins In legumes one protein is found like albumin in milk Some are like fibrinogen, some like albumin with similar properties

CARBOHYDRATES

All carbohydrates are derived from plants. The chlorophyll of the plant leaf (much like the hemoglobin in the animal's body) is able to take six parts of carbon dioxide (CO_2) from the air, combine it with five parts of water (H_2O) and produce starch, $C_6H_{10}O_5$, and then have some oxygen left over which it passes out into the air. Starch granules are built up, layer on layer, the primary factor in nutrition. Plants add nitrogen to starch and make proteins.

The starch granule has two substances in its composition: cellulose and granulose. The cellulose is fiber and gives plants their rigidity. When boiled it becomes soft but does not dissolve. Granulose will dissolve in boiling water. We find the starch diffused all through plants, some in seeds, some in tubers or roots, et cetera. Some starchy food has large amounts of water (potatoes), some very small amounts (grains). When we buy starches we compare them on the basis of their dry components.

As a practical matter, it is important to remember this: raw starch is not soluble in cold water but it does dissolve in boiling water. However, about twenty times as much water must be added for the dissolving to take place. Mixed with an equal amount of water, it does not dissolve. Dissolving starch does not materially alter its composition, but when dissolved starch cools it becomes solid. This unimportant change explains why pet-food canners like to add to their products some starchy foods which are poured into the cans before processing and come out solid chunks. Many are excellent food but are not the solid goodness the buyer might think, since they contain 70 per cent or more of water.

In order to make starch digestible for cats it is helpful to crack the granules by cooking. It can then be handled quite easily. Rabbits, cavies, and others digest part of the cellulose by enzymes and liberate the soluble starch; cats do not, but cats chew their food much finer than some animals kept for pets and thus get more good from it. We now know, that when potato, carrot, or any other starch food is cooked and mashed, cats can utilize it perfectly well.

Baking starch to 400°F. changes it to *dextrin* (not dextrose)—a gummy, sweetish substance, not unlike sugar, which dissolves easily. Biscuits taste good to animals because the heat has converted the starch to dextrin. They are sweeter but actually very little different from starch; they have one more molecule of water (H_2O), $C_6H_{12}O_6$ where starch is $C_6H_{10}O_5$.

Starch is found in the animal liver and muscles as *glycogen* or animal starch. It is soluble in hot or cold water. Animals quickly convert vegetable starch into animal starch, and they are able also to convert protein into glycogen.

Fasting uses up stored glycogen, eating replaces it, and quickly. Within a few hours after a meal of starch there are abundant stores to be found in the liver. As it is circulated for the nourishment of the body, glycogen is converted into blood sugar, *glucose*. And, as the blood leaves the liver, it may contain as much as 3 per cent. Sometimes animals are fed so much sugar they cannot store it. The excess is found in the urine; allowances for this must be made in tests for diabetes.

Besides the starches there are several carbohydrates common to most diets.

Milk sugar (lactose) is found in its only natural liquid form in milk. It is not, as a matter of fact, particularly sweet. Lactose is the food of acidophilus bacteria in the intestine. Many very difficult cases of intestinal trouble have been greatly helped by the simple expedient of adding milk to the diet or some food like bread, which has considerable milk in its composition. Lactose is easily dissolved by the acid digestive juice. Its action on the bowel is laxative, which explains the effect of skim milk.

Cane sugar is good for animals but spoils their appetites as candy spoils those of children. It is, of course, usually fed in artificial forms. Honey is composed of cane and fruit sugar. The latter is the sweetest sugar known.

FATS

The fatty acids are carbohydrates in a sense—being composed of carbon, hydrogen, and oxygen, but they have much less oxygen and more carbon than starches.

Unlike protein, fats contain no nitrogen. Like protein, they too are combinations of components, known as fatty acids. Only three of these are essential so far as we now know—*linoleic, linolenic* and *arachnidic* acids, all believed to be concerned with our pets' health in several ways. All are so very common in nature they may be almost neglected in our thoughts of nutrition. Some other nonessential ones are *butyric acid,* *caproic acid, lauric, oleic, palmitic, stearic acids.*

Fats melt when heated, are smooth, lubricating when warm. Some fats like tallow are comparatively hard and crystalline; some, like vegetable oils, are extremely soft and fluid. All are made by the plant and the animal body.

When an animal consumes fat he stores it in his body largely in the same form in which he ate it. A cat eating lard mixed with his food in a sense first becomes part hog. Later his body slowly changes the lard to cat fat. Cats fed mutton tallow, which melts at 40°C., become part sheep until they change the sheep fat into cat fat, which melts at 20°C. The same applies to vegetable fats. Cats first starved and then fed corn fat become part corn for a while. All the fats in the body are fluid and pliable because they melt at body temperatures and harden after death when the fat chills.

Fats have a number of interesting properties which should be remembered by the pet owner:

Fats are able to emulsify; when acted on by bile salts, for instance, they can split into tiny invisible particles which stay in suspension in water or gastric juice.

Fat acts as a vehicle for carrying some of the vitamins—A, D, E, K. Because of this fact, mineral oil can absorb them from food in the intestines and prevent their absorption.

Fat slows digestion and renders it more complete. It spares vitamin B in the diet, and is concerned with fertility.

A balanced diet should contain not less than 20 per cent fat. An animal living on prey often eats 30 per cent or more of fat. The amount of fat animals can utilize depends on the amount of exercise they are getting. Cats which stay at home, show but little activity, and are in danger of becoming overweight need only a small percentage of fat in their diets; but farm cats, which hunt and prowl, can easily handle 25 per cent fat in the diet.

Cows' milk, with the water omitted, contains about 25 per cent fat, and milk is an excellent food for many pets—almost a criterion of what a food should be. But note that it contains a goodly amount of milk sugar. Feed milk sugar alone and the pet's stools become almost liquid. Feed fat alone and the same thing happens. Feed the two as whole milk and the stool is perfect.

Physiologists say: *fat burns in the flame of carbohydrates.* When you feed fat always see that there is sufficient carbohydrates present. On the other hand, if you fail to provide enough fat, the pet has to manufacture his own from proteins and carbohydrates in his diet—a less efficient and more costly process.

The economy of fat in pet food can be easily and conclusively demonstrated. One pound of rendered suet contains about four thousand calories; one pound of the best dehydrated foods contains about one thousand five hundred and fifty calories; and the fat costs less than the food.

Fat in the diet contributes two and one quarter times as much energy as either proteins or carbohydrates.

For those who wish to compute the calories in any food formula, this is how it is done. Consider only the protein, carbohydrate (which may be expressed as nitrogen-free extract), and fat. Disregard the rest. Multiply the protein and carbohydrate by four, because a gram of protein, when burned, yields four calories. Multiply the fat by nine; a gram of fat burns to yield nine calories. This will give you the number of calories in one hundred grams of food. Since there are 454 grams in a pound, you can convert the answer to pounds by multiplying by 4.5

How many calories in a one-pound can of a certain canned fish food? The guarantee says:

Protein	9%
Carbohydrate	11%
Fat	2%
Fiber	2%
Water	74%
Ash	1%

Protein	9×4	equals	36	
Carbohydrate	11×4	"	44	
Fat	2×9	"	18	
			98	$\times 4.5$ equals 441 calories in a pound.

How many calories in a pound of top round? It contains about 21 per cent protein, 10.5 per cent fat, and the rest is mostly water.

Protein	21×4	equals	84	
Fat	10.5×9	"	94.4	
			178.4	$\times 4.5$ equals 802.8 calories in a pound.

How many calories in a pound of a certain dehydrated cat food? It has 25 per cent protein, 57 per cent carbohydrate, 4.5 per cent fat.

Protein	25×4	equals	100	
Carbohydrate	57×4	"	228	
Fat	4.5×9	"	40.5	
			368.5	$\times 4.5$ equals 1658.25 calories per pound.

It is also necessary, however, to consider what part of the total caloric volume is actually usable, because sometimes the protein and carbohydrates may not be so completely available as those in other foods. Even so, a dehydrated ration which furnishes sixteen hundred calories certainly should recommend itself for our consideration, especially since some fat could readily be added to it.

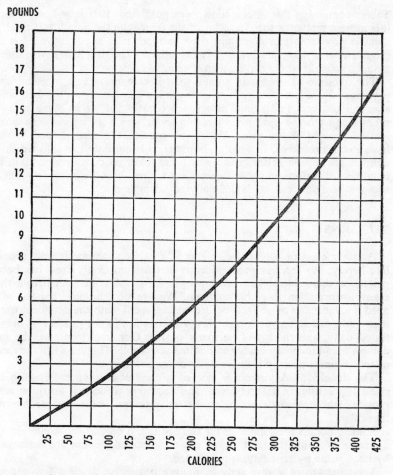

POUNDS

CALORIES

Approximate caloric requirements of cats by weight. Find the weight of your cat on the left-hand side and follow the line toward the right to its point of intersection with the heavy black line. Then drop downward to the bottom line, where you will find the daily calorie requirement.

LAXATION

Which brings us to the subject of residue. There often is considerable residue in the indigestible fiber and in part of the proteins and ash in many ingredients of pet foods. For a long while it was thought that the amount of this fiber was one of the criteria of how laxative a food would be.

Tables containing this information were published. It is now known that it is more a matter of the character of the fiber than the amount. If alfalfa meal is powdered like flour and used in food, it is not laxative; if it is ground coarse, like fine bran, it is exceedingly laxative; but if the same amount is fed as whole leaves, then it again is constipating.

The question of residue in animal food is of considerable practical importance to the pet owner. Cats eating mice pass much of the hair and stomach contents and skin, but are not constipated by it. Some pets—rabbits and cavies—eat only vegetable food, which if fed alone to dogs and cats would physic them. With each species, the natural food habits have to be considered. In general, however, it is quite well established that animals are kept in better health where the stool has considerable bulk. It is unwise, therefore, to try to figure diets with as little indigestible residue as possible. Some residue is definitely an advantage.

VITAMINS

Another class of essential elements in food is vitamins. It may sound like heresy, but there is good evidence that far too much stress has been placed on this subject. Too many people drew rash conclusions from the scanty information available to them. We are now finding that we will need a great many more facts before we can speak with the confident tone many adopted some years ago. New vitamins are in the process of being tested daily, and there will be many others. Our knowledge will be incomplete and inconclusive for some time yet. Table III gives a brief review of the vitamins about which we do know something.

The definition: A vitamin is one of a class of substances, existing in minute quantities in natural foods, and necessary to normal nutrition and growth, whose absence produces dietary diseases. Some are made synthetically.

Some vitamins are soluble in fat and are found only in foods containing appreciable amounts of fat. Some are water-soluble. Some are destroyed by heat, some by rancidity, some by age.

Vitamins are necessary only in minute quantities. With a few exceptions, all essential vitamins are present in the normal diet. When all our information is boiled down it seems certain that any animal among our pets, two- or four-legged, aquatic or terrestrial, can get all the vitamins it needs if its diet contains yeast, fresh alfalfa-leaf meal, and some form of vitamin D. This may be percomorph oil, in minute amounts, irradiated yeast, et cetera. It is as simple as that. Is it an exaggeration to say that the talk about vitamins, essential as they positively are, has been too free, and often misleading?

Many vitamins have individual but very similar functions. In maintaining health some are useful only in conjunction with others. It is often difficult to break down the better sources into their individual components. For our purposes it is quite unnecessary to discuss each of the vitamins individually in order to understand the effects of the groups in which they occur and in which we handle them. The B complex is an excellent illustration. It embodies many essentials. All may be found together and are used together medicinally. A veterinarian seldom gives thiamin, rather the whole complex, when he is using vitamin therapy.

Table III gives in outline form the major properties, functions, and sources of the principal vitamins and vitamin groups.

Table III—Vitamins: Their Properties, Functions, and Sources

VITAMINS	CONCERNED WITH	SOURCES
A (*and carotene*)		
Stable at boiling temperatures	General metabolism	Alfalfa-leaf meal
Spoils with age if exposed to air	Growth	Butter
Body stores it	Skin health	Carrots
Fat soluble	Muscle co-ordination	Egg yolks
	Fertility	Fish livers
	Calcium utilization	Glandular organs
	Digestion	Leaves of plants
	Hearing	Milk, whole
	Vision	Spinach
	Prevention of infection	Many dark green vegetables
	Nerve health	
	Prevention of one type of bladder-stone formation	
	Pituitary-gland function	
	Prevention of one form of diarrhea	
B Complex		
Biotin	Growth promotion	Yeast
Pantothenic acid	Nerve health	Cereals
Riboflavin, thiamin	Heart health	Milk
Folic acid	Liver function	Eggs
Niacin	Appetite	Liver
Pyridoxin	Gastro-intestinal function	Alfalfa-leaf meal
Animal protein factor	Intestinal absorption	Rapidly growing plants
Water soluble	Lactation	Bacterial growth
Body storage—small	Fertility	Cattle paunch and intestinal contents
Some destroyed by high cooking temperatures, but not riboflavin	Muscle function	
	Prevention of anemia	
	Prevention of black tongue	
Biotin effects robbed by raw egg white	Prevention of Vincent's disease	
	Kidney and bladder function	
	Blood health	
	Prevention of one type of paralysis	

VITAMINS	CONCERNED WITH	SOURCES
C		
Ascorbic acid	Prevention of scurvy in	Fruit juices and vege-
Water soluble	some pets	tables
Unstable at cooking temperatures	*Not necessary in cats*	Alfalfa-leaf meal
D		
Irradiated ergosterol	Regulation of calcium and	Fish livers and oils ex-
Well stored by body	phosphorus in blood	tracted
Stands considerable heat	Calcium and phosphorus metabolism	Some animal fats
Resists decomposition	Prevention of rickets	
Fat soluble	Normal skeletal development	
	Muscular co-ordination	
	Lactation	
E		
Tocopherol	Muscular co-ordination	Seed germs
Fat soluble	Fertility in some species	
Body stores it	Muscular development in	
Perishes when exposed to air	kittens	
Stands ordinary cooking temperatures	Sound hearts Survival of young animals Growth Pituitary gland health	
K		
Fat soluble	Blood-clotting Young kitten health	Alfalfa-leaf meal
Unsaturated Fatty Acids (sometimes called vitamin F)		
Linoleic acid	Coat and skin health	Wheat-germ oil
Linolenic acid		Linseed oil
Arachnidic acid		Rapeseed oil Many seed oils

Scientists have made careful studies of what they often call "nutritional wisdom" in animals. In doing so they expose animals of one species or another—children, rabbits, dogs, cattle, poultry—to separate dishes of all kinds of foods. Each day they measure what is left and keep track of what the appetite dictates the animal needs. In making these studies the scientist tries to rule out "conditioning." He knows that once an animal is conditioned or habituated to eat only certain foods it is almost useless for experimental study of nutritional wisdom.

If cat owners had only a little realization of the effect of food habits on animals, those who judge the value of a food by how greedily a cat eats it would revise their opinions completely. Students have consistently found that the taste test is nothing but a test of previous conditioning. It is difficult to understand why pet owners should sometimes be so reluctant to accept this fact. Anyone working with humans knows that undesirable habits in food selection are amazingly difficult to eradicate. A man is asked, "Why don't you eat cabbage? It's good for you." "Because if I ate it I might like it, and I hate the stuff," is his reply.

How many people prefer bread made of patent flour to whole-wheat bread! And yet it is distinctly inferior. Most of the better proteins, iron, manganese, magnesium, copper, calcium, thiamin, riboflavin, are removed. But white flour keeps better, so flour and bread manufacturers have conditioned the public to like it better. Fish is as valuable a food as meat and costs much less, yet many people refuse to eat it—and some have even trained their omnivorous pets to reject it.

A remarkable number of people have projected their own peculiar food habits to their pets. Animals can't reason, even as poorly as the man who wouldn't eat cabbage, but it is extremely easy to build up likes and dislikes by habit formations which are difficult to break. I have seen many cats, raised on complete dehydrated dog foods, which had to be starved several days to make them eat meat, and vice versa.

The point is—every cat should be trained to "eat what we set before it," so long as we know our provisions are wholesome and nutritious. All experience indicates that, given a very large assortment of foods, any unconditioned kitten will settle down to a certain diet of special foods he likes, mostly what is good for him. Among these might be a freshly killed rabbit, a juicy rat, or overripe meat. But since most of us can't offer such tidbits, or live in the same house with an animal which has eaten them, it behooves us to remember how important training is in the cultivation of appetite. A kitten reared on a diet of just one ready-mixed complete food mixed with water, and given nothing else, gets a treat in every meal. He's hungry for that diet when mealtime comes around. After he has become accustomed to it for a year, try offering him a dish of beef kidneys. He probably will have forgotten it is meant to be eaten.

HOW MUCH TO FEED

There are some general principles of feeding which are important to the health of every pet. Next to our consideration of what to do when the end comes, this is the most ticklish subject we have to tackle.

Nobody should have any difficulty understanding the fundamental rule: *In feeding mature cats, the less they eat,* compatible with keeping them in sound condition, *the healthier they'll be and the longer they'll live.* It goes without saying, of course, that they should have a complete and balanced diet. They should not be allowed to get too fat or too thin. If you try to keep them too thin, they may get too little of some essential ingredient; if you permit them to get too fat, you will shorten their lives.

In growing pets, the faster they grow the cheaper it is to raise them. Yes, *but*—will they live longer, be healthier? Probably the best rule for sound health and longevity is to grow them moderately fast, but not to force them. This applies to all species.

Nearly everyone overfeeds. And almost every animal will eat 20 per cent more than it needs. There are some animals, like some people, which never get fat even though they are chronically overfed. The way to feed —the way people who are good feeders feed their cats—is to find just the amount which will maintain your pet's weight and feed no more. No rule in feeding is as important as this one. It applies, of course, only to cats whose weights are satisfactory.

If only Mrs. Jones and all others who allow cats to become obese knew a few truths about food storage in the body and something about fasting —which some people call starvation—how much better off their pets would be.

Starvation is the long-continued deprivation of food.

Fasting is total or partial abstinence from food.

Starvation is forced; fasting is voluntary. A sick animal fasts; an obese animal must be starved but not necessarily deprived of all food. When an animal is too fat he won't really starve, even though he takes no food until his fat is consumed. We say "he lives on his fat." In the winter the raccoon fasts. Not that he reasons what he is doing. He lazily lives on his fat. He has stored sufficient vitamins and minerals along with the fat and moves about very little except during the warm spells of winter. No one need be sorry for raccoons. Why, then, pity our fat cats when they have to forego the habit of overeating for a while?

Most of this feeling sorry for pets which are reducing stems from the idea that starvation is painful. But it is not, so long as there is a reservoir of food in the stored fat of the body. If a little protein and a little carbohydrate is fed—say a slice of bread a day—to help burn the fat, there is no danger of acidosis developing. If a vitamin-mineral supplement is added, there is no danger of starvation at all.

Anyone who thinks starvation is painful need only try it. I once lost forty-two pounds in less than two months and smaller amounts on many other occasions, and I have never felt a pang of anything but hunger. Hunger pangs are habit pangs—not pain at all.

Starvation is painless until it reaches the point of emaciation, so humans tell us. There are many instances of cats living with only water for two months. So don't think your pet is going to die if he doesn't eat for a few days while you are accustoming him to what is good for him. His taste can become re-educated so he will like the diet you choose, and he will thrive on it if it is complete.

Clients whom I have advised to feed a certain diet ask if a cat doesn't need variety. How can a certain canned food or meal-type food which is fed day after day still be palatable? The reason is that our pets can smell each ingredient in a food. You and I smell hash. The cat smells separately each of the ingredients of which hash is composed. If you doubt this, watch a finicky cat trying to separate finely ground ingredients from each other in a mixture of foods. It isn't difficult to understand this ability if one thinks about it for a moment. Have you ever watched a cat raise its head and gently analyze air drifts for scents? They have uncommonly keen noses and are able to detect game for which they are sometimes trained to hunt at almost unbelievable distances. We so often overfeed house cats that few of them ever give us an opportunity to observe their actions when they are hungry.

It is far more cruel to overfeed than to reduce. It is a discredit to the owner. It shortens the life of the animal to be obese, and makes him sluggish and no longer fun to have around. It often brings great misery and suffering to pet and owner alike, because of the paralysis which so frequently sets in as the pet grows older.

Loss of weight can be accomplished in two ways: by reducing the amount of food or by exercising the pet. With most pets a decrease in food consumption is the more practical and effective means. With cats, however, the close personal feeling between the master and the pet sometimes makes it difficult for the owner to reduce feeding sufficiently to achieve the purpose. With cats the problem is not quite so important as it is in the case of other household pets, but it is probable that fat cats do not live as long as cats of normal weight.

4. Diseases and How Your Cat Catches Them

*I*F YOUR cat contracts pneumonia you will know that he is sick. But unless you know more than that, there is little that you can do for the animal. On the other hand, when you know something about the types of diseases and their causes and your pet becomes ill, you can handle the situation much more intelligently. You may be able to recognize the symptoms well enough to diagnose the condition and treat it yourself. If you do not recognize the symptoms, or if it is a serious disease which you cannot treat, you will realize the importance of having the pet properly cared for by a veterinarian. You will also be much better able to give the veterinarian the specific, accurate information he needs to have to treat the animal quickly and effectively.

A knowledge of the causes of the diseases to which your pet is subject and of the ways he may contract them is even more important from the standpoint of prevention. Many diseases can be avoided by observing a few simple precautions. Some of these maladies, once contracted, are difficult or impossible to cure. To the pet owner and to veterinary medicine, the prevention of disease in animals is as important as it is in the case of humans. A pet that is kept well is a good pet—a lively, active companion.

A simple understanding of the basic facts about disease is sufficient for the pet owner. He doesn't need to learn and remember a series of medical names or technical terms. He should know the broad general classifications into which all diseases are divided, he should be familiar with the common characteristics of each, and he should have a general knowledge of the way each affects animals. This is hardly too much to expect of any person who is really concerned with his cat's welfare.

To most pet owners all animal diseases are more or less alike—the result, they think, of some vague thing called "germs." Actually, of course, there are a number of distinct types of diseases, and they are classified according to their causes. Some are caused by bacteria, some by viruses, and others by fungi, or parasites, or growths, or deficiencies. To under-

stand the diseases themselves it is necessary to know something about
these causative agents.

BACTERIA

Bacteria are single-celled organisms; those which cause disease are
called *pathogenic*. There are many forms causing disease, and all are, in
some way, transmissible from one animal to another.

Since bacteria are too small to be seen without magnification, they must
be studied through the microscope. There they appear as different from
each other as the various farm animals. Some are spirals, some are little
balls, some have whiplike attachments, and some look like baseball bats.

(*1*) *Streptococci* (*grow in strings*); (*2*) *Staphylococci* (*grow in
bunches*); (*3*) *Bacteria*; (*4*) *Bacteria*.

Coccal bacteria are round. *Streptococci* (pronounced strep-toe-cox-
eye) are round bacteria which grow in strings. They produce such diseases
as pneumonia and pus infections. *Staphylococci* are round forms which
grow in groups like bunches of grapes. They are notorious pus producers
and abscess formers.

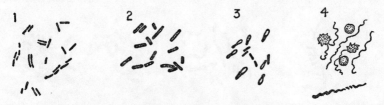

(*1*) *Bacilli* (*rod-shaped*); (*2*) *Bacilli* (*rod-shaped*); (*3*) *Clostridia*
(*form spores*); (*4*) *Spirochetes* (*among blood cells*).

Bacilli are rod-shaped bacteria, many of which are mischief-makers,
sometimes complicating other diseases. Rod-shaped forms, of which there
are many, cause bubonic plague, tularemia, and some poultry diseases.
Salmonella organisms cause food poisoning in man and other diseases in
animals. *Shigella* cause dysentery in kittens, and bird typhoid; *Clostridia*
cause lockjaw, food poisoning (botulism), gas gangrene; *Mycobacteria*
cause tuberculosis.

Spirochetes are corkscrew-shaped organisms which cause diseases such as trench mouth and leptospirosis.

Since these are all comparatively large forms, too large to enter the cells of the body, bacteria float or propel themselves about in body fluids or remain stationary. Some invade the blood; some are specific for certain tissue, such as pneumococcus types for lungs; others are found confined to the stomach and intestines.

RICKETTSIAE

Rickettsiae are different from bacteria. They are smaller—so small that they have been found inside of cells. They are responsible for such dis-eases as Rocky Mountain spotted fever, which is spread by the parasites of rodents, dogs, and humans.

FUNGI

A third class of infecting organisms most interesting to the veterinarian and to the cat owner is the fungus (plural, fungi or funguses). Fungi are plants of a low order; they produce spores which are like seeds. Spores resist drought, heat, cold, and other environmental factors. When condi-tions of moisture and temperature are right, they grow into mature forms.

Many skin diseases in cats are of fungus origin. Ringworm which grows in individual cells is a fungus. Molds are fungi. There are a great many kinds of fungi—good, bad, and neutral types. Penicillin, one of the most extraordinarily effective drugs ever discovered, is made from a mold.

(1) Mold; (2) Rickettsia (greatly magnified); (3) Fungi (grow by budding); (4) Fungi (grow in threads).

VIRUSES

Viruses live *in* the cells. They are so small that they are invisible through an ordinary microscope. Photographs of them made through the electron miscroscope indicate that, like bacteria, they grow in various forms. Their exact nature is not understood, nor has a cure for the diseases they cause been discovered. If your veterinarian diagnoses your cat's disease as a virus disease, and tells you that he has no medicine which can cure it, believe him. Don't run to another doctor expecting him to cure it with drugs. If he does effect a cure with drugs, your pet did not have a virus disease. At least this is true on the basis of what we now know about viruses.

Viruses, even more than bacteria, have affinities for certain tissues in the body. Rabies, for instance, is neurotropic, which means that it attacks nerve tissue. Distemper has an affinity for the epithelial tissue (skin and mucous membranes). Some viruses attack the lining of the nose and throat, and others attack lung tissue.

One of the tragic facts about viruses is that they so weaken tissue that bacterial diseases can get a start and develop. Certain bacteria are such constant companions of viruses that we once believed that bacteria caused a number of virus diseases because bacteria were constantly present. This was true, for example, of distemper, which we thought was caused by a bacterium called *B. bronchisepticus*. Bacterial pneumonia can be a secondary complication of cat distemper. Of course veterinarians should and do try to cure any part of the disease they can. If penicillin or sulfa drugs will destroy bacteria which complicate virus diseases, they should be used, *but not to treat the virus,* because they are worthless against it.

DISEASE TRANSMISSION

Before animals can contract a disease, they must in some manner be exposed to the infecting organism. Exposure can come about in many ways.

Bacterial diseases may be contracted by an animal's eating infected food, by getting the bacteria into cuts or puncture wounds. or by inhaling them. If a cat is bitten by another cat, the wounds may fester by the multiplication of bacteria inserted by the tooth. Bacteria may be drawn into the system, or they may be present in air passages, waiting for a virus or general loss of resistance to weaken tissue and set up conditions favorable to their growth.

Some virus diseases can be passed from one animal to another by inhaling one brief sniff of a sick animal's breath, or even by inhaling air in a room in which a sick animal has sneezed and left minute droplets floating about carrying the virus. Other virus diseases can be transmitted by bites, as in rabies.

Fungus diseases are spread in several ways: by contact, by wind, by water. Suppose your Siamese develops a concentric bare spot on his nose. How did it get there? Well, he may have pushed his nose against a spot on your infected dog, or he may have rested on a couch where the dog had been lying previously, or a breeze may have blown spores on him. Somehow they settled on his nose and grew. Some of the worst skin diseases a cat gets can be contracted by his lying on a lawn, or rubbing against another cat, or from dust blown on him containing spores that find entrance to his skin in fleabites.

IMMUNITY

Some knowledge of the body's defense against diseases and of immunity is necessary in understanding methods of prevention and cure.

When a cat which has been bitten develops an abscess, his body builds a dam around the area and walls it off from the rest. The next time he is bitten other infections may develop from the same bacteria. But if, instead of developing a localized abscess, the bacteria invade the blood stream, a different condition develops. *If the cat survives by its own bodily mechanism or chemistry,* it will be immune to that species of bacteria for a long time afterward. But if the cat is treated with medicine such as sulfathiazole, which destroys every bacterium of that type in the body within a few days, then solid immunity may not be developed. Why?

Because the body builds up defenses to overcome bacteria or viruses in several ways: white cells may engulf them, or the body may develop antitoxins which counteract the toxins elaborated by the bacteria. All animal bodies have the power to develop specific counter-chemicals which will act to destroy invading bacteria. We call these defense chemicals antibodies. It is amazing how specific they can be. The antibodies against one disease organism are seldom of value against another. If a cat recovers from virus pneumonia, for instance, he can still contract feline distemper. If he recovers from one species of coccidiosis, he can still contract another form. But if the cat is to develop immunity, he has to recover without medication. If the recovery from a bacterial disease is due to chemicals added to his blood, he does not always develop antibodies which will solidly protect him against that form of disease in the future.

There are different kinds of immunity. *Passive immunity* is conferred by additions of biologics to the blood which insure temporary protection. *Inherent or inherited immunity* is transmitted from parent to offspring. *Acquired immunity* is acquired after birth. *Active immunity* is produced by an animal's own tissues or fluids. It may be produced:

By having a disease and recovering.
By constant mild exposure to the disease-producing organism.
By injection of dead bacteria, or products of dead bacteria.
By injection of attenuated or dead viruses
   (a) Attenuated by the addition of chemicals to live virus.
   (b) Attenuated by passing the disease through another species.
By injection of toxins.

PARASITIC DISEASES

Parasitic diseases from which our cats suffer are real diseases, often tragic in their consequences. Have you ever thought of lice infestation as a disease, or hookworms, or mange? Fortunately these are the easiest diseases to manage, so long as we remember that the cure is only half of the job; the important part is to prevent reinfestation. For this reason every pet owner should know, in a general way, the life history of all of the common parasites.

External Parasites. THE FLEA: Those little elusive insects that jump so far and those big, brown, long-bodied insects that crawl about on our pets are fleas. The big ones are always females; the little jumpers may be either males or young females. Fleas are a serious threat to the health of animals. They carry and spread tapeworms, bubonic plague, and heartworm. They also help spread summer skin diseases, cause loss of weight and poor coats on their hosts.

There are four common types of fleas: the human flea, dog flea, cat flea, and the sticktight flea. The human flea may breed on cats as well as on humans. The dog flea and the cat flea infest either dogs or cats, but prefer their specific hosts. When they bite humans it is only because they lack a dog or cat to feed on. The sticktight flea is most often found infesting the rims of the ears of animals but may also be found attached to others parts of the body.

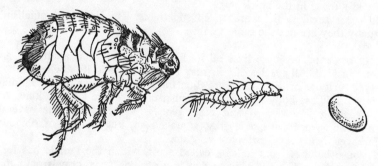

Stages of the flea, enlarged fifty times. Left, adult; center, newly hatched larva; right, egg.

Fleas produce large numbers of eggs, which drop off the host. The eggs sometimes get into cracks in the floor, into a sandbox, or into the furniture where the pet sleeps, and lie there in a dormant state for many months before conditions become right for their development. Some hatch very soon after they are dropped. Moisture and heat are essential for hatching. The egg is deliquescent, absorbing water from the air, so that whenever the weather becomes warm and humid, flea eggs soon hatch. In excessively dry climates fleas are almost unknown.

Out of the egg comes a worm, the larva. The worm feeds on organic matter such as scales from cat skin. It grows quickly. When it reaches the size of a very small maggot, it spins a cocoon and pupates like the caterpillar. Out of these cocoons come males and females, and at this stage they look very much alike. They are able to jump prodigious distances and are remarkably well protected against pressure. If you roll one tightly between your fingers and let it go, it will jump about as well as it did before.

After they hatch, fleas crawl up anything vertical and wait there, about a foot from the ground or floor, for a host to pass. If your pet is taken out of your home during the summer, you may find after a few weeks that the fleas are attacking you instead. The fleas you find in the house have developed from eggs which were dropped from your pet, and since the original host has been removed, they use you as a substitute. Nor are the fleas confined to the house or cattery. You may easily be flea-bitten in the garden if your pet had the run of the grounds and eggs were dropped there.

Sticktight fleas do not move about or jump, but cling to the skin, often in large clusters. The female burrows into the skin and lays her eggs in the ulcers she produces. After the eggs hatch the larvae fall to the ground, where they complete their development in about four weeks, when conditions are right. This flea is more prevalent in warm climates than in cold. Not only dogs, cats, and other four-legged pets are infested by sticktight fleas, but birds as well. Such an infestation is far more lethal to birds, especially those in the chick stage.

In some sections ticks are called sticktights. This is a colloquialism. Actually they are not the same thing.

THE LOUSE: The louse lives all its life—embryonic and adult—on an animal or bird. All species of pets may be infested, and it is believed that no type of louse can live for more than three or four days off the animal or bird on whose body it depends for sustenance. There are two kinds of lice—sucking and biting—and each type is subclassified into several species. Some are red, some gray, some bluish, but in spite of obvious differences their life histories are very similar.

A louse hatches from its egg, called a nit, which the female has fastened to a hair. The little louse, if it is a sucking type, crawls onto the body of the animal, fastens its mouth in the skin, and sucks blood. A large number can suck so much blood and give off such a toxin that the host often becomes anemic and dies. The biting louse, on the other hand, feeds on skin scales and organic matter as well as on blood. The males and females copulate, the female's body fills with eggs, the female lets go of the skin and, crawling on the hairs, attaches to them tiny silvery eggs which are large enough to be seen. The eggs of the biting louse hatch in five to eight days; those of the sucking louse in ten to twelve days. The young mature two or three weeks after hatching. Lice do not drop off their hosts spontaneously. In general, infestation is spread by contact and by close association. Apparently lice move from one host to another of a different species quite easily. For example, dogs and cats kept in close proximity are usually infested equally.

Lice are frequently a cause of death for whole litters of kittens. The owner may be unaware that the catta is infested with lice, but, when the pet has kittens, the lice tend to leave the mother and gravitate to the kittens. Apparently the latter are more tender morsels. Before the owner knows it, the kittens have developed a leathery feeling, fail to thrive, and

 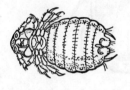 

Lice and nits, enlarged twenty-five times. Left, blood-sucking louse; center, biting louse; right, nit glued to hairs.

die. Every litter of kittens should be watched constantly for the presence of lice.

Scratching by cats is one of the means by which lice are spread. The cat's skin itches when infested, and his scratching will naturally remove a small number of the parasites. It is believed that this is one of the chief means of transferring lice from one cat to another, provided, of course, that the next cat comes along within three days. If nits are attached to the hairs which the cat breaks off in scratching, they may lie around for a considerable period before hatching.

One type of human louse, *Pediculus capitis,* can live on cats. In many cases, pets which have been treated for lice have become reinfested by lice from human beings. Fortunately, not all types of lice are able to infest both species.

THE TICK: Ticks are rapidly becoming a very great problem to cat owners and they are often a nuisance in the house, even in a home where no pet is kept. Ticks feed on many species of domestic animals as well as on wild ones, and some are found on birds. One characteristic of the most common ticks found on pets and man is the necessity for each to feed on blood at some stage of its life.

Dog ticks, wood ticks, spotted-fever ticks, Pacific Coast ticks, brown dog ticks, lone-star ticks, Gulf Coast ticks, blacklegged ticks—all are common names for the several kinds of ticks. Some kinds are known by several names. All of them are very much alike and all have similar life histories.

Ticks pass through four stages: egg, seed tick, nymph, and adult. The female lays enormous numbers of eggs in a mass on the ground or in a clump of grass. There may be as many as three thousand to six thousand eggs in one such mass. When the American dog tick hatches from the egg as a seed tick, it has six legs. It attaches itself to a rodent which car-

Ticks, enlarged six times. Left shows adult female before feeding; right, adult male.

ries it about for from two to twelve days and loses it after it has become engorged with blood. By this time the tick has eight legs, has molted, and is called a nymph. It again attaches itself to a rodent and for three to ten days rides and engorges blood, then drops off and molts again. It is now mature and, in order to attach itself to a larger animal, gravitates close to a path through the woods and climbs a bush, where it is rubbed off onto its new host. It is an interesting if unexpected fact that studies made of these pests show greater concentrations along paths than in the pathless woods.

After the female has attached herself to a host, the male crawls under her and mating occurs while the female is filling with blood. If you look under the big beanlike body of female ticks on an infested animal, you will almost invariably find a male—a small creature which does not grow nearly so large as his mate. The female engorges on the host for from five to thirteen days, then drops off, falls to the ground, and, being enormous and practically helpless, lays her eggs and dies.

Some ticks are not quite so discriminating as the American dog tick. Some spend their seed-tick and nymph stages on birds and even reptiles, and one, the Gulf Coast tick, spends its immature stages on birds which live on the ground, such as quail, turkeys, and pheasants. Still others feed on birds exclusively, notably *Argas reflexus,* whose host is the pigeon.

The brown dog tick, which is becoming the most widely distributed tick in the North, prefers to pass its early life inside dwellings. It is often found under picture moldings, behind baseboards, and in furniture. Even adults can be found in such hideaways. Fortunately they do not suck human blood as some other species do.

MITES: Mange on cats is caused by mange mites, which are so small that they cannot be identified without a microscope.

The *red mange mite* (*Demodex canis*) is also known as demodectic mange mite and follicular mange mite. When a cat shows a baldish area under the eyes, on the cheeks, on the forehead, or on the front legs, he may have red mange. If it is not checked early, it may soon have serious consequences. One of these is the bacterial infection which often develops, causing pustules and intense reddening of the skin, with violent scratching from the irritation.

The young mites, as they hatch from the eggs, appear to be elongated globs, but they mature very quickly to look like minute eight-legged worms. They live in sebaceous glands and in hair follicles, so that when an animal has been infected the hair soon drops off the infected area. They reproduce prodigiously. In eight days a thousand female mites may have increased to twelve thousand. In eight more days these may have become 132,000.

Sarcoptic mange mites (*Sarcoptes scabeii*) produce a disease called scabies. The mite is round, with four pairs of short legs. The female

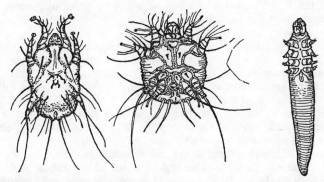

Mites which attack mammalian pets, all greatly enlarged. Left, ear mange mite; center, sarcoptic mange mite; right, demodectic mange mite, also called red and follicular mange mite.

tunnels into the skin and lays from twenty to forty eggs, which hatch in three to seven days. One female can easily produce 1,500,000 descendants in three months. The newly hatched larvae have three pairs of legs, but they molt to become nymphs which molt still again before they become adults. This process requires two to three weeks for completion. Only the adult female burrows beneath the outside layers of skin; males and immature forms live on the surface under scabs or skin scales.

Cat mites (*Notoedres cati*) are found on cats and rabbits. They are so similar to sarcoptic mites that it is not necessary to describe them.

Ear mange mites (*Otodectes cynotis*) are round and have somewhat longer legs than the sarcoptic mites. They live in the ear canal, causing a crumbly wax which is quite distinctive from normal wax. Actually the substance found in the ear is composed more of scabs than wax, because the mites pierce the skin to suck plasma or lymph. The irritation causes animals to shake their heads sharply, which helps distribute the mites to other animals. Some cats scratch their ears so vigorously that blood tumors develop between the layers of the ear flaps.

The life history of the ear mite is believed to be similar to that of the sarcoptic mite.

Sand flea (*Leptus irritans*) is also called chigger, harvest mite, chigga, chigre, jigger, red bug. Adult red bugs, which are quite large, do not bother humans or pets. Nor does the second, or nymph, stage. The larvae alone attack animals, and then only shortly after they have hatched. Like ticks, they suck blood and drop off to molt. After this molt the nymphs may even feed on plants, but not on mammals. The tiny larvae annoy pets a great deal. They often cause severe scratching and sometimes loss of weight, without the owner's understanding the cause.

Internal Parasites. Many pets suffer from parasites which damage the inside of the body, in contrast to those we have previously considered, which attack from the outside.

ROUNDWORMS include all worms under the classification of nematodes, such as hookworms, whipworms, esophageal worms, heartworms, lungworms, and kidney worms, as well as the large roundworms which most pet owners recognize. But as we use the term "roundworms" in this section, we shall limit it to the whitish or yellowish worm which grows up to five inches long in the stomach and intestines of pets, is pointed at both ends, and inclined, while alive, to curl up. When dead, it straightens out so that it may appear to be simply bowed at the ends.

Although there are several kinds of intestinal roundworms, their life histories are much the same. The eggs pass out of the animal with every bowel movement. In less than a week, if the temperature and moisture are propitious, a little worm forms in the egg. In other words, it has to incubate before it can hatch. Now this egg is in the infective stage and, as such, it will live for years, waiting to be picked up by a suitable host. It may enter the host in any one of dozens of ways. A catta may walk in a spot where feces have entirely disintegrated but where the eggs remain. They stick to her feet; she licks herself and becomes infested. Even cats which live all their lives inside homes, are pan trained, and never make mistakes, are frequently infested for the simple reason that the material in their pans is not changed often enough. Pans should be changed once every four days or oftener.

The egg enters the stomach, and the shell, or coat, is digested, liberating the embryo. If it happens to be an egg of *Toxascaris leonina* the larva moves along into the intestine, where it penetrates into the lining, remains there for ten days, and grows. Finally it returns into the lumen, or hollow part of the intestine, and continues to grow to maturity, feeding on the animal's partially digested food.

If the roundworms are of the *Toxascaris canis* or *T. cati* varieties, they are much more harmful to their host. In the intestine the little larvae bore

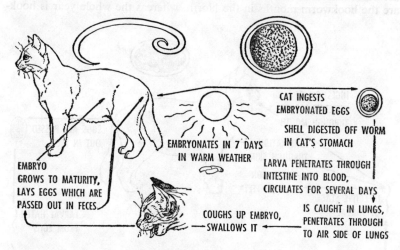

CAT INGESTS
EMBRYONATED EGGS

SHELL DIGESTED OFF WORM
IN CAT'S STOMACH

EMBRYONATES IN 7 DAYS
IN WARM WEATHER

LARVA PENETRATES THROUGH
INTESTINE INTO BLOOD,
CIRCULATES FOR SEVERAL DAYS

EMBRYO
GROWS TO MATURITY,
LAYS EGGS WHICH ARE
PASSED OUT IN FECES

IS CAUGHT IN LUNGS,
PENETRATES THROUGH
TO AIR SIDE OF LUNGS

COUGHS UP EMBRYO,
SWALLOWS IT

Life history of a common roundworm. Above, left, mature worm; right, egg magnified four hundred times.

through the intestinal lining and enter the blood stream, where they grow. Many may be found in the liver and spleen while on their way to the lungs. In the lungs they penetrate through from the blood vessels into the air spaces and are moved on to the windpipe. Up this they move in mucous secretions until the irritation causes the animal to cough and gag as if clearing his throat. The small amount of mucus with the worms in it is swallowed. Down the gullet go the parasites, which from then on until old age overtakes them, or worm medicine kills them, live in the intestine, migrating up and down at will, copulating and laying thousands of eggs.

Not only do roundworms give off a toxin, but the migrations of the larvae in the body, especially in the lungs, frequently cause death. The pneumonia they cause is called verminous pneumonia.

Hookworms are minute leeches, living on blood which they suck from the intestine, to which they cling with a set of hooks or teeth about the mouth. Hookworms cause anemia and loss of condition. A heavy infestation causes death.

The animal hookworm is not the same worm which causes so much hookworm anemia in humans. No animal hookworm is over five-eighths of an inch long for females and slightly less for males. Three types are found distributed in different sections. *Ancylostomum caninum* has a very wide distribution, while *A. braziliense* is more or less confined to the South and tropical regions. *Uncinaria stenocephala* is a northern hookworm.

The life history of the hookworm is interesting. The eggs, passed out of the host in the feces, need warmth to develop. Therefore the warm months are the hookworm months in the North, whereas the whole year is hook-

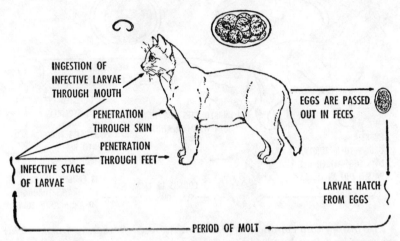

Life history of the hookworm. In the body, the larvae behave much like the roundworm larvae, spending their early days in the cat's blood and lungs. They are coughed up and swallowed. They then attach themselves to the small intestine by their hooks. Above, left, hookworm life size; right, egg enlarged four hundred times.

worm time in the South. After the eggs have incubated from three to six days, larvae emerge. These are called the first-stage larvae. Three days later the larvae molt and become the second-stage larvae. Eight days later they molt again to become third-stage or infective larvae and then lie waiting for a host. Hookworms can bore through the skin to reach the blood stream. More often they are ingested through the mouth and are sometimes inhaled with dust kicked up in a place where stools have disintegrated and become mixed with soil.

If the larvae have reached the blood stream by boring through the skin or internal tissues, they eventually reach the lungs, bore into the air sacs, are finally coughed up, swallowed, reach the intestine, and molt two more times. By three weeks after they first entered the body as larvae, hookworms are large enough to lay eggs. Sometimes hundreds cling to an animal's intestinal lining. They are very debilitating. A hookworm can suck half a teaspoonful of blood in a week. A thousand can suck one and a half drinking glasses *in a day*. No wonder hookworms cause anemia!

With these facts in mind, two questions can now be answered:

How can mother animals lick their offspring clean of feces without becoming infested with intestinal parasites? The answer is that all the eggs of parasites have to undergo several days' incubation to be infective. The eggs which the mother cleans from her offspring pass through her digestive tract and lie in her feces, unharmed, to become infective later.

How can two-weeks-old kittens be passing eggs of hookworms, for instance, when about three weeks are required for the eggs to develop into worms old enough to lay eggs? The answer is that the kittens were infected while they were embryos. Since several species of parasites spend some time in the blood, these larvae manage to penetrate through the placenta and into the blood of the embryos, whence they find the intestinal tract.

Whipworms: Considering its small size, the whipworm is one of the most debilitating parasites that pets harbor. The whip handle or body of the worm is approximately half an inch long, but the whip part is about one and a half inches. This part is sewed into the lining of the intestine,

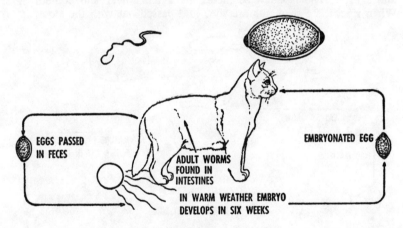

EGGS PASSED IN FECES

ADULT WORMS FOUND IN INTESTINES

EMBRYONATED EGG

IN WARM WEATHER EMBRYO DEVELOPS IN SIX WEEKS

Life history of the whipworm. Above, left, whipworm, life size; right, egg, enlarged four hundred times.

but the pest can withdraw it to move. The worm is very thin; even the body is no thicker than the diameter of coarse sewing thread. Whipworms lay yellowish eggs of a lemon shape. Incubation in the soil requires about three weeks at a fairly high temperature before the embryos are infective. So far as is known, upon being ingested, the larvae are liberated and fasten themselves at once along the intestine, chiefly in the large bowel or colon.

TAPEWORMS: It is comparatively easy to remove tapeworms from cats. The hardest part in their control is in the prevention of infestation. This requires a knowledge of tapeworm life history.

There are two general kinds of tapeworms—the armed and the unarmed. The armed have suckers and hooks with which they cling, while the unarmed are equipped with only a pair of grooves which hold to the intestinal lining. A large armed tapeworm has powerful devices which enable the worm to hold fast despite all of the pull exerted on it by the passing food. It seems almost impossible that the little head can hold all of the worm, yet that is what it does. Besides the host in which they spend most of their existence, all tapeworms require an intermediate host and, in some cases, two such hosts. All are composed of a head to which are added a series of flat segments, joined one to another.

The Flea-Host Tapeworm (Dipylidium caninum): This is the most common tapeworm of our pets and occurs in dogs, foxes, and cats. It is about a foot long. The head is smaller than a small pinhead and the segments close to the head are stretched to the thickness of a thread. This section is called the neck. As the worm grows, the segments become wider and shorter. The last few segments are again longer and contain eggs. When ripe, these segments are shed and passed out with the stool. If no

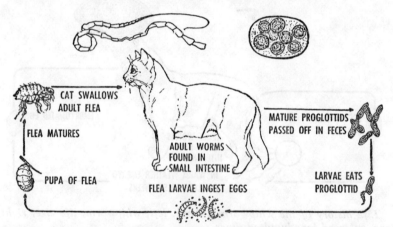

CAT SWALLOWS ADULT FLEA

FLEA MATURES

PUPA OF FLEA

ADULT WORMS FOUND IN SMALL INTESTINE

FLEA LARVAE INGEST EGGS

MATURE PROGLOTTIDS PASSED OFF IN FECES

LARVAE EATS PROGLOTTID

Life history of the flea-host tapeworm. Above, left, worm, life size. Often grows to be eighteen inches long. Right, capsule with eggs, enlarged one hundred and fifty times.

stool is present, the segment is moved downward to the anus, where it may cling until it dries into a small, brownish, seedlike grain which drops from the pet.

The eggs are not extruded without considerable pressure to the segment; then they appear in capsules and look, under a microscope, like bunches of grapes. When your veterinarian makes a fecal examination and tells you that your cat is free from worms, do not blame him for not detecting the presence of tapeworms. After you have seen a dozen segments, you may have an examination made and receive a negative report. Your veterinarian studies the stool for eggs, and if the tapeworm has laid no eggs before the examination, he won't find any. Finding segments is the only effective way to determine the presence of this worm.

Fleas and biting lice are the intermediate tapeworm hosts. When fleas are in their larval stage, they feed on tapeworm segments, among other foods. The eggs from these segments develop into tapeworm larvae as the flea matures. If an animal ingests the flea, the tapeworm larva is released and attaches itself to the intestinal wall, where it remains and grows.

The Rabbit-Host Tapeworm (*Taenia pisiformis*): This is a coarser worm than the flea-host tapeworm. Sometimes five to six feet long, its segments are larger and more active. The intermediate host is the rabbit or hare. This tapeworm lays many eggs which pass out of the cat in his stool and cling to vegetation. Rabbits eating the vegetation become in-

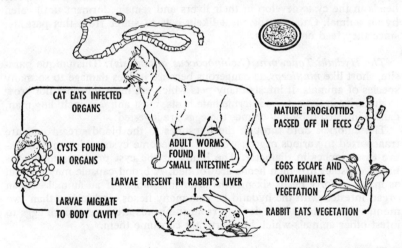

CAT EATS INFECTED ORGANS

CYSTS FOUND IN ORGANS

ADULT WORMS FOUND IN SMALL INTESTINE

MATURE PROGLOTTIDS PASSED OFF IN FECES

EGGS ESCAPE AND CONTAMINATE VEGETATION

LARVAE PRESENT IN RABBIT'S LIVER

LARVAE MIGRATE TO BODY CAVITY

RABBIT EATS VEGETATION

Life history of the rabbit-host tapeworm. Above, left, worm, life size. Often grows to be two or three feet long. Right, egg, enlarged four hundred times.

fested. The larvae work into the liver of the rabbits to develop, and from there into the abdominal cavity, where they attach themselves to intestines in small cysts. When a cat eats an infested rabbit, it too soon becomes infested.

Cats seldom kill adult rabbits and never kill hares. Baby rabbits, which are often killed by cats, are not likely to be infested with the cysts. How, then, do cats acquire the rabbit-host worms? It would seem by eating rabbits or hares which were shot and lost by hunters or killed by dogs or foxes. A healthy, hungry cat will not eschew so delectable an item. Since dogs, foxes, and cats have so many parasites in common, dogs and foxes often help spread parasites to cats and vice versa. This kind of tapeworm is an excellent illustration.

The Pork, Beef, and Sheep Tapeworms (Taenia soleum, T. saginata, T. marginata, T. ovis) have been reported as long as fifteen feet. It is rare to find these tapeworms in city pets. In country animals, which may feast on carcasses of dead animals, these infestations may occur. Hogs, cattle, or sheep which have fed in pastures where human excreta has been deposited can eat grass to which tapeworm eggs cling. The cat or other pet eats flesh from these animals and becomes infested from the cysts containing the tapeworm heads.

The Rodent-Host Tapeworm (Taenia taeniaformis) is a widely distributed form which probably does its worst damage to cats. Rats, mice, squirrels, muskrats, and other rodents may act as intermediate hosts. The heads in the cysts develop in their livers and remain dormant until eaten by an animal. Cats are the most likely pets to suffer from this parasite, since they feed on the host.

The Hydatid Tapeworm (Echinococcus granulosis): This unique parasite, short like *multiceps,* is dangerous because it does damage to so many species of animals. It infests many pets which eat meat but does not grow to maturity in the cat. As intermediate hosts, most animals, including man, can be infested if by any chance the eggs are ingested.

The embryos bore through the intestines to the blood stream and are transported to various organs where they become cysts which may measure three inches in diameter. The lining of the cyst produces numerous brood capsules in which heads are formed. A brood capsule may contain as many as forty heads six months after infestation. If an animal eats an organ infested with the hydatid he eats many heads, and in less than two months the worms which develop from the heads are laying more eggs to infest other animals which inadvertently consume them.

There are three unarmed tapeworms which are important to pet owners:

The Fish-Host Tapeworm (Diphyllobothrium latum) occurs in cats fed on fresh-water fish, generally within a few hundred miles of the Great Lakes in the United States. *D. mansoni* affects cats in Puerto Rico. *D. mansonides* has been reported in New York and Louisiana.

A human harboring the tapeworm passes out the eggs in feces which are dumped via sewers into the lake. Small crustaceans eat the eggs. In the first type, fish eat the crustaceans; in the latter two types, reptiles, such as frogs, or mammals which swallow the crustaceans can be the second hosts. Cats which eat the fish or reptiles or infested mammals become infested in turn. Raw whitefish, trout, salmon, pike, perch have all been incriminated as passing the cysts of these huge worms to pets.

Some of these worms have three thousand to four thousand segments and at their widest may be half an inch or even more across.

Taenia serialis: This is an intermediate worm between two and three feet long which dogs and foxes frequently carry in their intestines, and which they contract by eating cysts and their inhabitants—the heads which may number a dozen or more—when they eat hares, rabbits, or squirrels. Some cysts may be an inch in diameter and cause the intermediate host great discomfort. The rabbits or squirrels become infested from eating grass, nuts, or other vegetation to which eggs of the worm are sticking.

It should be noted in passing that many pets which are only intermediate hosts can be made very sick by the cysts of tapeworms developing within their organs and muscles as well as in their intestines. Rabbits are notorious in this respect.

PROTOZOA

Besides these already mentioned, there is a different kind of organism which produces diseases of a very serious nature in pets. This organism is the protozoa, the lowest form of animal life. There are several forms, of which the sporozoite named *coccidia* are most important. These one-celled minute organisms live among the cells of the intestinal lining. Their life history is exceedingly complicated, and the damage they do is accounted for by the enormous numbers that develop before the body eventually overcomes them. Two other types, piroplasma and anaplasma, cause considerable damage as parasites of pets.

Coccidia: Each species of animal and bird is infested by specific types of coccidia, but some have more than one. Dogs and cats have three principal forms affecting both species. Rabbits, poultry, and even reptiles are afflicted. All types of coccidia are extremely prevalent, the year round in warm climates and in the summer in the North.

In size, coccidia are microscopic. The form found in the feces, the egg or oocyst, is roundish with a nucleus inside. Some oocysts show divided nuclei. The forms infesting cats are *Isospora rivolta, I. bigemina,* and *I. felis.* Rabbits are principally infested with *Eimeria perforans.* Birds may be host to at least a dozen species. Some are residents of the cecum and some are found in the intestine. Guinea pigs, rats, and squirrels each have specific types.

After it has been outside of the host for several days, the coccidia egg form develops into the infestive stage, provided conditions are favorable. Flies carry it to feeding pans or animals pick it up by licking their feet or by getting feces into their mouths. Inside the animal the coating of the egg form is digested and the infestive forms which have developed in the egg are released. These bore into the cells lining the intestine and develop until they divide into other bodies.

Coccidia. Three common types as they appear when enlarged through a microscope. Left, Isospora bigemina; *center,* Isospora rivolta; *right,* Isospora felis.

This division and growth damages or destroys the cells, but these new forms now enter other cells and repeat the cycle. This goes on through several divisions and attacking of new cells, until at length male and female forms are produced. The males fertilize the females and thus produce the egg form which is passed out with the feces and deposited with the loose stool to infest other animals or birds.

Coccidiosis is a disease of self-limiting character. Once over a specific species of coccidia, the animal can no longer be infested, but this does not apply to all other species of the disease. A cat recovered from *I. rivolta* can be infested with *I. felis* as readily as though he had never been infested at all.

Piroplasma and Anaplasma: These are carried by ticks. They are minute animals which live in the red blood cells and produce diseases called piroplasmosis and anaplasmosis. Of course the disease is due to the enormous numbers of piroplasma which develop, and to their effect on the efficiency of the red cells in transporting carbon dioxide and oxygen.

Two or three days after infestation the first symptoms appear. The number of red corpuscles is reduced and the white increased. The color from the broken-down red cells being thrown off by the body causes reddening of the urine. The parasites multiply by division. New ones attack other red cells.

An intermediate form does not develop in the vector of this parasite as in the case of tapeworms or heartworms; injections of infested blood into a susceptible animal will be all that is necessary to start the disease.

So far the disease has been confined to the warm climates where ticks are prevalent, but with the increase of ticks in the North, piroplasmosis may become a Northern problem as well.

TUMORS AND CANCER

That lump growing under the cat's skin which develops slowly, that rapidly growing tumor on the shoulder, that soft pliant swelling, those lumps in the breast of your pet—what are they? Will they cost his life? Should they be removed? Will they return if they are removed? The veterinarian hears scores of such questions. Many cat owners have misconceptions about growths.

A tumor is a growth of new, useless tissue growing independently of the surrounding tissue but not replacing it.

In medical terminology the term *malignant* means a virulent growth that tends to go from bad to worse.

A *benign* growth is only a relative term. Compared to a malignant tumor, it stays within itself and does not recur elsewhere. But what growth could really be benign? A wart? Even so small and seemingly innocuous a growth causes itching and sometimes pain. No tumor is really benign in the common sense of the word.

Cancer is a malignant tumor. The word comes from the Latin, meaning *crab*. This implies that it is a growth which invades other tissue by extending crablike tentacles. But this is an old definition, hardly acceptable in the light of newer knowledge. There is cancer which grows in a lump apparently as benign as any nonmalignant tumor. Then this lump in the lungs, let us say, sends off a bud or cell into the blood stream which is halted in the skin on the pet's back, where it grows. Careful microscopic examination of the lump after removal discloses that it is tissue characteristic of the lungs, even though it is growing in the skin. This is called a *metastasis*. Surely such a tumor is a cancer.

Carcinomas arise in the skin, in the intestinal linings, and in all tissues which develop from the same original embryonic sources. *Sarcomas* are tumors made up of connective tissue—the part of the cat's body which binds it together and supports it.

Under these two classes, carinomas and sarcomas, fall the various kinds of tumors. If your veterinarian tells you your cat has a malignant melanotic sarcoma, you know it is a tumor of the connective tissue, that it gives off buds or invades the adjacent tissue, or both. Melanotic means black, so it is a darkly pigmented growth. A pigment cell must have gone wild.

What causes these growths? The causes of a few kinds are known. Some believe a virus is the initiating agent of certain forms, if not all. Irritation, such as the constant rubbing of a snag tooth on the lip, certain hormones, contact with irritating chemicals, inhalation of smoke—all are known to cause some types of growths; for others there is no explanation. Perhaps mutations or sudden changes in the characteristics of a cell are induced by irritation and, once started, simply grow out of control.

When a cut or abrasion occurs in an animal, the body heals it by the growth of surrounding cells. Something in the body applies a brake to this healing growth at the right time. If it didn't, every cut might grow out of all proportion. We are not sure what this brake is. The cancer cells have no brake applied by the body and grow by cell division on and on until they overwhelm the host.

Diagnosis of malignant growths is accomplished by removing a section of the growth and preparing it by an elaborate process of slicing and staining until it can be examined with a microscope by a pathologist who can classify it.

DEFICIENCY DISEASES

Negative as well as positive factors cause disease. Many pets have died from lack of oxygen. There are the obvious cases of suffocation; the carrying cage or shipping crate may be insufficiently ventilated, and when it is opened the pet is found dead. Lack of oxygen, obvious as it is, constitutes a deficiency disease. There are many more subtle deficiencies.

Some deficiencies produce what should be called conditions, not diseases. A disease is a morbid process with characteristic symptoms. Thirst is neither a disease nor the result of disease. The symptoms of dehydration are cured by water consumption. Anemia is a disease in one sense, a condition in another. Millions of humans go about in an anemic condition. In general, deficiency diseases are quite easily cured, simply by furnishing the body with the missing elements.

Anemia is caused by a shortage of oxygen. We have considered the obvious form but not the symptoms. *When an animal suffocates, the pink color of the tissue turns blue.* A lack of oxygen in the tissues can be produced by many causes other than lack of air. The blood may simply be unable to carry it about the body. This, in turn, may result from a diminished supply of red cells in the blood. There may be too few, or the chemical composition of their components may be inadequate.

Hookworms are the most common cause of an inadequate supply of red cells. Their blood consumption strains the blood-building equipment, which cannot keep up with the loss. A hookworm-infested animal lacks animation and gets out of breath easily. He shows all the symptoms of anemia, as though blood had been drawn from his arteries or veins. Little kittens are frequently found to be anemic because of hookworm infestation. There is so little iron in milk that they cannot regain their losses despite deworming, and they frequently die because of their owner's ignorance of this fact.

Heavy infestations of sucking lice may also cause anemia. Some cats harbor so many lice that they touch one another in places. The animal's gums reveal a sickly pallor; it can't stand cold and loses its appetite. The basic condition is probably aggravated by toxins from the lice. Animals are often seriously weakened by these parasites. Dogs have actually been known to die from lice infestation.

Blood diseases, rare in animals, produce an altered blood picture. Some ordinary diseases alter the proportion of red and white cells, not by reducing the number of red cells but by increasing the number of white cells. This is not anemia. Diseases which produce toxins or attack the blood-building apparatus of the body produce anemia by reducing the number of red cells.

A lack of iron or copper or both causes anemia. Insufficient iron is responsible for a shortage of hemoglobin, and though there may be a full quota of red cells, they can't pick up and transport oxygen. Copper deficiency also causes anemia. Copper is not part of hemoglobin, but is concerned with its formation.

Nicotinic-acid deficiency, which causes black tongue, a shortage of vitamin-B-complex factors, pyridoxin deficiency, all cause anemia.

Rickets: After anemia, rickets is probably the most common deficiency disease. It is a result of a lack of one or more of these factors: vitamin D, calcium, or phosphorus.

Eclampsia is a disease of nursing mother animals, caused by an inadequate amount of calcium or an inadequacy in the parathyroid glands.

Mineral Deficiencies: The only two minerals of great consequence to pets, especially cats, are calcium and iron, but in passing we must recognize that the absence of others causes dire consequences. Iodine is essential. Its lack causes goiter in animals, and when pregnant females are iodine-starved they may produce abnormal young called cretins. Common salt is also essential. Since 99 per cent of the calcium in the body is found in the skeleton, obviously a calcium deficiency results in poor skeletal development, as we saw in the case of rickets. But calcium does more than develop bone. It is necessary to proper nerve function and acts almost like some vitamins as a catalyst or "marrying agent" between other minerals. Bad teeth may be traced to a fluorine deficiency. Cobalt and boron, though needed in minute quantities, produce sickness through their absence. Potassium deficiency causes paralysis, and so forth.

Vitamin Deficiencies: The subject of vitamins has been covered in Chapter 3.

A number of deficiency diseases of an odd nature are due to what are known as inactivators. For example, a substance in raw fish destroys vitamin B, causing a deficiency, which in turn produces a paralysis known as Chastek. Cooking destroys the inactivator, which is, of course, why we recommend that fish be cooked for our pets. In raw eggs there is an inactivator, avertin, which inactivates biotin (one of the B-complex vitamins) and prevents egg-white digestion. Cooking destroys avertin also and prevents biotin deficiency.

5. Drugs and Their Uses

*N*OT long ago a cat with even a small spot of red mange was practically doomed. Pneumonia was a killer; leptospirosis, streptococcic, and meningitic diseases progressed unhindered; intestinal infections often proved fatal. Today we are able to treat all of these diseases with confidence. We have developed new uses and better methods of administering many of the older drugs. The discovery of the sulfas and such antibiotics as penicillin, streptomycin, and aureomycin has made it possible to cope with many of the most devastating diseases. We have developed new insect destroyers of great potency and seem to be on the verge of perfecting others in the near future. Equipped with a vastly improved arsenal of drugs and aided by an enormously expanded knowledge of the actions of those drugs, veterinary medicine has made astonishing progress in the last decade.

The value of these life-saving drugs is too often taken for granted by the cat owner. All of them are actually of the greatest importance to him, for in a very real sense it is they that have made it possible for him to own pets and keep them healthy and vigorous. If the owner is to be able to take full advantage of this new science of health, he must know some of the fundamental facts about drugs and their actions so that he can use them more intelligently and more effectively. Obviously there is no need for him to understand the pharmaceutical intricacies of the various medicinal preparations, but he should certainly know the characteristics of the several general types of drugs and be familiar with their common uses.

With a very few exceptions, there is no reason why your veterinarian should not tell you exactly what he has prescribed for your cat. Your understanding of what is being given and why will make for more intelligent home care. And there is no reason why you should not be able to understand what your veterinarian tells you and what he has prescribed. There is a small revolution coming to pass in prescription writing. Latin names of drugs are being dropped and the metric system is being used instead of the old avoirdupois with its minims, drams, scruples, et cetera. The U. S. Federal Food and Drug Administration insists that the simplest names or the exact chemical names be used on labels. A few years ago you might have found a label with *adeps* and *terebinthina* among its elements. Today you would find *lard* and *turpentine*.

In order to understand the uses of drugs, you must first understand that drugs work in several different ways. Some drugs do not kill germs outside of the body as well as they do in the blood stream; working in combination with the bacteria-destroying white cells in the blood, they are highly efficient. Without the white cells the drugs are of little value, and the cells without the drugs are helpless. This might be called a synergistic action. Phenols (such as creosol, thymol, tars), and mercurial salts, such as bichloride, kill by causing the protoplasm of the cells to precipitate. Other drugs, such as arsenic, prevent the multiplication of bacteria. Still others combine chemically with some constituent of the protoplasm of the organism. Some have oxidizing properties and some interfere with the functioning within the bacteria themselves. There are drugs that may not be given together, being spoken of as *incompatibles.* Those likely to be given from the home medicine chest are few and will be indicated in the course of the discussion. There are other drugs that are incompatible with species; for example, phenol for cats. Still others produce odd effects; for instance, morphine when given to a cat.

The success of all drugs depends on their being used in proper concentration. They must be strong enough to kill bacteria, yet weak enough to cause no harm to the tissues of the animal. The required strengths for the various drugs have been worked out by long study and testing, and your veterinarian's instructions should be followed explicitly. When he gives you pills or tablets with instructions to give them at certain intervals, he is usually calculating how fast the drug is eliminated, in order to be sure that your pet always has enough in his system to accomplish results. If you cannot give the prescribed doses at the prescribed intervals, it is better to leave the cat with the veterinarian, where the drugs will be given as they should be.

Which brings us to the question of body repair. Always remember that the body of a pet is composed of many delicate organs. Its potential length of life is more or less determined at conception. With good care and nonexposure to some diseases against which it may not be resistant, the pet should live its normal life span. But when it becomes sick there is no certainty that, with the jab of a needle and a dose of medicine, it will recover. Life isn't like that. Recovery takes care—and time. Think how long it takes for a cut on one's hand to heal. Cells slowly grow together, scar tissue forms and shrinks, and several weeks may pass before the area looks normal. Yet, too often, we expect pets to recover in a day or two from diseases more telling and debilitating than influenza is to humans. Drugs can and do have marvelous properties but they can't abolish the element of time.

Great care must be taken not to overdose, a common tendency on the part of laymen. If a teaspoonful cures, then three teaspoonfuls should cure in a third the time, he often reasons. Sometimes it kills. Doses have been worked out by pharmacologists with great care. The animal's size and the effect desired determine the dose. Overdoses are wasteful even when not dangerous. One most interesting fact is that the larger the animal, the less drug is needed proportionately. Doses are proportional to surface area rather than to weight, but weight is easier to measure. Whereas one might think that a smaller animal was tenderer and should have less than his proportional weight might indicate, the opposite is true.

GENERAL ANESTHETICS AND SEDATIVES

The drugs which allay pain and make surgery possible for cats include: those which are administered as a vapor, inhaled into the lungs, absorbed by the blood, and carried to the brain, where they temporarily deaden the sense of feeling and consciousness; those which are injected in liquid form; and those given by stomach.

Ether and **chloroform** are commonly employed in veterinary practice. Animals anesthetized with ether first experience an irritation to the nasal passages, then a moment of great excitement or stimulation, and finally a gradual loss of consciousness and inability to feel pain. The ether is lost from the body as it was gained, by being carried back to the lungs and exhaled until the blood is purified.

Ether is dangerous because it is explosive. All flames must be kept away. It is safer as an anesthetic than some others because an overdose will cause breathing to stop first and heart action last. Thus, if an animal stops breathing, artificial respiration often saves his life.

Chloroform, obtainable by laymen without a prescription, has been used widely for euthanasia. As such, it is a crude method, definitely inferior to the ether, chloral, or injectables which any veterinarian can give.

Among the general anesthetics used in small animal veterinary practice are those of a group usually injected into a vein, the abdominal cavity, or given by mouth. These are *chloral hydrate, phenobarbital, pentobarbital* (Nembutal), and *pentothal*.

Chloral hydrate is most dangerous because the margin of safety is less than that of the others. A very little more than the amount required for anesthesia will produce death.

Phenobarbital, well known to laymen under the trade name Luminal, is one of the oldest barbiturates from the standpoint of use. Its introduction followed that of the first barbiturate, Barbital. Given in both tablet and liquid form, it is one of the longest-acting of this class of drugs.

Barbiturates, of which phenobarbital is a good example, are composed basically of urea and malonic acid and have the following general actions:

Depressant. The size of the dose determines the degree of depression.

Sedative. Results are quickly accomplished, usually within an hour.

Analgesic. Barbiturates relieve pain without causing unconsciousness.

Anticonvulsant. Occasionally almost anesthetic doses must be given to animals convulsing severely, but they are effective even against the convulsions of strychnine poisoning. For this purpose, injectable barbiturates like Nembutal (pentobarbital) are preferable.

Anesthetic. Phenobarbital is seldom used for this purpose. When overdoses are given, the blood pressure falls and breathing becomes slowed.

Pentobarbital is the anesthetic most generally used for pets today—even more frequently than ether. It produces a deep sleep, which starts even before the hypodermic needle is out of the vein and lasts for several hours. The anesthetic dose is one c.c. of solution (one grain) for each five pounds of body weight. If the animal is kept quiet and in the dark, he may sleep until the last of the drug has been destroyed by the body, mostly by the liver. The pet may get up, stretch, drink, and show no ill effects. He has been unconscious long enough for a numbness to have set in around incisions and for all trace of surgical shock in minor operations to pass.

If your veterinarian is planning to use a barbiturate for an anesthetic, there are several things he should be told about your cat, if you know them. If your pet has had an increased thirst, it may suggest kidney disease. Animals with kidney diseases require much smaller amounts of barbiturates given by any route of administration. They are partially poisoned by the wastes in their systems. Liver disease and general debility also make a pet a poor subject for barbiturate anesthesia.

Animals terrified by thunderstorms, explosions from fireworks or blasting, or auto riding can be given small doses of pentobarbital with safety for partial sedation and to produce a temporary loss of fear and memory.

Pentothal is a short-acting general anesthetic which has many virtues but some disadvantages. Your veterinarian may offer you your choice of this or pentobarbital. Don't say, "You're the doctor," but consider the advantages of each. Suppose you want to wait until an operation is over and carry your cat home with you. This often happens in my practice. Do you want to wait for perhaps half an hour and take home an almost completely conscious pet, or would you prefer to take a completely anesthetized one which will lie perfectly quiet? Are you willing to keep him quiet? No radio, no moving about, nothing to disturb his deep slumber. If he rouses, you must realize that he may try to get up, try to walk, act for all the world as if he were intoxicated. He may lie making his legs go as if he were running, or he may moan, cry, even yowl. (People do strange things, too, as they come out of anesthesia.) If pentothal were used, your cat would be all over the anesthesia an hour or two after the operation, but his incision would pain him more. Pentothal is quite safe because, like ether, it first depresses the respiration.

Amytal is sometimes used, and its action is similar to that of pento-barbital.

Ethyl Alcohol. Clients are forever telephoning their veterinarians to say that they have just given their cats a dose of brandy or whisky as a stimulant. Somewhere the layman has picked up the idea that alcohol is a great animal saver. Actually it has so few warranted uses in veterinary medicine that it need be mentioned only to emphasize the fact that it is actually a depressant, rather than the excellent stimulant which most people believe it to be. It stimulates neither the respiration, the heart and blood system, nor the muscles.

Alcohol irritates the skin, injures the cells, has an astringent action, and shrinks tissues; it causes irritation and inflammation to mucous membranes. When injected into tissue, it acts as an anesthetic, but may permanently destroy nerve tissue. Alcohol anesthesia lasts longer than ether or chloroform, but if given in large enough doses to anesthetize, it is too near the fatal dose for safety.

Alcohol has very little germ-killing power, and only at 70 per cent by weight—a percentage difficult to approximate—is it worth using for this purpose.

Never give alcohol to "warm" a pet. All it does is lower the temperature by bringing the blood to the stomach and producing a false sensation of warmth. Nor should it be given as an aphrodisiac. I have known clients to use it in an effort to get shy breeding males to attempt copulation. They have found it often makes them worse.

LOCAL ANESTHETICS

These drugs, which can be injected to cause loss of pain in a given area, are a great boon to animals, doctors, and pet owners. They may be injected over a main nerve trunk, around the area to be anesthetized—for example, around a bad gash which needs to be sutured, or around a tumor which requires removal.

Cocaine is not made from opium, as so many think, but from leaves of trees which grow in Peru and Bolivia. It is dangerous to humans because of addiction, but animals cannot develop addictions without human help. Used locally, it blocks off nervous conduction. Much higher concentrations are needed for main nerve trunks than for terminal branches.

Procaine (also called Novocaine), **butyn,** and **nupercaine** are being more and more widely used. The first is used more widely than the others in veterinary practice. Butyn is frequently used in the eyes to relieve soreness. When adrenalin (epinephrine) is combined with any of the above, the capillaries of the anesthetized area shrink and bleeding is greatly reduced. It is well to remember this if you take home a pet that has been operated on or sutured under a local anesthetic of procaine and adrenalin. When you start for home from the doctor's, there may be no bleeding, but as the effects of the adrenalin wear off, considerable bleeding may ensue, so be prepared. It is nearly always better to leave an animal that has been operated on in a hospital for twelve to twenty-four hours, but so many veterinarians maintain only offices and operating rooms with no facilities for keeping pets that it is often necessary to look after your own pet at home.

Some doctors prefer combinations of local anesthetics, and there are many new ones coming alone. **Urea-and-quinine** is a favorite where very long-lasting anesthesia is desired. Its effects may last for several weeks.

TOPICAL ANESTHETICS

Several of the drugs we have mentioned are also used to deaden pain simply by allowing them to soak through tissues. In addition to butyn, *procaine, quinine,* a coal-tar derivative called *phenol,* and *benzyl alcohol* are often used as topicals. Such anesthetics stop itching when they are incorporated in salve applied by being rubbed in, and relieve pain when they are ingredients of ointments used in cuts, sores, anal ills, or ear canker.

In using them it is essential to keep them in contact with the tissue. If the cat persists in licking or rubbing them off, they must be replaced. Let me stress a warning which will be repeated throughout this book: phenol must not be applied to cats.

Benzyl alcohol is a useful local anesthetic for surface application. It will dissove in water one part to twenty-five. Its pain-quieting power is of short duration. When first applied there is often a stinging sensation, followed by numbness. It is used in ointments to quiet skin irritation, in ear remedies to reduce the itching, and in salves applied to cuts or sores. Four per cent solutions are strong enough. It must not be used full strength.

PAINKILLERS

Acetylsalicylic Acid (Aspirin). "Doctor, how about an aspirin for my cat?" How many times I have heard these words over the telephone! The client sometimes goes on to tell me that she has already given Fifi three and the little thing still seems to have a pain. Fifi is a twelve-pound Siamese.

The derivatives of salicylic acid, a synthetic drug made from coal tar, are numerous, but only acetylsalicylic acid (aspirin) is of much interest to pet owners. The salicylates act to reduce fever slightly. No effect on heat production is noticed, but the heat loss is heightened by bringing the blood to the body surface where, in short-haired animals, it tends to dissipate. The dose is never more than a grain for a seven-pound cat.

We can judge the effect of aspirin as a painkiller only by questioning human subjects. Students assure us it does not relieve sore throat, or toothache, or pain in the intestines. It does afford relief from neuralgia, rheumatic and headache pains. In some cat diseases, when they seem to have headaches, aspirin may be effective. Salicylates do not exert germ-killing power in the blood, so should not be given to cure disease.

Acetanilid (Antifebrine) and **Acetophenetidin (Phenacetine).** These coal-tar derivatives belong to still another group of painkillers. Neither is as safe or as valuable as the salicylates, but both cause a lowering of a fever temperature as well as some relief from pain. A seven-pound cat needs no more than one eighth of a five-grain tablet.

Aminopyrene and **Antipyrene** are drugs similar in action to those above. We used to hear about them frequently, but today they are little used because of their inferiority to the salicylates.

Bromine. Bromides are used in medicine as depressants of the nervous system. They are prescribed less frequently today than formerly. However, many drugstore remedies sold to pet owners as sedatives are bromides. Whether they are *sodium, potassium, calcium,* or *ammonium* bromide makes little difference; the bromine does the work. Sodium bromide is probably the safest and ammonium bromide the least desirable. Since no prescription is required, it is sometimes advisable to resort to bromides when no veterinarian can be reached.

Their action is to cause a general quieting which results in drowsiness and sleep; overdoses and continual dosing may even produce coma. When given in just the right amounts, the animal calms but remains alert to his surroundings. The principal use of bromides recently has been in the prevention of convulsions. But in this respect they are inferior to pheno-barbital. Since too large doses often cause vomiting, they are considered fairly safe drugs. When it is desired to give large doses, they had best be given with or after meals. The bromides give longer sedation than other drugs used for the purpose but produce "hangovers" far more severe, and their sedation to prevent fits and epilepsy in animals is only a fraction of that produced by other drugs.

Laymen almost always give too large a dose of bromide. When we realize that five grams a day is a maximum human dose, then one quarter gram is a safe dose for a ten-pound cat. One gram is fifteen grains, so that one five-grain tablet every eight hours is enough. Yet I have seen cat owners give twenty-five grains a day and wonder why the cat became sicker. Bromine poisoning may be worse than the condition for which the bromine was given.

STIMULANTS

Caffeine. Besides having a slight stimulating effect on the peristalsis in the intestine, caffeine is useful because it (1) stimulates the general circulation by accelerating the heart, increasing its force and raising the blood pressure. It affects the heart muscle directly. Overdoses cause such rapid heartbeat that blood pressure drops. (2) It increases the rapidity and depth of respiration. (3) It stimulates the nervous system. (4) It increases muscular strength and power. (5) It stimulates the production of urine by heightening the activity of the kidneys without irritating them. Thus it is a *diuretic*.

Caffeine can be given in pill form as caffeine citrate, as an injection in the form of caffeine sodiobenzoate, or as ordinary coffee. If an old cat can be taught to take coffee, it may be a lifesaver. Sugar and cream with it are not harmful. Very little coffee is required as a good-sized dose for a cat. The error most people make is in giving their pets too much. In proportion to the human dose, when used as a stimulant, a Persian weighing fifteen pounds needs only one third to one half a cup, while half that amount is enough for a small cat. Yet an owner will often mistakenly give one cup to a cat if the cat is hungry for it.

As a stimulant to counteract a narcotic or barbiturate poisoning, fairly large amounts of coffee should be given, but great care is necessary to prevent some from running into the lungs of the anesthetized animals. It is safer to give it via a stomach tube, or let your veterinarian inject caffeine sodiobenzoate. If coffee is not handy, strong tea is an excellent substitute. A cup of tea contains almost as much caffeine as a cup of coffee. Cocoa contains theobromine, whose action is similar to that of caffeine.

Ammonia. Aromatic spirits are often given to cats to sniff, or by mouth as a stimulant. A cat can stand four drops in water, but very often large doses are given mistakenly. Ammonia has also been given to stimulate kidney action, and to help the animal to raise phlegm from the windpipe, but for these purposes it is inferior to other drugs for pets. Best to forget it.

Camphor. Many laymen apparently believe that camphor, by its odor alone, has some extraordinary power to avert disease. Often veterinarians also find that the owner has hung a wad of cloth soaked in camphorated oil about his cat's neck, in the expectation that the camphor would somehow stimulate it. Contrary to the earlier belief that camphor was one of the heart stimulants, studies show that its value is so small as to be inconsequential.

Strychnine. The seeds of a small tree called quaker-button, growing naturally in the East Indies, yield a drug called *nux vomica*. From this in.

turn are isolated strychnine and brucine. The former is available to laymen at drugstores in some states. They need only sign in a book as receipt for the poison and it is theirs. Safe doses of strychnine do not stimulate respiration, as many people think, nor has it value as a heart or intestinal stimulant, or to strengthen muscles, though it is often given for these purposes. Despite all you may have heard about its value, the best place for strychnine is in the drugstore, where it cannot poison some person or animal who might inadvertently swallow it.

DIURETICS

Agents which increase the flow of urine are diuretics. We have noted earlier the action of several drugs which incidentally increase urine flow, although they are used primarily for some other purpose. In addition to these, certain drugs, such as salines, by increasing thirst, cause the blood to absorb a surplus of water which later escapes through the kidneys.

Diuretics are occasionally useful to flush some circulatory poison from the blood or to pull dropsical fluid from the abdomen and relieve pressure on the heart and lungs without resorting to tapping. Sometimes when cats have bladder infections, copious urine formation and elimination helps wash that reservoir clean. There are also times when abundant urine helps prevent formation of urine crystals and flushes out those which have formed.

It need hardly be said that while you are trying to eliminate part of the dropsical fluid by diuresis without tapping the abdomen, you must prevent the cat from drinking more water. You are trying to make him soak this surplus fluid back into his blood vessels. To do that you cause him to urinate copiously, which reduces the water content of the blood, which in turn causes him to replenish it from his abdomen.

Water. The basis of diuresis centers about water. Reducing the percentage in the blood is one thing that is striven for. This in turn creates thirst; more water is drunk, more eliminated. So your veterinarian may inject water with added salt to make a "physiological solution." Or he can inject a small amount of common salt in solution, or even give it by mouth so that the pet will drink copiously.

Urea, in its pure chemical form, is coming more and more to be used. It is not necessary to administer it as an injection, but it may be given mixed with fluids such as meat broths. It is not advisable to give it to an animal with kidney disease. Your veterinarian will suggest the proper dose, if any is needed.

Sugar. Either glucose or cane sugar, or both, may be given, but in such large amounts that the pet can't utilize it all. It must be given by vein, and when so given, especially in poison cases, helps detoxify some poisons and hence is worthy of use for several reasons. A 50 per cent solution is generally used. Cane sugar is used intravenously in double the dose of glucose and in some ways is preferable.

There are also proprietary drugs and mixtures, such as *calomel, squill,* and *digitalis,* which your veterinarian may favor, or he may tell you to use coffee for its caffeine.

When cats are known to have infected or defective kidneys, your veterinarian may prescribe some mercurial drug. One dose in combination with, say, theophylline, either injected or used as a suppository, may keep up its good work for nearly a day and reduce the dropsy and edema considerably.

HEART STIMULANTS

Digitalis. Of the drugs whose action is specifically on the heart, digitalis stands first. The dried leaves of the lovely garden flower, foxglove, are the source of this remarkable drug. Several other plants produce the so-called digitalis principles: squill, a sea onion; strophanthus, a tree whose seeds are used; and even the bulb of the lily-of-the-valley.

Digitalis directly affects the muscle of the heart, whose force of contraction it greatly increases. The rate is also slowed. It is useful in many disturbances which result from heart failure—and heart weakness is heart failure. Dropsy and edema of the tissues may be due both to heart and kidney failure. Digitalis gives relief in some cases. It is not, however, the universal remedy some people think. Digitalis is not a useful stimulant when a quick one is needed, because it takes too long to establish the desired effects. It is almost useless in some forms of heart trouble, in pneumonia, in shock. The dose is such a tricky matter it should be left to your veterinarian.

Epinephrine (Adrenalin). When your veterinarian injects a small dose of epinephrine into your cat, to treat him for shock after an accident or severe intestinal bleeding, he does so because of certain life-saving properties which this drug, produced by the adrenal glands, has demonstrated. Of its many effects, those he desires are contraction of the capillaries and arterioles sufficiently so that a clot may form without being washed off from the injured tissue or organ, so that some increase in blood pressure may occur to help the animal recover from shock, and so that breathing may be easier and oxygen-absorption promoted. Its affects are of short duration—only a matter of minutes—but those minutes usually are all that are required to save the pet's life. This wonderful drug can be relied upon to produce all these effects; it is the perfect antidote for shock.

Suppose sometime in the past your cat was given a dose of anti-tetanus serum. Again he receives a puncture wound filled with filth difficult to remove. You rush to the nearest veterinarian and forget to explain (or don't know that it is necessary) that the cat had had horse serum previously. Another dose of tetanus serum is injected. Shock! Anaphylaxis! Adrenalin may save your pet.

Mixed with procaine and used as a local anesthetic in surgery, epinephrine helps prevent capillary bleeding. In cases of heart failure or stoppage, adrenalin, injected directly into the heart, may sometimes cause it to beat again. In acute bronchial asthma it brings relief. The dose is very small. Your veterinarian usually uses a 1:1000 solution and injects fractions of a cubic centimeter.

Ephedrine. Another drug, this one of plant origin, has similar properties. Unlike epinephrine, it has the advantage of being absorbed from the digestive tract; it need not be injected unless quick action is required. Moreover, it has much longer effects. Practically everything said regarding epinephrine applies to ephedrine, except that it is sometimes harmful when used in shock treatment. In pet medicine it finds a wonderful use in emphysema in old, wheezy animals. Animals which cough constantly, apparently trying to raise phlegm from the lungs, are often benefited by a little ephedrine. A mixture with atropine sometimes works wonders.

Your veterinarian will advise you on its use and dosage, but it must be remembered that one tenth of the smallest human doses obtainable from drugstores are enough for large cats and should be divided to make the proper amount for smaller pets.

SECRETORY GLAND DEPRESSANTS

Belladonna. All the old veterinary books had much to say about the wonders of belladonna. It was a favorite remedy used by all sorts of people. The old horse "jockeys" used to give mixtures of it with arsenical preparations to give temporary relief to horses with heaves, so that they could trade them to some unsuspecting victim.

Today belladonna is seldom used by small animal practitioners, but one of its derivatives, *atropine*, finds many uses. Atropine does almost everything that the parent product will do. Other drugs with the same effects, such as *Metropine*, are also used. All are given principally to cause dilation of the pupils, as in eye examinations, to dry secretions, because they inhibit glandular secretions with remarkable efficacy, to aid in preventing car sickness, and to counteract overdoses of drugs such as arecolene or Lentin, as well as poisoning by such drugs.

If a cat has been eating plants in a garden where there is deadly nightshade (a rich source of belladonna), and you see him bumping into objects, trying to get into a dark spot; if you open his mouth and find it dry; if his temperature is high, heart very rapid, pulse weak, and gait abnormal; if he is restless and excited—call your veterinarian. He can flush out the offending herbage, inject arecolene, pilocarpine, or Lentin repeatedly until the pet's mouth shows moisture, and thus save him

DRUGS ACTING ON THE ORGANS OF REPRODUCTION

Nearly every pet owner has wondered what drug he could use in some particular phase of his pet's reproduction cycle. Could males be made to stay home if certain drugs were fed to them? Could other drugs cause a catta to dry up? Would others stop a tomcat from wetting on the furniture? Could a pure-bred show catta have her heat period postponed by injections? Could anything be used to stop the undesirable results of a mismating? In these matters the up-to-date veterinarian can often be of the greatest assistance.

The Female. Starting with preparation for breeding, we know that certain vitamins are essential for reproduction. Chief of these is vitamin A. Vitamin E is essential for rats; despite the testimonials you may have seen to the contrary, it has not been demonstrated as necessary for other species. These facts are covered in the chapters on feeding, since vitamins are not drugs, but food. Here we need only repeat that no supplementary vitamins or drugs are apt to have beneficial effects on reproduction, provided the animal has been fed a complete diet.

What can you do if your catta is bred by accident to an undesirable male?

Lose no time! As quickly as possible have your veterinarian inject her with heavy doses of estrin, which will prevent the ova (eggs) from nesting in the uterus. You may douche her, but that can be risky, and the estrin treatment is preferable. Pressure douches are needed. Nearly always laymen fail to hold the tube in long enough to get the douche fluid up to the uterus through the Fallopian tubes, and in to the ovarian capsules. There is also danger of overdoing it if the pressure is sustained too long, for then the fluid may spill into the abdomen, where it can cause trouble.

How can a pregnant female animal be helped at the time for parturition? Is she sluggish? Your veterinarian can inject an extract made from the posterior pituitary gland. It may be one of the many put out by drug houses. Pituitrin is of great value. Pitocin has been of even greater worth because it has its principal effect on the uterus and less nausea accompanies its use. Any of these drugs should be injected only by your veterinarian. None of them should be given to an animal with a constricted pelvis. If a kitten is obviously too large for passage through the pelvis, it would be cruelty to inject the mother. What she needs is a Caesarian operation.

At weaning time should we rub the mother's breasts with camphorated oil or other substances? No, let them cake naturally and they will soon stop secreting. Drugs are unnecessary.

Very old cattas often resorb their partially developed fetuses. How can the veterinarian help them carry to full term? He may give small amounts of stilbestrol, the female sex hormone, at regular intervals.

The Male. Male animals have had all manner of drugs fed them and injected into them to make them eager to mate and fertile if they do. Some drugs make matters worse. There was a vogue for using testosterone until it bcame apparent that it was making animals sterile instead of fertile.

Kittens whose testicles are not descended are often rendered normal by A-P-L (anterior-pituitary-like) injections. And this synthetic hormone may have some effect on sexual vigor in mature animals. In either case it is worth a try, but you must be prepared for a series of treatments.

DRUGS TO KILL INTERNAL PARASITES

The drugs which are used to eradicate the worms which infest cats (the helminths) are called anthelmintics. Some are flat worms (platyhelminths) and some are round (nemahelminths). This class of drugs is of vital importance to us all, since the most prevalent group of diseases to which pets fall heir is caused by worms and external parasite infestation, with the consequent symptoms. The life histories of all of the common parasites have been considered in an earlier chapter. Here we will discuss only the drugs used in their elimination.

Male Fern. One of the oldest worm expellers is the dried root of a common fern (*Aspidium*) or extractions from it. It has been used since ancient times and is still in use where people do not know of more efficient drugs. However, with the greatly improved anthelmintics available, there is little reason to use male fern today.

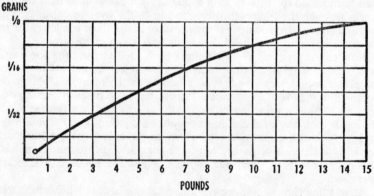

Safe doses of arecolene hydrobromide. Find the weight of your cat. Follow the line vertically until it intersects the heavy black line, then follow to the left to read the dose. Doses are given in divisions of one eighth because the drug is most often sold in one-eighth-grain pills. You may have to cut pills in halves, thirds, or quarters, etc.

Arecolene Hydrobromide. We have few more efficient expellers of tapeworms than this drug with its unique properties. Since it not only causes the tapeworms to let go, but also has a vigorous flushing action on the intestine, it performs the feat of expelling tapeworms in as little as twenty to sixty minutes. But it may produce griping pains. Fifteen to twenty hours' fasting should precede the dose. The dose is about one tenth grain for each fifteen pounds of weight.

If possible, animals given arecolene should be exercised about half an hour after dosing. Cats may be given as much freedom as possible. This tends to prevent griping.

Arecolene comes in sugar-coated pills in a variety of sizes, from one sixtieth grain to one half. It is cumulative, so that when a normal dose

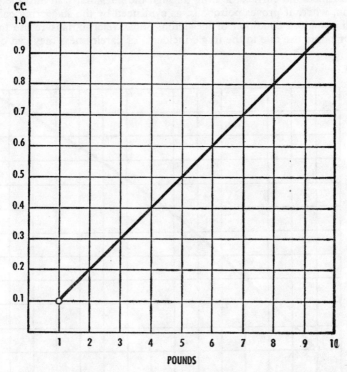

Safe doses of tetrachlorethylene for robust, empty cats. Find the weight of your cat. Follow the line vertically until it intersects the heavy black line, then follow to the left to read the dose. Doses are given in multiples of one-tenth c.c. because the drug is often sold in two-tenths-c.c. (three minim) size capsules. You may have to prick the capsule with a pin and squeeze some of the drug out to make the proper amount.

causes vomiting, it may be given in three or four split doses about seven minutes apart and will do its work admirably. The dose for small cats is necessarily larger in proportion than that for large.

Nemural is a proprietary drug whose characteristics are similar to arecolene. The manufacturers advise no more than twelve hours fasting before dosing. The recommended dose is one pill for each eight pounds of body weight, given in a little food. It seems especially useful for cats. The drug is dispensed only through the veterinary profession.

Tetrachlorethylene. This is a common drug of commerce. As an anthelmintic it is safe provided there is no fat in the digestive tract of the animal. Because of its affinity for fat, it quickly combines with it. The fat is absorbed and carries the drug through the intestinal wall into the circulation, where it proves poisonous, as evidenced by the staggering gait and even comatose condition of its victim. Some veterinarians refuse to give it for home use due to the tragic incidents of carelessness they can cite.

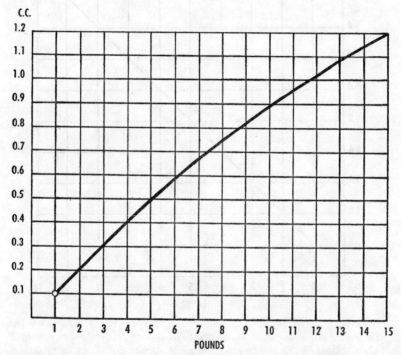

Safe doses of N-Butyl Chloride for robust, empty cats. Find the weight of your cat. Follow the line vertically until it intersects the heavy black line, then follow to the left to read the dose. Doses are given in tenth c.c.s.

However, if you could be absolutely sure that your cat had been completely starved for twenty-four hours before dosing, you could give several times the recommended amount without harm. It may be given to very young kittens safely, even at the rate of one tenth c.c. for each twelve ounces of weight. But for grown cats, if one c.c. is given for each ten pounds it is highly effective, killing roundworms, hookworms.

It should be followed in an hour to two hours by a saline physic, such as milk of magnesia or Epsom salts or arecolene hydrobromide. Giving arecolene or Nemural after tetrachlorethylene is a reliable way of expelling several kinds of worms at once.

Normal Butyl Chloride. While tetrachlorethylene was hitherto the drug usually sold in drugstores for the home deworming of pets, N butyl chloride has now largely replaced it. This is not because it is any more efficient, but because it is safer if the pet has been fed by mistake. It is more toxic to little kittens than the former, and I personally prefer the tetrachlorethylene for most purposes.

Some starvation is necessary to prevent dilution of the drug. Eighteen hours is recommended, but twenty-four hours is preferable.

DRUGS TO KILL EXTERNAL PARASITES

Dozens of drugs can be used to kill insects, but most of them will kill mammals and humans too. There are four modern drugs which are quite safe if used with reasonable care, and new ones are appearing and being tested annually.

Rotenone. This drug (and related resins) is obtained from the roots of tropical plants, notably derris in the East Indies, cube in South and Central America; it is one of the most potent insect killers known. It kills animals by paralyzing their respiratory tracts. Pets can eat it in small amounts usually with no ill effects. It is more poisonous if inhaled, and is especially so if it gets into fresh open cuts.

Rotenone also kills fish. If you use it, don't allow rotenone to blow onto the water in a fishpond. And don't dust your cat close to the home aquarium.

Probably rotenone in dusts, diluted to 1 per cent, is as safe for flea and louse powders as anything one could ask. While other powders are dangerous to cats, which lick themselves, rotenone is not. No cat should be put in a closed box and dusted, since it is then forced to breathe the dust. It is hard to believe that pets could be so mistreated, but they often are— by people who want to keep the powder off their clothes.

Incidentally, with some people—not all—rotenone causes numbness of the lips and tongue tip. The sensation soon passes. If you are sensitive, dust the pet in the open where the breeze blows the dust away from you.

Rotenone is an ingredient of some of our best dips and rinses. A one per cent solution in pine oil to which an emulsifier has been added kills all insects except ticks.

Pyrethrum. Chrysanthemums contribute pyrethrum to our store of drugs. In pure form, the chemical agents made from it are called pyrethrins. They are mentioned here because they are so often ingredients of flea powder, but the fact that they are included here is not an endorsement, since they merely stun the insects. The early powders were sold with the advice that you dust the animal, brush the fleas and lice onto a newspaper, and burn the paper. You burned it because the insects usually refused to "stay dead" and manufacturers knew it.

Pyrethrum has a wonderful psychological effect on the cat's owner. When it is used as an ingredient of a powder or rinse, the insects appear to die instantly. They drop off, and that is what the owners love to see. Mix in some rotenone and the bugs not only drop off but they stay dead! The combination of the two drugs makes a fine treatment for the owner as well as for the pet.

DDT. This is also called by the simple (to a chemist) name of diphenyldichlorotrichloroethane. It really kills insects and lasts for weeks without decomposing and losing its potency. It finds uses in fly sprays, mists, dusts, rinses, and all vehicles for spreading bug death. When it is used in liquid-soap shampoos at a low concentration of 2 per cent, the effect will last in the animal's coat for a week or more, killing any insect that gets on the fur.

DDT's lethal properties against warm-blooded animals are not so dire as many think. Cats lick themselves, so it must be used on them with great discretion.

Benzine hexachloride, also called *Sixide* and *cyclochlorohexane,* is the newest of the lethal products to date, and it kills ticks as well as other insects. It is probably one of the safest for pets, since it may be used in powders at a dilution of 1 per cent. This is relatively non-toxic to pets in the amounts that would be used to kill fleas or ticks. The form called *gamma isomer* is the most toxic to insects and animals too. Like DDT, this drug has a long-lasting effect. It is used in a very wide variety of ways, even for killing mange mites.

The chief drawback to benzine hexachloride is its obnoxious musty odor. Since the nearly pure gamma isomer, now called Lindane, has been produced and sold, the product is almost odorless.

Chlordane is one of the most recent insect killers and is used in many proprietary powders. It is one of the best tick killers, as well as being exceedingly effective against fleas and lice. Being a poison, it must be used with discretion.

DRUGS APPLIED TO THE SKIN

Possibly because vanishing and other creams are thought by many to be essential aids to beautify the human skin, many pet owners have come to the mistaken conclusion that there must be skin lotions necessary for animals' skins. Some think there are miracle drugs or vitamins which may be given to make an animal's skin and coat shine and his eyes sparkle. There are no such lotions, nor does a healthy animal need any.

What we are going to consider here are the vehicles, skin remedies, drugs used in burn treatments, antiseptics for cuts and scratches, and liniments.

Vehicles for Drugs Applied to the Skin. WOOL FAT, also called lanolin, forms an excellent vehicle because it holds most drugs and, when it is absorbed into the skin, carries the drugs with it. It is coherent, sticking even to surfaces which are moist. Wool fat of the ordinary variety contains about 25 per cent water. It can also be obtained in an anhydrous form (without water).

PETROLATUM is available as a liquid (mineral oil), or as a jelly (vaseline). When used as a vehicle, it is not absorbed, and drugs used with it remain more or less outside of the skin. Depending upon whether a liquid or solid non-absorbable is desired, one or the other form is used.

LARD is still a standard base, as is *suet*. Everyone knows that it is usually advisable to mix some pleasant odor with them when they are used in medication.

GLYCERINE. This thick, sweet, syrupy material is mixed with innumerable drugs for skin application where liquids are used. But glycerine absorbs water from the tissues. Because it finds so many uses in human medicine, one would expect more in veterinary practice, but cats often lick the sweet substance and may be sickened by the accompanying drugs unless they are repellent.

Skin Disease Remedies. Almost every veterinarian has his favorite remedy for skin diseases. Some smell so unpleasant that the cure is almost worse than the disease. Some require such frequent application that treatment becomes a great bore. Some irritate. It is unfortunate that one general remedy cannot be given which will cure all such diseases, but since some are caused by mites, which require special drugs, others by fungi, and probably still others by bacteria and viruses—not to mention occasional cases resulting from some food idiosyncrasy—no one remedy can be suggested. Here are the common effective drugs and chemicals used today:

SULPHUR. This is one of the oldest and still one of the most reliable of skin remedies. Sulphur should not be used alone—as such it is useless. But when oxygen in the air combines with sulphur it forms sulphur dioxide, a gas deadly to fungus diseases and to some insects. It is this constant gas formation which cures. Sulphur, to be of value, must therefore be kept in position by some base which holds it in place and yet does not cover it to such an extent that air cannot reach it. The old lard-and-sulphur or axle-grease-and-sulphur treatments had some virtues, but they cured very slowly because the grease coated the sulphur particles.

The fineness of the sulphur particles, too, makes a great difference. Coarse sulphur crystals are not so effective as the sulphur which is close to the colloidal state. Colloidal materials are so fine they will stay in suspension as if they were in solution and never settle out. It is possible to obtain colloidal sulphur, but it is expensive and its results are not enough better than those obtained by the finest air-floated mechanically ground product to warrant the additional cost.

Sulphur mixed with vegetable oils produces better results than that mixed with heavy greases, but other drugs can be added which help materially, as we shall see.

TAR. This is a product greatly prized by the old farriers. It is much too irritating to be used full strength, and is diluted in various ways. Pine tar, juniper tar (also called oil of cade), coal tar, and oil of tar are all available.

Pine tar has a turpentiny taste and a typical pine odor. Its medicinal agents are chiefly creosotelike chemicals. Oil of tar is a distillation product made from tar. Many veterinarians use it as the principal ingredient of skin remedies. If you can stand the odor, it has some advantages. To my mind its disadvantages far outnumber them—the way it discolors coats, the fact that, used injudiciously, it may burn, and the odor.

OIL OF TURPENTINE. Many skin preparations employ gum turpentine. It was and still is used widely for horses, but for pets this product finds small usage. Besides its use in skin remedies, some is incorporated in liniments, where it has some value.

In curing skin diseases and relieving soreness, a veterinarian depends upon bringing blood to the skin—practically producing a mild inflammation. Turpentine in full strength would burn, but dilutions are often of value. When it is used, the proportion is small—not over 10 or 15 per cent when mixed with oils, and even less when mixed with other irritating products. Turpentine has a mild antiseptic effect.

One should be very sure not to use it on old cats, especially those with kidney diseases. It has a strong diuretic effect, and even the amounts absorbed may damage kidneys irreparably. Occasionally we see blood in the urine of cats when turpentine has been applied to the skin and absorbed through it. Turpentine as an ingredient of skin lotions should be used prudently.

CALAMINE LOTION. Some mild forms of skin disease are cured by this white liquid, which needs shaking each time before application. Calamine itself is a 98 per cent zinc-oxide preparation with a little iron rust mixed with it. Calamine lotion contains 8 per cent calamine. It is effective in certain cases where only the surface layers of the skin are attacked. The ear is part of the skin, and quite good results have been obtained by pouring the ear canal full of calamine lotion and allowing as much to stay as possible after the pet has shaken his head. But it had best not be used when the eardrum is broken, since it may cake around the delicate mechanism of the middle ear.

BORIC ACID. The medical profession has prescribed boric acid for so many years for so many millions of people that the first thing the layman thinks of to cure almost anything is boric acid or boracic acid. Boric acid and boracic acid are the same thing. In skin disease its value is questionable. It does not kill germs, but does retard their growth.

SALICYLIC ACID. One of the reasons salicylic acid is useful in skin remedies is that it destroys the outer layers of skin but does not destroy the growing layers. Who hasn't used corn removers, most of which contain salicylic acid and collodium? When applied, the skin swells, becomes soft, and the outer layers slough off. Like boric acid, its action on bacteria is to slow their growth but not to kill them. Salicylic acid is seldom used stronger than 10 per cent of any solution or ointment.

POTASSIUM PERMANGANATE. A favorite water solution, this useful drug is more valuable in human skin treatment than for animals. In humans, dressings can be applied and allowed to stay in place; animals often tear them off. Laymen often apply too strong solutions. One part to one hundred parts of water is as strong as should be used when applied uncovered. If a wet dressing is used, a solution of 1:10,000 is strong enough. And don't forget that it leaves a purple discoloration.

GENTIAN VIOLET. Speaking of stains, gentian violet, a dye, will really leave its mark. Used at 1:500 parts water when applied to the skin uncovered, it kills many kinds of germs. Even a 1:1,000,000 solution will kill some. If a pet licks it off, no harm is done, since it is safe enough to use in internal medicine. It may be applied many times to skin sores with no harm to the cat. The 1:1,000 strength usually proves practicable. Its one great disadvantage is its color. Few people want great purple patches on their pets.

TANNIC ACID. This is an astringent—an agent which causes shrinking and stops discharges. Considerable difference of opinion exists among veterinarians as to whether it is preferable to apply an astringent, and dry up an area affected with dermatitis, or to inflame it with some substance like turpentine and, with the aid of the inflammation, to cure it with other drugs.

In a 5 or 10 per cent solution, tannic acid is effective over raw areas such as those eroded by disease organisms or sore from constant scratching, since it causes a film of protective protein to form. But there is a question whether, except in the case of burns, this is always desirable. Cats may bite and scratch the film off as fast as it forms.

PHENOL (Carbolic Acid). This is a coal-tar derivative. Again let me remind you never to use it or any of its relatives on cats or foxes. A few drops will kill a kitten; a few drops will make any cat sick. And it can be absorbed through the skin.

Phenol is the standard by which other germicides are compared. We speak of Phenol Coefficient of 5, meaning that a comparison of germ-killing power of a certain dilution has been made with a given dilution of phenol.

ICHTHYOL was once widely employed as an ointment, but today it is used to a lesser extent. It is a dark gummy substance made by distilling the bituminous remains of fossil fishes. Some think it is because of its 15 per cent sulphur content that it exerts a curative property. In my experience it is inferior to many other skin remedies.

IODINE. This old stand-by of a generation ago is slowly being replaced as a skin remedy, as it is as an antiseptic. For ringworm in animals, it is used in the proportion of 50 per cent of the tincture with an equal amount of glycerine.

SPERGON. Since so many skin diseases are of fungus origin, a search is now under way for fungicides harmless to pets but deadly to fungi. One of these which offers much hope is Spergon (tetrachlorobenzoquinone). Mixed with flea powder, it has proved an effective preventive against some skin diseases and has even cured some.

Burn Remedies. When a cat is burned either by fire, scalding, or corrosion, by acids, caustics, or other chemicals, the capillaries of the skin become dilated in all the burned area. You will remember that any skin burn seeps a moist material. This seepage goes on and on until, in cases of large burned areas, so much plasma escapes that the animal's blood-volume loss is extremely serious. That is point one to remember. The second point is that all of this area affords an excellent growing medium for bacteria, whose toxic by-products may cause death to the burned victim. The third is that supportive treatment for the animal is essential because one often finds a temporary improvement followed by prostration, due to shock. What drugs can you use for burns?

TANNIC ACID is now the first thought of many doctors. When a fresh 10 per cent solution is used, a thick scab forms over the burn and to a large extent prevents the loss of plasma, although under the scab the tissue may remain moist.

To prevent growth of bacteria, some veterinarians use *gentian violet, acriflavin,* or *brilliant green.* Others prefer application of *powdered sulfa drugs* or solutions of *penicillin* or *streptomycin.* Still others use *tannic acid and dilute silver nitrate* with excellent results. Some favor salves embodying combinations of drugs, but spreading salves over painful burned areas adds to the pain. In first aid, however, it's a case of any port in a storm, and salves may be the only available remedy besides tea, which may be used for its tannic-acid content.

After the burn itself has been treated, supportive treatment is often necessary. If the pet seems to be in shock, an infusion with saline solution and glucose often saves its life. Clients often want their veterinarians to give sedatives in such cases, thinking it is the pain causing the shock. If they are given, the dose must be small or the drug may cause death.

Drugs for Cuts and Scratches. Does it sound unprofessional to say that any ordinary cut or scratch or scraped area which the pet can reach to lick is just as well off left untreated? If it is so small or unimportant that it does not need suturing, it does not need medication—if Dr. Cat can reach it. The scales on our pets' tongues can clean a wound beautifully, and clean wounds heal well. There are, however, many wounds in places our pets cannot reach, such as those on the head, neck, and shoulders, abscess formations under the skin, and wounds under long hair. These should be cared for by the owner. The variety of drugs available for treatment is wide, and the list is growing. Here we need discuss only the most important ones.

Disinfectants, germicides, antiseptics, bacteriostatics, fungicides, bacteriocides—what are these things? Disinfectants free areas of infection by destroying bacteria, fungus organisms, viruses—all kinds of infective organisms. Antiseptics inhibit the growth of bacteria or other infecting agents, but do not necessarily kill them. Germicides and bacteriocides are agents that kill germs. Contrary to what you may have thought, there are not very many which will kill germs and not injure tissues too. Bacteriostatics arrest the growth of bacteria. A viricide is an agent which kills viruses. Fungicides are agents which destroy fungi.

TINCTURE OF IODINE. One of the mainstays of veterinarians of a few years ago, as it was in the average household, tincture of iodine still has its uses. It is germicidal against all bacteria and many fungi and viruses, regardless of their race, creed, or color. It is twice as potent as phenol as a germ killer. Since a number of applications to the same area may result in burning, when several treatments are indicated it is better to use the tincture diluted by an equal amount of water. Iodine discolors, and animal hair once discolored with it may retain the stain for months. This, plus the fact that the treated area burns and smarts when it is applied, makes its use of limited value for pets.

HEXYLRESORCINOL is a remarkable product in that even in dilutions of one to one thousand it is highly bacteriocidal. The drugstore product may be obtained in a glycerine solution. If cats lick it off, it does no harm. Its disadvantage is that, like iodine, repeated applications irritate tissues.

CHLORAMINE is one of the antiseptics that kill by the liberation of chlorine. It is excellent when used on wounds which are covered, and its effects are quite long-lasting. When it is applied to dressing in dilutions of one to one thousand, healing progresses nicely.

HYDROGEN PEROXIDE. When you apply this product to raw tissue there is a strong fizzing, and a white foam appears. This means that the peroxide is decomposing into water and oxygen. And only while this decomposition is progressing is the treated area being disinfected. But this fizzing helps wonderfully at times to loosen debris in wounds. As a germ killer, it is less efficient than many others. Phenol is about one hundred times as potent. In wound and external treatment it is best employed to cleanse wounds and to flush out the sheaths of male cats when they become infected. The drugstore strength is 3 per cent, which has been found best for all such tasks.

POTASSIUM PERMANGANATE. There are many veterinarians who use this chemical for wound treatments, though it is now used less than formerly because we have so many better antiseptics. It is a brownish crystalline substance, generally used in concentrations of about one to five thousand parts of water.

MERCURIC COMPOUNDS. Our first thought is bichloride when we think of mercury. The large coffin-shaped blue tablets are synonomous with poison in the minds of many and are dangerous to have around for humans or pets. Best forget bichloride.

But there are many other useful mercuric compounds. What household does not have Tincture of Metaphen, or Mercurochrome, or Merthiolate? Recently much publicity has been given to the failure of these mercury compounds to kill germs. The inference is that they are worthless. Actually, at the "drugstore" dilutions, they are bacteriostatic, and to some extent bacteriocidal. To my knowledge, that is all the manufacturers ever claimed for them. If bacteria or their spores cannot grow in the presence of these drugs, then they serve a useful purpose.

SILVER. In veterinary medicine, silver is used as silver nitrate, silver oxide, and in colloidal form. Silver nitrate will kill bacteria, but it is a caustic and astringent. Except in burns (in dilute solutions) and in wart removal, it has few uses. Silver oxide is used in ear-canker unguents. Colloidal silver is greatly prized by some. It is not caustic or astringent and can be used safely, but the field of use is restricted, since many bacteria are not killed by it. Moreover, it stains hair black and stains clothes as well.

THE DYES. Acriflavin, a yellow dye, methylene blue, gentian violet, methyl violet, crystal violet are in use—one can judge how often by the number of vividly stained areas he sees on cats. Unfortunately these dyes are effective against a limited field of infectious organisms.

THE SULFA DRUGS

The person who did not own cats B.S.D. (Before Sulfa Drugs) can possibly appreciate what their discovery has meant to pet owners. True, some are already outdated, and all are being replaced for some purposes by the antibiotics, but veterinary medicine is now a far happier profession because of them.

The first to be discovered was sulfanilamide. Shortly thereafter unfounded claims were made for it as a cure-all; it was said to be a specific for coccidiosis, viruses, including distemper in dogs, all kinds of bacteria. But genuine study showed that its field was very narrow—that it killed only a limited number of bacteria and was ineffectual against viruses, coccidiosis, warts, bad disposition, or ingrowing toenails!

Laymen cannot obtain sulfa drugs without prescriptions. Let your veterinarian tell you why he prescribes the sulfa drug he prefers for your cat. Here, in general, are a few things you should know about them, which will save his time in instructions and explain why he tells you to use them as he does.

Some of the sulfas do not kill certain bacteria. Some are more toxic than others. Some are much more soluble. Sulfathiazole and sulfadiazine accomplish approximately the same germ-killing effects, but the sulfadiazine, being more soluble, is a better bladder and kidney disinfectant. Some sulfas are but slightly absorbed from the digestive tract. Sulfathalidine disinfects the colon principally; sulfaguanidine, the whole tract. Some leave such acid residues that it is wise to prescribe bicarbonate of soda with them. Some do their best work when injected, some when taken orally.

In spite of all their wonderful effects, no sulfa drug and no combination of them has yet been found which will kill all the bacteria, and none affects viruses.

One of the most important facts to remember when you use the sulfas, which are absorbed, is that many of them are excreted via the kidneys quite soon after they are administered. Others, sulfamethazine, for example, need be injected only once a day. If your veterinarian says "give every six hours," don't stretch the interval to eight hours. For some, his instructions may be every four hours. The reason for giving them frequently is that sulfa drugs will not kill germs when their concentration in the blood drops to below one to fifty thousand. Your veterinarian may prescribe one grain, split in four doses, to each pound of body weight of your pet. When the drug is first absorbed, the concentration may be 1:25,000, but after a few hours it will have left the blood and the concentration may fall so low it can no longer kill germs in the body, so they grow again unimpeded. It pays to follow your veterinarian's instructions.

Powdered sulfa drugs are often sifted into surgical incisions and wounds, where they are of great help. Now they are being used in solutions, as in propylene glycol, and poured into inaccessible wounds where they often prove to be true miracle drugs and lifesavers.

THE ANTIBIOTICS

When researchers learned that some bacteria and molds give off substances toxic to others, a new branch of bacteriology was born. When further research demonstrated that these substances would kill bacteria and not poison animals, a lifesaving blessing of inestimable value was bestowed upon both us and our pets. And we are told that wonderful as penicillin, streptomycin, and aureomycin are, they are but heralds of far more wonderful drugs to come. Several which are still in the experimental stages, including aureomycin, have a specificity for certain types of bacteria. As yet none has been found specific for viruses, except aureomycin in the case of human virus pneumonia and possibly for ornithosis.

The antibiotics, like sulfas, are prescription drugs. At first they were given in quickly absorbed doses, mostly intramuscularly and at very frequent intervals. Later a way was found of combining them in a wax-and-oil solution from which they are slowly absorbed, so that injections once in twenty-four hours now suffice to furnish a high enough concentration in the blood to destroy effectively the germs against which they are being used. Aureomycin is eliminated so slowly that one dose a day, given orally, is sufficient.

EMETICS

Hydrogen Peroxide. Used at half the ordinary drugstore strength, which is 3 per cent, this drug probably is the best emetic yet discovered for cats. Mix equal amounts of peroxide and water and either make the animal swallow it or administer it with a stomach tube. Vomiting occurs in about two minutes and is repeated at intervals of about thirty seconds for several minutes thereafter. Dose for a cat is two tablespoonfuls.

Apomorphine is a prescription drug. It can be injected, or it can be given by dropping in the eye, from which it is absorbed. Your veterinarian usually uses a solution and gives an injection. The animal becomes restless and may shake. Sometimes a severe depression follows its use.

Copper Sulfate.   When neither of the above is available, copper sulfate, given at the rate of a tiny pinch in a little water for a large cat, often proves effective. A grain is about as large as a grain of wheat. It leaves no depression.

Mustard.   This is difficult to administer orally and had best be given via stomach tube. One quarter of a teaspoonful will cause vomiting fairly effectively for a ten-pound cat. Larger doses may continue the vomiting for too long a time.

Ipecac.   Although many laymen try to use ipecac to make cats vomit, it is about the slowest-acting emetic of any and therefore of small use in emergencies. Drugstores carry syrup of ipecac. The dose is generally ten to fifteen drops for a ten-pound cat.

Salt.   Common table salt may be used, but it is hard to give. A strong solution is administered, so that the animal—our ten-pound cat—receives a quarter teaspoonful of salt.

Lentin.   This is an injectable drug which causes very rapid vomiting and also acts as a violent physic. It must not be used where only vomiting is desirable.

CATHARTICS

These drugs, which promote defecation, may be classified in a variety of ways; according to their severity (mild, medium, violent); according to their natures (oils, salines, metals, glandular stimulants, et cetera); according to their action (lubricants, bile-flow stimulants, et cetera); and so on. I shall simply list the most easily available cathartics and a few of those prescription drugs which your veterinarian uses or prescribes, and tell you why. The order of their listing is no indication of their value.

Castor oil is a fairly quick-acting cathartic. Cats usually defecate about two hours after dosing. The stool is not fluid but only slightly softer than normal, unless overdoses are administered. Castor oil should be given on an empty stomach for the best results. The dose for a ten-pound cat is one quarter teaspoonful. Remember that in giving castor oil you are not trying to lubricate the intestinal contents, but that an irritant acid is causing a speed-up of evacuation. Racinic acid does the physicking; the oil is partly digested. Sometimes well-meaning cat fanciers give large doses to cats. This is a mistake.

Mineral oil. In contrast to castor oil, the oral dose of mineral oil is almost all deposited with the feces. It is a lubricant. Larger doses may be given, but overdoses are inadvisable because they run out, and cats, especially, will lick themselves and thus take feces into their stomachs. Overdosing is common. I have known clients to give a cat a tablespoonful, which would be equivalent to the owner taking more than a glassful.

The chief danger in using oils is that inadvertently some—even a little —may be poured into the windpipe and cause pneumonia. However, some cats will often lap mineral oil out of a dish. It may be mixed with food and not be refused. Cats which refuse it will usually lick it off their paws if it is spread on them. There is little difference in the cathartic effect of the light and heavy mineral oils. A cat takes one half to one teaspoonful without discomfort.

Long-continued use of oil is not advantageous, since it dissolves the fat-soluble vitamins out of the food, preventing their absorption.

Milk of magnesia is magnesium hydroxide, one of the mildest of cathartics. Less than 10 per cent of milk of magnesia is hydroxide. It is therefore a moderate, harmless laxative. Doses of a teaspoonful produce laxation in a ten-pound cat in about six hours. Overdoses do little harm but do retard digestion because of their reduction of stomach acidity. In pets, the pill form is seldom satisfactory.

Epsom Salts. This would be the perfect cathartic for cats were it not so intensely disliked, even in solution, because of the bitter taste. Several theories have been advanced as to how the salts accomplish their results. Probably they do it by drawing large amounts of water from the intestine (osmosis) and, by thus filling the intestine, soften the contents and mechanically stimulate its action.

The dose for a ten-pound cat is a half teaspoonful, usually partially dissolved in water. Try to give that much; you generally lose some. Its action is fairly rapid, and evacuation occurs in two to four hours after dosing.

Phenolphthalein. For those who want a mild laxative for pets, phenolphthalein is among the best and deserves much wider use. It is combined with chocolate to form some of the more common human laxatives. It has a slightly irritating effect on the intestine, but, interestingly enough, exerts its principal action on the colon. Generally five or six hours elapse before the pet wants to defecate. Despite the fact that it is a phenol derivative, it is reasonably safe for cats. The dose is one half a grain for the average sized cat.

An excellent home remedy consists in dissolving one grain of phenolphthalein in two ounces of mineral oil. The dose is divided proportionately. Two ounces equals sixteen teaspoonfuls.

Arecolene Hydrobromide and **Lentin.** Few cathartics have been found to act more rapidly than these. Arecolene can be given in tablet form or injected; Lentin must be injected. Their action is to cause a profuse out-pouring of the glandular secretions, which loads the intestines with fluid, and they, in turn, stimulated by the presence of the fluid, work to eliminate it. Lentin first causes prompt vomiting. Hence it is almost the perfect treatment for poisoning. Defecation occurs in a matter of minutes. Arecolene requires twenty to forty-five minutes for drastic doses and longer than that when milder doses are given.

The dose of arecolene is one tenth grain to each fifteen pounds of body weight. Lentin in a 1:1000 dilution is injected hypodermically at the rate of one drop for a five-pound cat, two drops for a ten-pound cat.

VACCINES AND SERUMS

Antiserum. If your veterinarian tells you there is only one hope for your cat—antiserum, or "serum" for short—he means that he feels the cat should be given, by injection, the liquid part of the blood of an animal which has recovered from the disease the cat has. This is *homologous* serum. If it is produced in another species it is called *heterologous*. Great care must be exercised in a second injection of the latter type if more than a week elapses after the first injection.

There are several different types of serum, depending on their source. *Convalescent* serum comes from the blood of an animal just recovered from a disease. *Immune* serum is that which has been produced from an animal immune to the disease in question. *Hyperimmune* serum is made from animals which have been hyperimmunized against the disease, that is, by subjecting an already immune animal to massive doses of the virus. All these types are in common use in veterinary medicine.

Serum, having been made from the blood of recovered animals, is full of antibodies. When we inject it we simply add these antibodies against the disease to the blood of the animal we want to protect or try to cure. This addition does not in any way cause the body to produce more antibodies, and after a few days they are lost and the body is no longer protected. When serum is used as protection against disease it must be given repeatedly at not more than two-week intervals.

Vaccines are biologics for preventive inoculation. They may be bacterial or virus, and induce the body to produce antibodies against the disease-producing agents.

Vaccine may consist of several different materials. It may be bacteria, live or dead; virus, live, dead, or attenuated. If we are vaccinating against a bacterial disease we sometimes use live bacteria of some strain that does not produce a disease of much intensity. This is done to vaccinate against undulant fever. The animal is given the real disease, but of a strain which has proved from long study to produce mild symptoms. The animal actually becomes sick, recovers, and is henceforth immune. *Autogenous* vaccine is made from the very organism affecting an animal and then used against the disease.

Dead bacteria in suspension form a common type of vaccine which is used for several diseases of pets—always as a preventive. Sometimes several species of bacteria are mixed in one vaccine in order to immunize our pets at one time against all the diseases these bacteria cause.

Virus vaccines may be of *live virus,* so the animal actually is given the disease. *Attenuated virus* vaccines are those which have been either attenuated (weakened) by passage through a different species or by chemicals. Everybody has heard how smallpox, if given a calf, produces cowpox, and how if we are given that disease it immunizes us against smallpox.

Part Two

6. What You Should Know about Restraint and First Aid

ADEQUATE care and intelligent handling are usually sufficient to keep a cat in good health. But even a healthy animal—like a healthy child—cannot be perfectly guarded against every eventuality. Accidents do happen; emergencies arise in spite of every precaution. The most conscientious owner cannot prevent his cat from killing and eating a poisoned rodent that wanders across his back yard.

Two things the owner *can* do. By exercising reasonable and humane precautions, he can avoid the accidents resulting from carelessness. He can learn how to cope with emergencies when they do arise.

Every year thousands of cats are lost needlessly simply because their owners have never taken the time to familiarize themselves with a few simple principles of first aid and emergency treatment. The owner who has never learned how to handle the common emergency situations becomes panicky and does nothing to help his injured pet—or does worse than nothing, the wrong thing. The person who has no understanding of the normal recuperative processes or powers of animals too quickly assumes that the best he can do for an animal that has been hurt is to put it out of the reach of pain and so destroys his pet when it might have recovered easily and completely.

Too many pet owners feel that since they prefer to have their veterinarian prescribe for all serious pet problems, there is no necessity for them to be able to handle difficult or unpleasant situations themselves. Such owners should remember, however, that emergencies have a way of happening at inconvenient moments. Even in metropolitan areas there are often times when a veterinarian is not immediately available, and in most sections of the country it may well take several hours to reach a veterinarian when he is needed. So long as that is true, the owner who doesn't take the trouble to find out what he can do to help his pet in an emergency is risking the animal's life foolishly.

Any owner can be and should be prepared to administer first aid to an injured pet. He should know how to restrain an animal that is frightened or in pain so that it will not harm itself or others. He should know how to stop the flow of blood from a wound, how to relieve the pain as much as possible, how to protect the pet until the veterinarian reaches it. He should know *what not to do*. The skills and techniques are not difficult to learn or to apply. They are available to everyone—the cheapest and best insurance a person can get against the loss of his pet.

HOW TO RESTRAIN A CAT

Before you can attempt any sort of treatment for an injured animal, you must know how to protect yourself and how to prevent the patient from doing damage to himself or escaping before you have taken care of him properly. Restraint of some sort is usually necessary to administer first aid and always necessary when surgery of any sort is involved. With some unruly pets it is even necessary when the animal is being groomed.

Your cat's defenses consist of biting and clawing. He must be held so that he cannot reach the handler. His head must be covered or his mouth must be tied closed. An injured pet is often a panic-stricken animal. Under such circumstances even the most gentle animal may bite and scratch when you attempt to help him. Don't blame him, and *don't destroy him as vicious*. Remember that biting is a normal reaction of a frightened or injured animal. Remember, too, that his pain may have subsided for the moment and that in handling him you may have caused it to recur with terrible intensity. Don't expect the animal to respond as he usually does. Expect him to act like what he is—an animal in pain.

Restraining a cat is ordinarily a simple matter, even though he defends himself with his claws and teeth. The easiest method is to wrap a heavy folded blanket around him and grasp it firmly from each side. It usually requires no more than this to control the most vicious cat.

Because of an inherited reflex action cats almost invariably succumb to the firm touch of a strong hand which lifts them by grasping a large handful of skin on the back of the neck. Some of the most ornery old toms will curl up like little kittens when handled in this way.

Many ingenious devices are produced commercially for restraining and carrying cats. The heavy duck zipper bag is one. The cat is placed in it with his head resting through one end of the opening. The zipper is drawn from the rear, over his body to his neck. He can't get his legs out or his head in. A stout laundry bag with a drawstring is popular with cat owners.

For examining a cat which is badly frightened or in pain, two people are required. One can hold the cat's head, with fingers of one hand under her chin, and thumb behind her head, and the other hand holding both front legs tightly. Both hands must hold tightly. The examiner holds the two hind legs in one hand and examines with the other—let the cat squirm as it may.

The inept and often ineffectual attempts of the average person to con-

White Persian *Paul E. Robinson*

Short-Haired Black

Russian Blue *Casa Gatos Cattery*

Siamese *International News Photo*

Peke-Faced Red Tabby

Abyssinian *Chirn Sa-hai Cattery*

Dosing a cat is simple if you are quick. Tip her head back and straight upward. Have a pencil as well as the capsule or pill in your fingers.

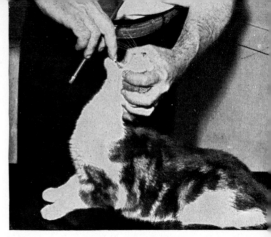

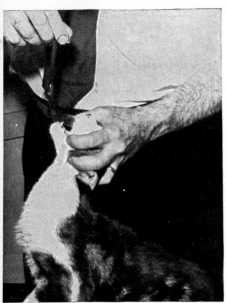

Drop capsule far back in her mouth. If she wiggles her tongue, it will slide over the back and she will swallow it if you close her mouth quickly.

If she doesn't swallow it, quickly push capsule down with pencil eraser and hold her mouth closed for a moment. In this way you won't be bitten.

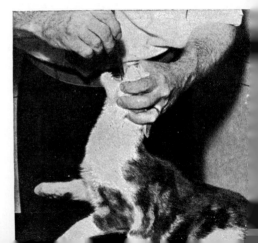

Restraining a cat can often be accomplished by merely grasping a large handful of skin on the back of the neck and lifting the animal.

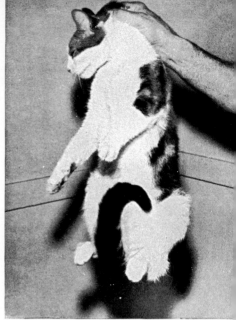

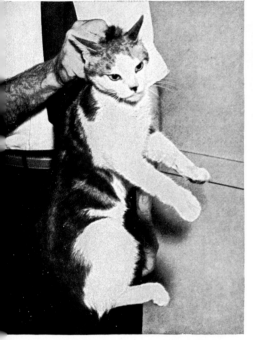

Another view. Even fierce cats may become subdued in this way. There is no pain. It's the way his mother carried him as a kitten.

Two persons are needed to restrain some cats. Three hands hold, and one is free to examine or medicate.

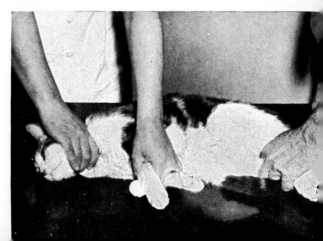

Smoke Persian Kittens *Mrs. Bellows*

Manx *Marshall Clemeau*

Blue Persian *Purri-Isle Cattery*

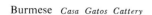

Tortoise
Calico

Mollie Brennan

Black Persian *Hermscrest Cattery*

Burmese *Casa Gatos Cattery*

Persian *Azulita Cattery*

trol cats are amazing. Don't be afraid to hold and don't let go when the patient struggles. If either person fails to hold tightly, at least one will be scratched and the cat will probably get away. Be sure of your assistant and be sure the assistant has no cause to distrust you.

FIRST AID

The principles of first aid which the cat owner needs to master are simple and relatively few, but they are of vital importance in handling emergencies. Whether an animal that has been injured is to recover quickly or slowly, whether it is to be completely restored or marked or scarred—indeed, whether the animal is to survive at all—often depends upon the treatment it gets immediately after it is hurt. The balance of this chapter is intended to give the cat owner the general information he needs and at the same time to provide him with a reference manual in which he may quickly find the specific way to handle any emergency that may arise with his pet.

Shock. Any severe injury—a burn, a struggle, a fight, or even a severe fright—may bring on this condition. The animal usually seems to be prostrated in a semi-oblivious state, yet apparently anxious. The nervous system is in depression, sometimes so severe as to cause complete immobility. On the other hand, an occasional animal may suffer the opposite effect, so that it seems to be in a state of nervous excitement. The pulse is slow and weak, the breathing shallow. Often, as the animal recovers, the pulse becomes too rapid and the temperature may rise well above normal.

First aid consists in covering the cat so his temperature will rise to normal. High artificial heat is not necessary if the animal is at home in familiar surroundings. Administer a stimulant, such as coffee, then let him rest. Occasional fondling is often reassuring and helpful. Recovery may sometimes take an hour or more.

Heat Strokes. We are all conscious of the refreshing sensation of a breeze in hot weather. This is due to evaporation of moisture from our bodies and the consequent cooling of the surface of the body. The bodies of animals are cooled by the same process, which is aided by evaporation in the throat and mouth when the pet becomes overheated and pants. Cats have few sweat glands in the skin compared to humans and horses, but they do have some. When an animal is sufficiently cooled by bodily evaporation, he stops panting.

In itself, panting is a normal method of reducing body temperature. It may sometimes be an indication of thirst.

Accidents. The most common cause of accidents among pets is the automobile. So common is it that companies which insure pets' lives often exempt death by automobile from policies.

When a cat is struck by an automobile, you must first restrain him and then treat him for shock. Look at his gums to see if he is losing blood too rapidly. If his gums appear gray or white, he probably has suffered an organic injury and is bleeding internally. Roll up long strips of bandage —an old sheet may be torn in strips for the purpose. Have an assistant stretch the pet out and hold the front and hind legs. Then wrap the bandage around the pet's body tightly, corset-fashion. Keep on wrapping it until you have made a good firm support. Be sure that it will not pull together in a narrow roll around his abdomen when he moves. It must form a long tube, which holds the animal's organs relatively immobile, so that a clot can form and remain in place. Without this firmness and pressure, the organs can move freely and break the blood clot loose. Do all you can to keep the animal quiet. The veterinarian, when he comes, will administer a drug to check bleeding and may decide upon a transfusion if he feels that the transfused blood will not run into the abdomen and be wasted. Whatever you do, do *not* move the pet far after an accident if there are indications of internal bleeding. He can bleed to death very quickly. He may be saved if you keep him quiet.

If an animal does bleed internally, what becomes of the blood which runs into the abdomen? When a clot forms, it is composed of red and white cells, plasma, and fibrinogen, which causes coagulation. As it forms, the clot squeezes out a fluid or serum. This serum can be, and is, soaked up by the peritoneum (the lining of the abdomen and covering of the organs). Obviously the serum gets back into the circulation and thus helps to increase the blood volume. Many of the red cells which transport oxygen through the body are in the clot. This clot does not persist permanently as a liverlike lump. Instead a process called *lysis* occurs. The cells simply dissolve into the fluid in the abdomen. Their covering disintegrates and releases the contents. The fluid is now circulated, but only a small amount is utilized by the body; most of it, including the red pigment, is passed out of the body through the urine as waste. When you see your weak but mending patient urinating what appears to be blood, don't presume he is passing blood from his kidneys and bladder; it is probably blood-coloring matter. Indeed, anticipate his doing this. This fact is sometimes used as a diagnostic means of demonstrating internal hemorrhage which occurred several days before the red color is seen.

Mad Cat. The cry of "mad dog" is no longer heard in America as it used to be, or as history tells us it was in Europe. Nevertheless, it *does* occur. An animal which manifests *any* symptoms of rabies is suspect. Rabies is discussed in detail in Chapter 15, and here we need only concern ourselves with the problems of first aid—first aid to the cat and to the animals or humans he has bitten—and the subsequent management of the incident.

For the suspected mad cat, sure isolation must be provided. Shut him in a cage or room and call your veterinarian immediately. Keep people and animals away from him. Your veterinarian and the health authorities will diagnose his condition, using a mouse test if advisable. Either the local authorities or veterinarian will provide isolation until the diagnosis is clearly established. If an animal *is* infected, the local authorities will determine its disposition. Frequently they prefer to let the disease progress until Negri bodies have developed in the brain.

Any pet that has been bitten by a rabid animal should be quarantined. Since a high proportion of all animals—75 per cent of all dogs, for example—are susceptible to rabies, no other course is safe. The period of isolation is long. An exposed animal must be confined for six months. Will it pay to maintain him so long at possibly a dollar a day? Will he still know you when he is returned? Will you ever have complete confidence in him? Rabies is such a horrible disease that it is advisable that all rabid animals be destroyed.

Needless to say, if a human is bitten, call a doctor immediately. Only a physician is qualified to decide on the treatment or prophylaxis for the humans involved.

Cuts.   Cats hustling through barbed-wire fences, stepping on broken bottles, scratching in ash piles, and stepping on concealed metal scraps come home gashed, bleeding, and torn. They seldom bleed to death.

Most of the cuts which occur on animal skins are triangular tears. Some, of course, are clean, straight cuts. In either case only a limited kind of first aid should be administered. In animal saliva there is an enzyme which digests germs. The surface of an animal's tongue is made up of small, tough scales so strong that he can wear flesh away if he wants to. There is no better way of cleaning a cut than allowing him to do it. He will lick away all dead flesh or debris and kill germs as he does so. He will heal his own wounds.

First aid consists not of strapping the cut together with adhesive tape, nor of binding up the wound, unless it is bleeding badly, but of allowing the patient to clean his wounds and then having the veterinarian treat them. So there need be no hurry in rushing your pet to the doctor. When you do he will cut away any dead edges on the flap and suture it in place, so that when it has healed no ugly scar will remain.

There are cuts which cats cannot reach to lick, however. In long-haired cats these may be covered with hair, which should be trimmed off about the area. Or they may be on areas of the body, such as the neck, head, face, and shoulders, which the cat cannot reach. In such a case, clean the cuts yourself (peroxide is excellent for this purpose) and take him to the hospital as soon as possible.

Cuts deep in the feet usually cause profuse bleeding, since this area is filled with blood vessels. A cut of this sort should always be examined to see if a long sliver has remained in it. After this examination it is necessary to stop the bleeding. A plug of cotton pressed against the opening and a pressure bandage which holds it there will quickly check the bleeding. If the cut should hemorrhage, apply a tourniquet immediately above or below the wrist joint. It must be loosened and reapplied every ten minutes.

On the trip to the veterinarian take along some cloths to absorb blood which may stain the car or clothes.

The most dangerous cuts are those made by filthy objects. These cuts may heal or mat over with hair which becomes part of a scab, and tetanus (lockjaw) germs frequently infect such wounds. Since they can develop only in a cut or puncture wound which the air cannot reach, cuts of this sort must be opened, cleansed, and kept open until they have been disinfected and sutured. There are some wounds which are best left unsutured for a considerable length of time. These must be flushed daily while they heal from the bottom out, and they are sutured to avoid unsightly scars only when the healing process has reached the surface layers of the skin.

Bites.   Animal bites and poisonous snake or insect bites need very different treatment, so we shall consider them separately.

ANIMAL BITES.   It is sometimes important to determine the kind of bite to be treated. The bite of a dog, cat, and even that of a rat, can usually be distinguished by the number of teeth marks. When a large dog attacks a cat, if one dog tooth mark is found, three others can nearly always be located. The distance between these skin punctures, as well as their size, gives some idea of the size of the attacker. Little dogs sometimes open their mouths wide and leave impressions of their upper and lower canine teeth perhaps four inches apart, but the distance between the two upper canines will still be small. Large dogs may happen to get hold with only a small nip, but the distance between their upper canines may be as much as three inches in some breeds.

Because of their size and strength, large dogs inflict greater damage than do small dogs. Ordinarily, a dog attacking another animal does not simply attack, hold on, and squeeze; he shakes his head and thus drives his fangs deeper. These teeth wounds can be cleansed by shaving the hair away and filling them with antiseptic from an inserted medicine dropper. The attacker may have pulled the skin loose from the underlying connective tissue over a large area. In such cases your veterinarian will flush this area clean and bind it down. It usually heals in a few days.

Cat bites on dogs or other cats often become infected. The skin should not be allowed to heal quickly over them. First aid often consists in hurrying the animal to the doctor. If infected, the punctures become large abscesses which burst, carrying with them large areas of skin which has been killed in the process of abscess formation. A bite that has been allowed to abscess takes much longer to heal than does a properly treated bite, and the new skin which eventually covers the sore spot will never have hair.

Cats are frequently bitten. Old tomcats may attack castrated males, and even cattas fight at times. Cats are also bitten by rats. If your pet comes home and shows by her licking that a spot or spots are sore, look at these moistened areas and try to find tooth marks. Flush them out with peroxide (never use phenol derivatives on a cat). Cats are particularly prone to staphylococcic infections. When such abscesses open, a whitish or yellow pus is usually exuded. Watch the bites every day for swelling (abscesses), and have the swellings opened while they are small. It will be worth while. Often bites in or just above the paws, where many small bones and tendons lie, are neglected and infection creeps all around the area so that it becomes difficult to cure.

"But," you may say, "look at all the old tramp cats; they get in fights and nobody bothers about them." Look at them! They often have several patches of bare skin from these very abscesses which have broken and healed without hair to cover them. They show battle scars from fights, and they are so often infected with abscesses that they are not a pretty sight. Perhaps that is why they are tramps—nobody wants them.

SNAKE BITES. First aid in snake bites is extremely important. When you suspect a rapidly increasing swelling to be the result of a rattlesnake, copperhead, or water-moccasin bite, there is usually sufficient time to reach a veterinarian. If you can't reach him, try your family doctor. Many physicians have saved animal lives in emergencies. If neither a veterinarian nor a doctor is available, buy some potassium-permanganate solution which a druggist will prepare for you. Make a deep X-shaped cut right over the fang marks, remembering that they are pushed in at an angle and not straight. This cut induces bleeding. Drop the potassium permanganate into the cut and hold it there for a moment. Apply a tourniquet above the bite, if it is on the leg or foot. If the swelling ascends the leg and reaches the body, you may lose the animal.

SPIDER BITES. The only dangerous spider bites are those of the black widow. This spider has a predilection for old bones. Spiders are often found inside old skulls of horses and cattle that have died and been left unburied. Cats prowl around such things, and so are often bitten by these poisonous insects. The bites are usually on the lips or face. Swelling occurs and increases proportionately with the amount of venom the spider injects. One bite may kill a cat, although it is unlikely. Very little can be done at home. If you know where the spider that bit your pet lives, a fine opportunity is offered to do some spraying and exterminate the spider and possibly all of her young, thus saving others pets and humans from being bitten.

Foreign Bodies.   No first-aid discussion could be complete without suggestions as to the removal of foreign bodies.

IN THE MOUTH: Cats sometimes overestimate their ability to manipulate certain bones. It is common to find such bones caught in various positions: wedged across the roof of the mouth between the back teeth; driven down into the gum beside a tooth; driven through the soft tissue below the lower jaw; stuck between two teeth; stuck on top of a molar tooth; or covering several teeth.

A T bone from a lamb chop is sometimes caught across a cat's mouth between the back teeth, with its sharp point sticking into the throat. The cat paws desperately at his mouth, and the owner often thinks that the end has surely come. Cats sometimes chew two- or three-inch shank bones from lamb so that the rounded bone slips down over their teeth and they can't close their mouths without forcing the sharp edges of the bone farther down against the gums. These cats become frantic.

Many other kinds of foreign bodies become wedged in the teeth or stuck in the mouth. Any cat may have such accidents. The mouth must be opened and the object pulled out. Whenever possible, it is wise to rush the pet to the veterinarian, who has the instruments to remove the obstruction without difficulty.

IN THE STOMACH: If you do not actually see a cat eat a foreign object, you can never be sure that the cat does have it in his stomach. You may have seen him eat gravel or sand, or chew on an old doll. But circumstantial evidence is usually all that is necessary. If a small item the cat was playing with is missing and the cat begins to show evidence of stomach pain, it is time for action.

Suppose you suspect that your small cat has swallowed one of your child's iron jacks, the crisscross gadget the child picks up when he bounces a ball. The cat will probably show some evidence of stomach pain, and you should act at once. Mix about an ounce of peroxide with an ounce of water and pour it down the cat's throat. Vomiting will occur very soon. When it begins, lift the cat by his back legs so that his forepaws are touching the ground and his head is down. In almost every case the jack will be regurgitated the first time.

You may be surprised sometime to pick up your cat and hear stones rattling together in his stomach. Actually you shouldn't be too astonished, for this is a fairly common occurrence. And it shouldn't worry you very much. Stones can always be recovered with the peroxide treatment. Cats with gravel impactions in their stomach can be relieved by the same means. Mineral oil should be given fifteen minutes after the peroxide, to help move along the gravel which has entered the intestine.

Remedies of this sort for the removal of foreign bodies are properly classified as first aid. More difficult cases should be left to the veterinarian. With X-ray he can locate bullets, needles, pins, spark plugs, and any of the hundreds of other odd and dangerous objects that cats have been known to swallow.

IN THE RECTUM: If your cat squats, strains, cries, and possibly exudes a little blood from his anus, the likelihood is that he has a foreign body in the rectum. If a constipated mass is considered a foreign body, he surely has. Not infrequently the stoppage is caused by sharp bone splinters which were not properly softened and digested in his stomach. Poultry, pork, and lamb bones are the most likely to cause such difficulties. Since any movement of the sharp bones is extremely painful, the cat refrains from defecating. In time the fecal material piles up behind them and soon a solid, dry mass with sharp bones sticking out of it precludes all passage.

First aid consists of enemas to soften the mass, though they often are not sufficiently effective to allow passage of the material. Humane considerations indicate a prompt visit to the doctor, who will probably first soften the mass and then gently reach in with an instrument and crush it into small particles. Occasionally an oily enema is sufficiently lubricating to permit the stool to be passed without great difficulty or pain. In difficult cases the veterinarian may have to pull out the sharp pieces with his instrument to avoid cutting.

Needles are frequently found in the rectums of cats. Often a thread hanging from the anus is a good indication of the cause of the pain. If the needle is just inside and can be felt, an ingenious person with a small wire cutter such as electricians use can snip the needle in half and remove the halves separately. Generally, however, this job is best left to the doctor, who will use anesthesia and a speculum to see clearly what he is doing.

IN THE SKIN: Foreign bodies in the skin or feet are usually splinters or bullets, although other objects, such as pitchforks tines, glass chips, and porcupine quills, are not so uncommon as most people think. Common sense dictates the quick removal of such objects, whenever possible, in order to relieve the animal. It also dictates the injection of an antiseptic into the wound. If a bullet has come to rest against a rib and it can be seen through the hole, you should—for once—do what your first impulse tells you: pull it out with the family tweezers and cleanse the wound.

Children often put elastic bands around the neck, leg, tail, ear, or even the penis of their pets. The hair covers the band and it goes unnoticed by adults until swelling starts. By that time it may have cut through the skin. There is little the owner himself can do after he has removed the band. If the skin gaps too wide, have the veterinarian suture it to prevent formation of a hairless scar. Ropes and small chains may also cut deeply through the skin. Most people have seen at least one animal with a hairless band of skin around the neck—mute evidence that some negligent owner left a rope or chain on until it cut the animal's neck. Having callously injured the animal, he failed even to have the gaping skin sutured.

Skunk Spraying. Skunk odor has chemically a rather simple formula —a mercaptan, a sort of alcohol-sulfur combination. It is a volatile substance. Volatile chemicals usually turn into gas with heat and maintain their liquid character in cold. The way to dissipate skunk odor, therefore, is to get clothes hot; not to bury them. Hang them in the sun in the summertime, or in a garage attic—anywhere that is dry and hot. The odor leaves quite quickly. A hot bath with lots of soap will usually remove most of the odor from a cat—or from an owner, for that matter. Several baths certainly will. If the cat is left where it is hot, the odor more quickly evaporates to a point where it loses its unpleasantness. After all, it was once used as a basis for fancy perfumes. Washing the pet in tomato juice is said to be most efficacious in removing the odor. The amount used depends on the size of the animal.

Drowning.   If a pet can be pulled out of the water while his heart is still beating, he can almost always be saved. Slow, steady artificial respiration does the trick. Not as you may have been taught to work on a human. Place the animal on his side and push with the flat of the hand on his ribs. Then pull your weight up quickly. Repeat at regular intervals about once in two seconds. He'll usually start to breathe very shallowly, and gradually breathe more deeply. Even when the heartbeat is faint, there is hope. It pays to try.

Electric Shock.   Since animals' bodies are such excellent conductors of electricity, the shock of 110 volts—which ordinarily merely jolts a human—may kill them. When shocked, they sometimes stiffen so rigidly that they appear to leap into the air. There is a great temptation for a cat to chew a dangling electric cord, and many have been badly injured when they tried it. One such experience is sufficient to teach a cat's owner the hazard of loose electric wires—often at the cost of his pet's life. If the shock has not killed the animal, artificial respiration should be administered immediately. If he cannot let go of the wire, be careful when you pick him up. He may have urinated; you may step in the urine and, in touching him, the current may pass through you. It is always safer to pull out the plug first or take hold of the wire with a wad of dry cloth and jerk it out of his mouth. Call the veterinarian immediately. He will probably administer a drug to stimulate the heart and breathing when he gets to the animal.

Burns.   If you are called upon to treat a burned animal, clean off all the hair which can mat down on the burned area. Then apply a solution of one part tannic acid to one hundred parts of water (strong, strained tea may be substituted). Then cover gently with vaseline. Your druggist will furnish his best burn remedy and help in an emergency.

Your veterinarian should be called on for all except very minor burns. The anesthetic and treatment he can administer may save your pet. Burns scab over and heal under the scabs, if left alone; but sometimes infections grow under the scabs. Tannic acid promotes healthy healing.

If half of an animal's skin is destroyed by fire, steam, acid, or any agency of burning, it is kindest to put him permanently to sleep. Burned areas usually fail to grow hair, and the period of healing is protracted and painful. Even the duration of shock that usually follows severe burns is long. The owner of any animal that has been badly burned must always decide quickly, "Is it worth it?"

Fits.   The various kinds of fits, their causes, and the means of preventing them are discussed in later chapters of this book. They should be read carefully. Here we are concerned only with the first aid the owner should be prepared to administer.

The handling of a fit depends upon where it happens and also upon its nature.

You can't stop the fit, but you can reduce the amount of damage the animal may do. He probably won't bite you unless you get in his way. If you can guide him into a room where he can't do serious damage, by all means do it and close the door.

Let your cat alone until he has recovered from the fit and then look for the cause. Prevention of future attacks is the best first aid. Your veterinarian will help you to locate the cause and provide the cure.

A cat should not be handled while it is having a fit. Some leap up in a corner, others run for the darkest spot they can find. Let them be, and wait for the fit to be well over before you touch them.

Bruises. It requires a hard, glancing blow to bruise a cat. Even those cats which have been skidded along on a road until the hair was scraped off and the skin left bloody seldom swell as do some other species. Probably the looseness of the skin over the cat's body is one of its prime protections. When uninfected swellings are found they need only cleansing. They soon subside without further treatment.

Broken Bones. You may find, when you examine an injured pet, that he has a broken bone. To treat a fracture properly you should understand the principles of bone growth and healing discussed in Chapter 2. You will also need to be familiar with certain first-aid techniques to prevent additional damage to the cat.

A broken leg is the most common animal fracture, and requires immediate attention. Its care involves straightening the leg and immobilizing it. Sometimes this takes courage. A splint is needed. A barrel stave, a tine from a bamboo rake, a yardstick may serve as an improvised splint. The leg should be tied to the splint below and above the break and wrapped with anything suitable to hold it securely in place until you can get the pet to the veterinarian.

A splint should be applied at once. If the broken bone slashes about the flesh, it can easily cut a major vein or artery and then the area around the break will become a large pocket filled with blood, greatly complicating the task of setting. It is just as important to splint a greenstick fracture, because movement or a fall may break it further.

If ribs are broken, keep the animal quiet. It is possible for ribs to puncture lungs, so lay him down with the broken ribs up and keep him as calm as possible until the veterinarian arrives.

A fractured pelvis heals slowly. Little can be done to repair pelvic breaks or to hasten the natural process of reconstruction. Occasionally only one side is broken and the cat can continue to walk on three legs. More often the pelvis is fractured in such a way as to preclude walking until the usual numbness develops and anesthetizes the area. For several days after the break the animal may be unable to raise himself without help. Gradually he takes a few unstable steps and soon is waddling about. Don't expect him to run for at least a month after the break. Even after the healing is well started it may be necessary to help him up, carry him outside, and sometimes hold him in a position to defecate. Some animals learn why they are taken outside surprisingly soon, and, as quickly as they are placed in position, will void. Standing the animal up and putting pressure on the bladder from both sides usually causes urination, and it is not uncommon to have a cat so co-operative that just touching his sides is suggestion enough for him to urinate.

Not all broken backs are hopeless. Many backs are set and wired so that the cats can live normally again. Palpation will usually determine where the tips of the vertebrae are out of line. Get your pet to the veterinarian as quickly as possible with as little jolting as you can. The spinal cord is a delicate structure. If the animal is to survive, the nerve-fiber damage must be held at a minimum.

One of the most usual back breaks comes at the point inside the body where the tail vertebrae start. The tail in such a fracture hangs limp and lifeless. It is often soiled with feces because the animal cannot raise it to defecate. Sometimes there is enough muscular strength left to move it slightly. If it is not set, it may retain its life; more often the tail loses all its feeling and dries up with dry gangrene. In this case your veterinarian will have to open the skin over the break and remove the useless appendage.

Bee Stings.   It is not uncommon to hear of pets being stung to death by bees. Cats frequently swell from single stings and not uncommonly come home drooling with mouths partly open from pain and swelling occasioned by snapping up a stinging insect—wasp, hornet, or bee.

The painful stings, the poisonous effect of the toxin, and, worst of all, the sensitivity to the foreign material developed by having been previously stung many produce a severe shock.

Treatment may be intravenous calcium gluconate, four or five c.c.s of a 25 per cent solution for a ten-pound cat. Nembutal, at the rate of one grain to each fifteen pounds, or paregoric in fairly large doses, say a quarter teaspoonful for a ten-pound cat, will help ease intense pain. If nothing better is available, aspirin may be given.

Poisoning.   Pain, trembling, panting, vomiting, convulsions, coma, slimy mouths are all symptoms of poisoning. Any of these, except a caustically burned mouth, may also be a symptom of another malady. But if your cat should manifest any of these symptoms, you should investigate immediately to see if he has been poisoned.

Animals are very seldom deliberately poisoned. Usually they are poisoned either by chewing plants which have been sprayed, by gnawing at a piece of wood which has some paint pigment on it, by catching a ground mole which has been poisoned with cyanide, by consuming poison put out for other animals or insects, or by eating infected garbage. Since none of the poisons is easily traced, you ought to know the procedure to follow *in case* your pet may have been poisoned.

An emetic *must be administered immediately*. The loss of a few minutes may give the poison time to do irremediable damage. Mix equal parts of hydrogen peroxide and water. Force your pet to take one and a half tablespoonfuls of this mixture for each ten pounds. In two or three minutes the contents of his stomach will have been regurgitated.

Either mustard or a strong salt solution can be used as an emetic, but hydrogen peroxide has proved to be most effective.

Following the administration of this emetic, call your veterinarian. If you know the source of the poisoning and can look at the package it came from, you will find the antidote on the label. If you don't know the poison to which your pet has been exposed, your veterinarian will probably identify it from its symptoms and give further appropriate treatment.

If there is any chance that poison can be the cause of intestinal trouble, it is imperative that all traces of the poison be eliminated before giving the animal drugs which will stop bowel movement and allow the intestines to become quiescent—paregoric, for instance. But if the intestines are badly corroded, it is dangerous to give violent physics. I have been able to save more poisoned animals by using two simple drugs than by any other method I have ever heard of. The drugs are hydrogen peroxide and Lentin. The Lentin is used in all cases where the animal is known to have ingested the poison recently. Since it produces both emesis and purgation, it seems the ideal drug to use, and its swift action, coupled with the fact that it causes prolific outpouring of gastro-intestinal secretions, eliminates the entire stomach and intestinal contents before too great harm is done.

The dose is a matter of drops of the 1:1000 solution. Once the offending material is removed, our job is to give such common home remedies as milk of bismuth, paregoric, strong tea for its tannic-acid content. Strangely enough, some cases are benefited by castor oil, which removes the cause and tends to be followed by constipation. Veterinarians can prescribe sulfaguanidine and sulfathaladine and other prescription drugs.

The same drugs which are useful in human care can be employed. Today a variety of mixtures embodying kaolin, bismuth, pectin are available, and your veterinarian will advise you on their use.

Table IV—Household Antidotes for Common Poisons

POISON	ANTIDOTE
Acids (Hydrochloric; nitric; acetic)	Bicarbonate of soda; eggshells; crushed plaster (tablespoonful)
Alkalies (Sink cleansers; cleaning agent)	Vinegar or lemon juice (several tablespoonfuls)
Arsenic (Lead arsenate; calcium arsenate; white arsenic; Paris green)	Epsom salts (1 teaspoonful in water)

POISON	ANTIDOTE
Hydrocyanic Acid (Wild cherry; laurel leaves)	Glucose (2 tablespoonfuls dextrose or corn syrup)
Lead (Lead arsenic; paint pigments)	Epsom salts (1 teaspoonful in water)
Phosphorus (Rat poison)	Peroxide of hydrogen. (Peroxide and water in equal parts, 1 oz. to each 10 pounds of weight of animal)
Mercury (Bichloride of mercury)	Eggs and milk
Theobromine (Cooking chocolate)	Pentobarbital, phenobarbital
Thallium (Bug poisons)	Table salt (1 teaspoonful in water)
Food Poisoning (Bacteria from garbage or decomposed food)	Peroxide of hydrogen. Give enema after stomach has emptied
Strychnine (Strychnine sulfate in rodent and animal poisons)	Sedatives such as phenobarbital, Nembutal (1 grain to 7 pounds of cat)
Sedatives (Overdoses in medicating)	Strong coffee (2 tablespoonfuls)
DDT (Flea powders; bug poisons)	Peroxide of hydrogen and enema. No antidote known

GENERAL ADVICE IN TREATING POISONING. Immediate action is essential. Some poisons are absorbed at once. If you can get Lentin in 1:1000 strength, inject one drop to each ten pounds of cat. If you have to take the cat to your veterinarian get there with all possible haste.

7. Minor Operations and Home Surgery

*F*IRST aid and minor surgery are closely allied and at times almost indistinguishable. Adequate first aid for an injured animal sometimes involves more than merely moving him to a place of safety and preventing additional harm until the veterinarian arrives. Emergency surgery may be necessary to save his life.

This chapter is intended to acquaint the owner with the basic skills and techniques which he will have occasion to use in any operation he may undertake.

RESTRAINT

This is nothing more than an adaptation of the restraint used in first aid. It must, however, be dependable and certain. During surgery, the animal must often be held securely in a supine position, perhaps on its side or on its back. When a local anesthetic is used, sometimes only a hitch to the collar is enough and the operation can be performed with the cat sitting or standing on the table, but it is usually safer to use a few ties on the legs. If the operation is in the abdominal area, a kitchen table top can be used for the emergency operating table, with a cord running from each table leg to one of the pet's legs.

Anesthesia. Ether is probably the safest general anesthesia for the home veterinarian to use. It can be administered through a tin can with one end removed, the sharp edges covered with adhesive tape and the other end perforated with nail holes and an inch of gauze stuffed into the bottom. As much ether is poured on the gauze as it will absorb. A cloth is wrapped about the patient's face covering the eyes, and the can placed over it. Air is drawn through the gauze, which evaporates the ether and as vapor it is inhaled and absorbed by the blood from the lungs, carried to the brain, and brings unconsciousness. Before complete anesthesia, a period of excitement and struggling occurs. Sometimes two persons are needed to hold the patient until this initial struggling ceases.

It is imperative not to overanesthetize. A limpness which occurs in all the muscles is indication that a state of anesthesia exists. If you can touch the patient's eyelashes with a finger tip without causing any blinking, you can be sure that the animal is anesthetized. The ether container must be removed and the patient watched by the anesthetist to make sure that it is breathing regularly and that there is no evidence of pain. If the breathing becomes shallow and quick, too much anesthetic has been given. Watch out for a complete cessation of respiration and be ready for artificial respiration. If a very large overdose has been administered, the heart, too, will stop, and revival is then usually impossible. The person giving the ether has a task which requires his complete attention, and he must not allow his interest to be diverted to the surgery.

If the home veterinarian is sufficiently competent to use an injectable anesthetic, pentobarbital sodium (Nembutal) is excellent in the proportion of one grain to five pounds of body weight (one c.c. of solution to five pounds). This is a prescription drug and you must first find a doctor willing to give it to you. Injection is made directly into the abdomen. Anesthesia will occur in ten to fifteen minutes.

CAUTION: Pentobarbital should not be given to a cat in shock, nor to an old one with kidney or liver disease.

Local anesthetic applied with a hypodermic syringe can employ procaine (Novocaine), or a mixture of it with adrenalin (epinephrine), available in most drugstores. A 23-gauge needle is large enough. Without knowledge of nerve pathways, the home surgeon will inject a c.c. here and there about the area to be anesthetized. Remember that each layer of tissue must be anesthetized separately. If a deep rent is to be sutured, anesthetic in the skin is not sufficient to deaden the area underneath. The skin is first treated and incised, and then the next layer similarly anesthetized.

WOUND CLEANING

Soap and water clean the skin fairly satisfactorily; a razor can be used to shave the area to be opened; if a gash needs suturing, scissors can be used to trim away the hair. Ragged tissue is removed because if it has no blood supply it may become gangrenous. Blood clots, dirt, gravel, and any other foreign bodies, including hair, which retard healing, should be meticulously removed with tweezers. The area is flushed out with pure water and a gauze swab—cotton leaves lint. When it looks clean, hydrogen peroxide may be used to further cleanse it, or any household antiseptic in weak dilution, according to directions on the bottle. Powdered sulfa drugs, if you can get them, may be sprinkled in and the wound closed.

If there is no infection, the pet will usually leave any sutured wound alone. When he can smell pus, however, he will try to open the incision to lick the pus out.

TISSUE JOINING

You already know that the deepest layer of the skin is the growing layer. Hence it is the layer to be joined with its opposite. The amateur often folds the skin inward, suturing the outer layers together, and then wonders why it refuses to heal. The peritoneum, which covers the intestines and such organs as the bladder, stomach, kidneys, and uterus, must be joined if an incision through the abdominal wall is to be sutured. It heals together in a day or two. Making sure that peritoneum is joined to peritoneum, thin though it may be, is absolutely essential. Even the tissues it covers will often heal cleanly if the peritoneum is well joined.

Suturing muscle tissue is accomplished by sewing together the covering of the muscles (fascia). If this is joined, the muscle within heals more quickly. This layer is fairly tough too.

The periosteum (the skin around the bones) should be drawn together where possible. The capsule around the joints, when ruptured, should also be joined.

If, in an emergency, you can only remember to join like tissue to like tissue, your chances of success are good, provided reasonable care is taken with cleanliness.

SUTURING MATERIALS

Absorbable material, such as catgut, is generally used where the new tissue itself will be strong enough after healing. In hernias and in emer-

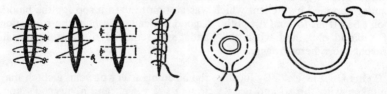

Common surgical sutures. Left to right: interrupted; continuous; Halsted; mattress; purse-string; Lembert.

gencies when nothing else is available, silk can be buried provided the knots are left without dangling ends. Linen sutures are preferred by many. Horsehair has been used in some emergencies—hair pulled from a horse's tail or mane—and many disfigurements have been prevented by its use.

Kinds of Sutures. Only a few of the surgeon's stitches need be remembered or will be useful in home emergency operations. What is of great importance is the kind of knot. Granny knots may loosen; square knots will not. If nylon sutures are used, at least three knots must be made or they will work open.

If tissue tends to pull apart as it is sutured, the surgeon's knot is used. Two twists instead of one are made of one thread about the other, followed by a one-twist ordinary square knot, to hold it securely.

Two correct surgical knots and an improper one. Left to right: square and surgeon's knots, both approved; granny knot, disapproved.

STOPPING HEMORRHAGE

In Red Cross work thousands of volunteer workers were instructed in hemorrhage control by temporary methods, such as by pressure bandages, tourniquets, and finger pressure on arteries and large veins. The same principles apply to pets, but with animals there is more that can be done.

Pressure bandages must be applied with real pressure. A wad of cloth is made and placed on top of the spot from which blood is gushing. A bandage is wrapped tightly about it and the pet is hurried to the veterinarian. For some reason the amateur is invariably unwilling to bind a wound firmly. In not one case of a badly cut foot have I ever seen a bandage applied by a client which was any more than a sop for the blood. Don't be afraid to bind it tightly. A good bandage will help the formation of a blood clot, and when the bandage is removed the clot itself will prevent more hemorrhage.

Tying Off Vessels. By locating the bleeding artery or vein, a stitch may be taken with thread and needle circling the vessel, and a surgeon's knot then tied tightly. In open wounds tying off is the safest assurance.

Stretching Arteries. If a little artery spurting blood is located, it may be grasped with forceps, pulled out, twisted, and then released. The flow is generally stopped effectively. Arteries are quite tough. In cat castrations, most veterinarians rely on this method. The blood vessels are stretched until they part and no hemorrhage results.

DEVICES TO PREVENT SELF-INJURY

After any operation, or even to prevent a cat from chewing or scratching at an area of skin infection, it may be necessary to apply one of several devices designed to permit healing without interference.

Boxing Gloves. If scratching is the difficulty, the cat may have "boxing gloves" put on the feet. These are applied by first placing a wad of cotton around the foot, winding gauze over it, and then covering the whole pad with adhesive tape. The tape should be started an inch above the gauze in order to fasten it to the hair and prevent it from slipping off. Batting itself with such soft devices often entirely discourages a pet from scratching.

Tying the Legs. Where a cat refuses to let his face alone but insists on scratching with his front paws, and if only a day or two of prevention is

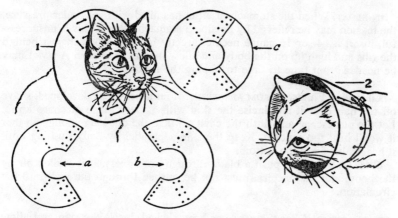

Devices to prevent self-injury. (1) An "Elizabethan collar," improvised from thin plywood or extra-strong cardboard, is helpful in preventing an animal from chewing on cuts or sores or removing bandages. a., b., and c. show how collar is made and put together. (2) Head funnel of plastic or heavy cardboard prevents an animal from scratching sores or irritations on its head or ears.

required, the front legs may be crossed and taped together at the wrists. The tape is, of course, removed while the owner takes the cat outside.

Elizabethan Collars. These may be purchased as inflatable rubber collars which are slipped over the neck and then blown up. They may also be made, easily enough, by using two pieces of thin plywood or heavy stiff cardboard, which are put together and held with shoelace or cord ties.

The Cone Collar. A piece of flat, flexible plastic is cut to make a partial cone. The edges are punched and the device is brought together around the head. The small end of the cone may either be fastened to the collar or left free; the larger end of the cone (the base) is a little beyond the cat's nose. See illustration.

MINOR OPERATIONS

Tapping. IN DROPSY. For the relief of a cat whose abdomen is filled with dropsical fluid so breathing is difficult, when there is not time to wait for absorption and excretion of the fluid, use a sharp 14-gauge hypodermic needle. Plunge it through the abdominal wall halfway between the ribs and pelvis and allow the fluid to drain into a pan. There is no appreciable amount of pain to the pet.

IN BLOAT. When the stomach of a pet has filled with gas under pressure, the tension may be relieved by passing a stomach tube. If this is unsuccessful, insert a 14- or 16-gauge needle directly into the stomach just behind the ribs and high up on the body and allow the gas to escape. A stylet may be needed from time to time to unplug the needle.

Liberating Fluids. FROM ABSCESSES. If an abscess has developed, shave off the hair over it and incise the skin with a razor blade or sharp knife. Let the pus escape and flush the cavity. Make the cut long enough so that it won't heal too quickly. Keep the skin separated by daily flushing until it has healed from the bottom.
CAUTION: Don't push a blade through an abscess. It is walled off by the body, and the bacteria must not be pushed through the wall into the circulation.

FROM CYSTS. After the area has been shaved, incise the skin and allow the fluid to escape. Make a long enough incision and retard skin healing by daily opening and flushing until the pocket has shrunk to normal size. Cysts, especially cysts of the salivary glands, occasionally have developed linings which are of a secretory nature and cannot be healed without dissection of the entire lining. This is a delicate task even for a skilled veterinarian. Cats may develop cysts under the tongue (ranulas). Let the veterinarian remove them, as they should be done under general anesthesia, for there is danger of pneumonia if the pet inspires some of the viscous fluid with which the ranula is filled.

FROM FISTULAS. A fistula is an opening or passage between two parts of the body, such as from the larynx out through the skin of the neck. A fistula may result from a gunshot wound. A sharp stick or a splinter may remain in the cat's body unknown to the owner. The passage, an unhealing ulcer, in time becomes filled with fluid. The condition may be remedied by liberating the fluid and removing the foreign body. If this does not effect a cure, your veterinarian will have to resort to surgery.

FROM SERUM POCKETS. After accidents, great pouches of fluid often develop under areas of skin which have been loosened. Sometimes they fill with blood which clots and from which the plasma is absorbed back into circulation. If the injury was serious enough, bacteria may have gained access to the pocket. After the skin is shaved, an incision at the lowest part of the pocket should be made and the fluid and clots squeezed out. The area may be flushed with peroxide or sulfa-drug solutions and the body bound to press the skin against the underlying layers to promote rapid healing.

FROM EAR HEMATOMAS. Hematomas are pockets of blood between layers of the skin. The most common location is in the ear. Cats with ear mites bruise the ears by constant scratching. Let the fluid out by a slit through the skin on the inside of the ear. If the blood is not drawn off, it will clot, and the clot will shrink and pull the ear into a gnarled deformity. Let the veterinarian operate. If no veterinarian is available,

A hematoma in the ear, and surgical treatment to facilitate rapid healing without puckering. The gauze, which is moved back and forth to prevent the middle strip from healing, is removed when the sides have healed down.

anesthetize the ear along its base with a few drops of procaine. After shaving the area, make two parallel slits through the skin, three sixteenths inches apart, the length of the hematoma. Clean all clots and fibrin strings out of the pocket. Then tie a small piece of gauze around the narrow slit to keep it from healing. Move the gauze up and down the slit once a day as you flush it out. Let the pockets heal together on both sides of the slit before removing the gauze. The strip of skin will heal in place promptly after the gauze has been removed.

Suturing. SKIN CUTS. The edges are shaved or trimmed with sharp scissors, the tissue cleansed, and the skin brought together. If a cut is long, use Halsted-type suture; if short, an interrupted stitch is adequate. Be sure the lower layers of skin are joined. It is necessary to pull the skin together as quickly as possible because it shrinks rapidly. V-shaped areas especially should be treated immediately, since the loosened skin retracts so much that it is difficult to stretch it sufficiently to cover the wound. Where skin grows together from the sides no hair will cover it and a scar is left.

EAR CUTS. Notches in the ear flaps of cats tend to grow deeper as the cat shakes his head. Healing is often completely prevented, and even after the area has healed, the cat may open the tissue to blood flow by shaking his head incessantly. The bleeding can be greatly reduced by taking a stitch which circles the blood vessel at the base of the notch. A fresh cut can best be repaired by your veterinarian, who will use local anesthetic and carefully suture both layers of skin together separately. One stitch through both skin layers and the cartilage is seldom entirely satisfactory, but if the skin is sutured neatly, the cartilage between the layers will heal together evenly.

Growth Removal. WARTS. Simply cutting a wart off results in hemorrhage. To remove one successfully, the skin below the wart must be dissected out along with the protruding part. A few drops of local anesthetic under the wart is enough to deaden the area. A single suture bringing the skin together usually results in perfect healing.

POLYPS, PAPILLOMAS. Little toadstool growths on the body or in the mouth or on the lips of a pet may often be removed by simply tying them at the base with a surgeon's knot and letting them drop off.

PROLAPSED RECTUM. It is not uncommon to find a cat which from long-continued straining at stool—frequently occasioned by the administration of laxatives, by coccidiosis, or by a disease which produces loose bowel movements—has suffered a prolapse of the rectum.

A red, tumorlike body protrudes from the anus, becomes inflamed and increases in length and diameter, and gradually turns black as the tissues dry and die. If your veterinarian is not available within a few hours, gently push the spongy enlargement back inside. Find a smooth object, such as a one-half-inch rubber tube, insert it into the rectum to be sure no intussusception remains inside and that the prolapse is entirely gone. Withdraw the tube and insert a purse-string suture around the anus, which will have become quite numb from the prolapse. Leave the ends long enough to tie in a bowknot. Release the sutures twice a day to permit defecation.

Castration. Millions of farm animals are castrated annually by farmers. Pet animals are also operated on, often very crudely. Without proper knowledge, home veterinarians often kill their pets by clumsy castration. The technique is actually quite simple.

After proper restraint and local or general anesthesia, the incision is made through the skin of the scrotum. This exposes the covering of the testicle (the tunic). It is actually an extension of the peritoneum. Now, too many times the home operator pulls out the testicle and cuts it off. The cat frequently bleeds to death. Instead, the tunic should be incised and the testicle itself exposed. The tunic is folded back over the testicle, remaining attached at only one point from which it must be peeled off. In young animals the testicle and its cord, composed of a muscle, blood vessels, nerves, and seminal vesicle, is then pulled until all these have snapped. The stretching of the artery prevents bleeding. The tunic withdraws into the abdominal ring and heals quickly.

CAUTION: If any vestige of the tunic is left sticking through the skin incisions, as it often is in cat castrations, a little lump will grow out and the skin will be prevented from healing. The home operator should always examine the scrotum to be sure the incisions are empty.

A mature pet needs a gut ligature about the blood vessels to prevent hemorrhage. It is not necessary to place sutures through the skin incisions, since they keep themselves licked clean and are not likely to pick up infections.

Cryptorchidism. Removing hidden testicles is a task for the veterinarian.

Spaying. Spaying should be done only by a professional. Considering the number of cattas lost by those who have attempted it without knowing some of the finer points, it is far better to leave it to one who knows and can perform the operation neatly, quickly, and humanely.

Teeth Extractions. Loose teeth are so simply extracted—sometimes with one's fingers—that veterinarians often wonder why they find so many in pets' mouths. Some teeth need special instruments to split them and remove them in pieces, but the incisors and premolars are sometimes so loose that they can be pulled with small tweezers or forceps, or with clean automobile pliers. If you are uncertain about how firmly set the tooth really is, better let the veterinarian attend to it even though you have to wait a week or two. If a tooth can't be moved by the finger tip, it probably is a job for the doctor.

Hernias. A hernia is a protrusion of tissue, organ, or organs through an abnormal opening. Reducing a hernia is a job for a veterinarian.

FRACTURES AND DISLOCATIONS

The most common disorders of the bones are fractures—all of which can be observed easily by the layman. Dislocations, too, are frequent. The causes of both breaks and dislocations are so varied that it would be of little use to list them; they range from the kick of a horse to catching a toenail in a crack between boards.

Before discussing specific types, let us consider the general categories of fractures.

Three different kinds of break are most often found:

In a *greenstick fracture* the bone breaks but stays in its natural position. Usually one side is broken but the other only bent.

A *simple fracture* is a clean break in which the tissue surrounding the bone is left intact.

A *compound fracture* is one in which there is an opening connecting the site of fracture to the outside of the body. This opening may be due to a wound inflicted from without or to a hole punched outward by the end of the bone being driven through the surrounding tissue and skin.

In addition there are other descriptive classifications. There are com-

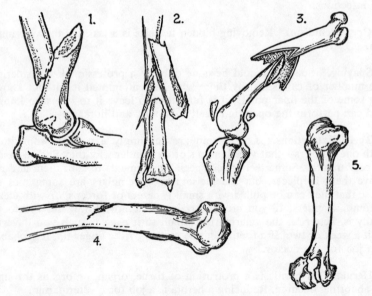

Common fractures. (1) Simple, (2) Compound, when some of the bones penetrate the skin, (3) Comminuted, (4) "Greenstick," (5) Condylar.

plete fractures where bones are broken clear across; comminuted fractures where bones are splintered; linear fractures in which the break is lengthwise of the bone; neoplastic fractures where the bone breaks from a growth in its substance; sprain fractures in which a tendon tears away a piece of bone to which it is attached, and numerous other variations.

Besides learning a little about the kinds of fractures, it will be helpful at this point if you will review that part of Chapter 2 concerned with how bones heal. You will have a clearer understanding of how fractures should be treated and why.

The owner should know how to treat his cat for shock when it suffers broken bones (see page 127). If a veterinarian is near, the owner is well advised to call him immediately. The animal should be kept warm until the doctor arrives to give the necessary treatment and set the bone.

Dislocations must be "reduced"—slipped back into place—and this, too, usually had best be left to the veterinarian. Breaks of almost any bone can be set. Some, like broken jaws, may need wiring; some may require complicated pegging, or joining by grafting. These matters require specialized study and are definitely outside the realm of this book. The methods require considerable study and a great deal of experience. So does the decision as to whether to use splints, and what kind of splint—yucca, Stader, Thomas—or plaster casts interspersed with cloth, with or without windows, if the fracture is compound. Even the cat's character must be considered. Some cats will chew almost any appliance off; others will co-operate as good patients should.

Every fracture case should be observed by your veterinarian once a week, so that he can check on the apposition, the healing, the straightness, and so he can remove the splint or cast at the right time. In growing kittens it is often safe to remove a splint three weeks after the break; in mature cats a month is the usual time.

Pelvic Breaks.   Probably the greatest number of breaks are caused by automobile accidents, and, in my experience, of these, pelvic breaks lead all others in frequency.

It is not difficult to tell when the pelvis is fractured. Usually the cat will not be able to stand, or, if he is stood up, his hind legs spread apart and he either collapses in pain or waddles with difficulty. The tail may hang inert.

If the examiner will soap an index finger and, after placing the cat on its side, insert it into the rectum, he will feel the break or breaks clearly. He may even find that a bone edge has cut through the rectum, or he may be able to push a collapsed pelvis back into place by finger pressure and thereby relieve the cat considerably. He may feel a break in the spine where the first tail vertebra joins the last sacral, which would account for the dead tail. If the cat can wag his tail, it is conclusive evidence that the backbone is not broken.

A ruptured pelvis may involve any of the six bones which comprise it (three pairs of bones), and sometimes, as we have said, the spinal column is involved. The bones of the pelvis are the ilium, ischium, and pubis. Look at the diagram of a cat's skeleton (page 32). Now imagine it is covered with flesh and is your cat. Imagine you can see that skeleton through the flesh and skin of your cat. The bones of the pelvic girdle are these six plus the sacrum, that section of the spinal column consisting of five or six vertebrae ending where the tail vertebrae start. When the pelvis is ruptured, any of the six pelvic bones may be broken or torn, or the injury may be to the backbone, the joints where the sacrum and the ilium join, one on each side, to make the sacroiliac joint, or the muscles and ligaments which hold this whole box together.

Fractured Femur. The examiner may find that nothing is wrong in the pelvis, that no bones feel as though they were broken, and yet the cat appears lopsided when viewed from behind. This may be an indication that the head of the femur—the head of the thigh bone—is broken off. It may also mean that the hipbone is dislocated, a condition which we will discuss under dislocations.

In my experience, fracture of the femur is the second most common break. Such a fracture is frequently surrounded by a pocket of blood because, as the cat trots home on three legs, the bone edges rub on the muscles and cut arterioles or venules—sometimes even a large artery or vein. An animal with such a break should be hustled to a veterinarian. He will have to anesthetize the patient to set the break. Anesthetics not only render the cat insensible but also relax the muscles and so make the job easier for the doctor.

Many a well-set bone separates and slips so that it sets in a side-to-side position instead of end to end. If this should happen, the healing process will take longer and the broken leg will be shorter than normal. Even so, the cat will manage to get about with less limp than one would expect.

Fractures of the Toes and Tails. Dislocations which amount to breaks occur in the toes and the tails of cats of all breeds. Kittens born with tails that bend backward actually have dislocated vertebrae, and bending the tail to straighten it usually results in breaking it or damaging it so severely that the end below the break dies and must be removed.

Toes which are broken at the joints usually are easily repaired by applying casts to the feet after reduction or setting. But when a ligament of the toes is cut or broken, it seldom regenerates and the nail bends upward. This is a familiar sight to veterinarians, who see so many steel-trap wounds. I have repaired feet where these little ligaments were cut on three of the four toes. Thereafter the cat may be unable to extend or retract her nails and her foot may appear dissimilar to the opposite foot.

Head Fractures. Head fractures result from a variety of accidents— from being struck by a baseball to being hit by a truck. If the skull is cracked above the brain case, the cat may live, but generally so much brain concussion occurs that the prognosis is unfavorable. If the skull over the brain case is not fractured, very often some other part of the skull is. A favorite spot is the bone covering the sinus in the forehead. The sinus itself may be penetrated and infected. Your veterinarian may have to pick pieces of bone out, flush the sinus, and cover the hole with skin.

The arch of bone over the eye, which has a fixed joint through it, often breaks and presses inward, causing the eye to bulge. This necessitates pulling the arch back into shape, where it usually stays because the cat lets it alone after he learns that pressure against it occasions pain. The eye generally becomes inflamed and may even be damaged so that it has to be removed.

Jaw injuries are common. Breaks in the center of the jawbone occur more frequently in my practice than breaks involving either of the bones (mandibles) which together make the jaw. The mandibles are joined by a cartilaginous attachment. When the break occurs here, it is obvious, because the jaw loses its firmness. If it is permitted to heal without attention, it often sets crooked. A veterinarian will wire it together so neatly that it will heal like new and much more quickly than true bone. Nursing is of primary importance. The saliva seems to prevent infection, so that no medication is required unless the wire is placed from below after the skin has been parted. Then the sutures need attention. The diet must be of a nature requiring no chewing—milk and mushy food.

Hip Joint Dislocations. Cat's hip joints come apart (are dislocated) more often than any other joints. This ball-and-socket joint, like most others, is surrounded by a capsule. Ligaments and muscles, too, hold it in place. In spite of the fact that it is held very strongly in place, falls and blows such as those inflicted by automobiles somehow get the ball on the femur out of the socket (acetabulum).

This dislocation may be such that the ball is above, below, or in front of the rim of the socket. Even the rim itself may be damaged so that it is extremely difficult to get the joint to stay together. Often the capsule, ligaments, and muscles which hold the joint together are so mutilated that the femur can be put back with ease, only to slip out again just as easily.

I have seen some dislocations of this type in large cats so difficult to reduce that three strong veterinarians struggled until sweat stood out all over them before the muscles relaxed enough to let the joint slip together. I've seen others which were snapped back by merely bending the leg and giving it just the right kind of twist. You may say, if you watch your veterinarian set one, "It's all in knowing how." But no expert, even with the use of a fluoroscope, can get all hip joints together easily.

Shoulder Dislocations. These can be observed by comparing the feel of the two shoulders. Generally a quick forward pull while someone holds the cat firmly will snap a dislocated shoulder into place, with very little resulting pain. But a difficult dislocation should not be pulled more than once. There may be tissue between the two parts. Your veterinarian can locate the trouble quickly, and by anesthetizing the cat and then twisting the leg, he will be able to replace it quite simply.

Wrist and Hock Dislocations. When dislocated, these joints are usually said to be broken. The many little bones of which the joints are composed are held together by ligaments which may be ruptured. The leg may hang sideways with skin and ligaments on one side torn away, and yet when it is straightened in a splint and held immobile, the joint heals and in time the animal will be able to walk as well as before the accident.

Such injuries may require many weeks of careful nursing. Ligaments do regenerate and skin does grow across, but the spot will be bald. That is why the veterinarian tries to draw the skin as closely together as he can—that and because the skin makes the best and the natural covering.

This has been a long chapter, filled with the details of surgical methods. No one can tell you just how you will use this information or when you will need it. As you read it you may have felt that parts of it were unnecessarily detailed. But these very details may someday save the life of your cat. Isn't he worth it?

8. How to Give Medicines and Apply Accessories

*A*LL cat owners should know how to administer the common drugs used with animals, how to give their cats medicine in liquid and capsule form, how to apply the standard bandages, how to take the temperatures of animals—in short, how to handle all the little problems of caring for a sick or injured pet.

Your veterinarian will diagnose your cat's condition, prescribe the proper medication, and tell you the kind of care and attention your pet needs. That alone is not enough to restore the animal to health. In most cases you will treat your pet at home, and it is your responsibility to carry out the veterinarian's instructions. The most effective drug ever prescribed will not help your pet if you cannot manage to get more than 5 per cent of the dose down his throat. If you allow the animal to remove the bandage the veterinarian has applied and permit him to expose an open wound to infection simply because you don't know how to apply a bandage that will stay, you can hardly expect a quick and satisfactory recovery.

Your veterinarian will outline a course of treatment for your sick cat, but the way you carry out his instructions and the care you give the animal will usually determine how effective the treatment will be. If you can give the doctor the kind of intelligent co-operation that he has a right to expect, your pet's chances for recovery will be greatly increased.

METHODS FOR GIVING MEDICINE TO ANIMALS

Liquids. When done right it requires less skill than many think to dose a cat with liquid by mouth. Whenever a liquid is to be given, you should always remember that if certain of them enter the lungs they can be very dangerous. The first question you should ask yourself is: What would happen if the animal inhaled some?

Pure water solutions of quickly soluble drugs are least dangerous. Hydrogen peroxide turns to water and oxygen when it decomposes in the fizzing effect known to everyone. On the other hand, milk, which is sometimes used as a base or vehicle for drugs, contains solids. Fat is one of them, and fat in the lungs is especially dangerous. If the drug used is harmless if it gets into the lungs—that is, if it is a water solution —it is fairly safe to fill the animal's mouth and throat and force him to swallow it. If some of the medicine trickles down the windpipe, the only unfortunate thing that can happen is a blast of the medicine in your face or on your coat sleeve when the patient coughs. But when a solution dangerous to the lungs is to be administered, a little at a time had best be given.

In either event there are two practical ways of giving a liquid medicine: the lip-pocket method and by stomach tube. Let's see how and when each of these is used.

THE LIP-POCKET METHOD: Although an experienced person can accomplish this alone, you will probably find that two people are necessary for satisfactory results. Place the animal on a table broadside to you. Make him sit. Tilt his head back so that he is looking at the ceiling. With your right hand hold his chin in this position. Slide the fingers of your left hand under his lip, push back and catch hold of the angle where lower and upper lips join. Pull this out and upward. Now you have a cup or pocket which will hold a considerable amount. While you hold the patient thus, with one hand your assistant holds both front paws firmly so that the cat can't pull them loose, and with the other he pours the medicine into the lip pocket. As it runs between his teeth and onto the back of the tongue, he will swallow it. When this is gone, more is poured in, and soon he has the whole dose. A word of caution: the assistant should stand out of the line of fire, for if the animal coughs, he or she is liable to be thoroughly sprayed.

Some cats will shake their heads violently and lose some of the medicine. For that reason it is well to quickly set the medicine container down and place your hand about the cat's head to hold him until he has swallowed all the drug.

THE STOMACH-TUBE METHOD: What seems a great task is in reality a simple and safe method if two people co-operate to dose an animal. A piece of rubber tubing, one eighth inch inside diameter and twelve to eighteen inches long, depending upon the size of the animal, is large enough for a cat. You can get both the tube and a syringe—either glass or rubber will do—at your druggist's. The syringe should be filled with the medicine and left within reach. When you are ready to insert the tube, hold the animal as described above with the head straight up. As the tube is pushed over the back of the tongue into the throat, the patient will gulp and swallow it down. If it has been moistened, it will slide down the gullet with reasonable ease.

There is one danger to guard against. You must be extremely careful not to get the tube into the windpipe, for if fluids are squirted down the tube into the lungs by mistake, the results may be tragic. By holding the upper end of the tube close to your ear, you can tell whether the other end is in the windpipe by the purring sound of air rushing in and out of the tube. If the tube has entered the gullet properly, you will not hear any sound at all. Another method of being sure where the tube is is to feel the throat. The windipe is in front and closest to the skin, and in animals which are not too fat you should have no difficulty in feeling the tube in the gullet behind it.

When you are certain that the tube is where it should be, have your assistant—who needs both hands for the job—connect the syringe to the tube and squirt the medicine or liquid food down the tube. In mature animals the stomach tube may be left in for several minutes without causing strangulation; the patient goes right on breathing normally.

This stomach-tube method is particularly useful in feeding tiny kittens which are too cold or too weak to suck. I have saved dozens this way and have taught many assistants to do it, using a urinary catheter, or small rubber tube. It is a quick way of feeding and one that is most useful in supplementing an inadequate maternal milk supply. To be sure, you must always be certain that the tube is in the gullet, but that is not hard to determine, once you have done it a few times.

You should never try to squirt a drug into your cat's mouth, snap it shut, and expect the animal to swallow it. Most of the solution runs out. The animal shakes his head and the administration is a failure. You can sometimes overcome the patient's dislike for some drugs by disguising them in sweet syrups thinned down. Glucose (dextrose) is often administered to advantage to sick animals, but if given in the form of corn syrup it is difficult to pour. It must be thinned. If any sweet substance is given carefully and without a struggle, the subsequent dosages will be simpler.

Pills and Capsules. It doesn't require sleight of hand to get a pill or capsule down the throat of a cat, even when the cat resists. It's all in knowing how. Opening the animal's mouth, dropping in the medicine, closing his mouth, and rubbing his throat may work now and again, but it's not a sure enough method to rely on.

Some capsules contain bitter or choking drugs. If a cat bites them they may cause him fright, suffocation, and a taste so obnoxious that he will try for many minutes to cough or scratch it out. If you are giving your pet medicine of this sort, you will want to be certain that no capsules are dropped between his teeth or insufficiently pushed down his throat.

Giving pills to cats is quite simple. After you have had a little practice you can do it so quickly that before the cat has time to think about scratching the job is done. With the cat sitting in front of you on a table, facing toward your right, grasp the whole head in your left hand with your thumb and fingers pressing from opposite sides of the upper jaw. Pull her head gently backward until her nose is pointing straight up. Hold it in this position. With your right hand pull down her lower jaw and, as you do so, with the left hand push her lips between her teeth so that she can't close her mouth. Now drop the pill or capsule on the back of the tongue, where it touches the palate, and as the tongue wiggles watch the pill slip over the back of it. It will slide out of sight. Let the cat close her mouth. She will seldom spit up the pill. If you find she is inclined to, then hold a pencil in the right hand as well as the pill. The moment the pill lands on the cat's tongue, give it a gentle quick push with the eraser end of the pencil and it will surely be down so far she'll swallow it when you let go of her head.

BANDAGES AND THEIR USES

Applying bandages of various dimensions to the outside of the body for the many purposes for which they are designed is truly an art if it is done properly. A few simple basic directions will be useful to those who have never bandaged an animal. Not that these will make an expert nurse of the beginner. But these instructions should make it possible to apply most of the common types of bandages securely and with reasonable facility.

Cats need bandaging to keep them from licking or tearing at newly sutured wounds or surgical incisions, to hold dressings in place, to prevent their chewing their skin when skin irritations itch them, to hold broken limbs straight in splints while waiting to set them, to stop bleeding.

Of the many kinds of bandage used by physicians and nurses, only a few are very useful in veterinary work. Rolls of muslin and gauze, many-tailed bandages, and adhesive are those needed. Anyone can rip an old sheet into three-inch-wide strips to make a bandage in a pinch. But those strips had best be rolled tightly before applying. A four-foot bandage, two inches wide, serves nicely in bandaging a cat.

Many-tails are simply strips of cloth as wide as the area to be bandaged on the patient and torn in the same number of parallel strips from each end toward the central area.

Adhesive tape one inch wide should serve almost any purpose. To cover a wide area it may be lapped, and if a narrower strip is desired, it may easily be ripped.

Most bandages will be applied by the home veterinarian for minor cuts and blemishes, or as stopgap measures before taking the pet to the veterinarian, after which, if bandaging is necessary, the veterinarian will have instructed the client as to how he wants the bandage applied in the future. This may save him giving instructions.

The most common use of bandages in pets is to prevent self-injury. Suppose a cat has been caught in a steel trap. She is found before the part of the leg below the trap bit has died. The skin has been cleaned and the veterinarian has sutured it. If she is not prevented from licking it, she will remove the stitches and open the wound. Moreover, after the bandage is applied, there will be considerable weeping from the wound and, despite antiseptics, an odd odor will develop. This is not a bad sign but rather a good one. The cat smells it and becomes frantic to lick it, since there is something about the odor which animals either enjoy or which excites them to lick. At any rate, they may rip bandages off, necessitating application of new ones fairly often.

In covering such an area, several things must be kept in mind. The bandage cannot be wound too tightly or circulation will be impeded and the area below it will swell from blood and lymph. It must be wound tightly enough not to slip. If swelling occurs, the bandage may be cut but not necessarily removed. New adhesive must then be wound around it.

First some surgical dressing, powder, solution, or salve is applied, and usually a sponge of several thicknesses of gauze put over it. The bandage is unrolled about the wound firmly until several thicknesses have been applied. The end is torn lengthwise to make two tails, which are tied in a knot at the bottom of the tear and then wound around the leg in opposite directions and tied in a knot again. When the bandage fails to go on smoothly, or when it is necessary to go from a thin place on the leg to a thicker section, if the roll is twisted occasionally, it will go on with professional smoothness. If one layer of adhesive tape is then applied, making sure that at least one half inch sticks to the hair above the bandage, it will hold the bandage material in place and be sufficient protection against the patient's efforts to remove it.

One of the most frequent uses made of bandages is to check blood flow. In this case we call them pressure bandages.

To stop the flow of blood, apply a small cloth sponge directly to the cut and quickly wind a bandage tightly about the foot many times. It may become red from blood soaking through it, but it will slowly stop bleeding.

Tourniquets are so often recommended to stop bleeding in human beings that pet owners sometimes resort to them injudiciously. With a pet, a strong elastic band can suffice or even thumb pressure over the cut artery. If a tourniquet of any sort is applied to a whole limb, it is important that it be released occasionally to let blood in and out of the part tied off.

Many-tailed bandages are usually used about the body. When cats scratch and chew holes in themselves because of skin infections, there is often no better accessory treatment. Skin remedies are applied and the bandage put on. Depending upon how much of the body it is to cover, the bandage generally has two or four holes cut to allow the legs to go through. Then a row of knots is tied along the back and left in bows, so that it can be untied to remove the bandage, which may be used again. Long surgical incisions on the sides, back, or belly can sometimes be kept covered by many-tails. Head operations, ear troubles, such as splits or sutured ear flaps, can best be protected with many-tails.

USING THERMOMETERS

Ordinary rectal thermometers, which one can purchase in any drugstore, are adequate for taking the temperatures of our cats. It is a simple matter to shake one down, then dip it in vaseline or mineral oil and insert it three quarters of its length into the rectum. It should be left in for more than sixty seconds, removed, wiped clean with a piece of cotton, and read. Don't wash it in hot water. Anyone can read such a thermometer by twisting it slowly until the wide silver stripe appears and reading the figures opposite the top of the column. Most thermometers are graduated in fifths, and since each fifth equals two tenths, the reading is usually expressed in tenths, i.e., 102⅕ °F. is 102.2°F.

The arrow at 98.6° represents the normal human temperature, and this of course is disregarded, since the normal for the cat is 101°.

It is always better to take temperatures when animals are not flustered or excited. This is especially true in the case of cats. An excited cat will show at least one degree above her normal temperature and sometimes more.

9. Problems of Reproduction

$\mathcal{T}$HOUSANDS of people breed and raise cats. Some enjoy breeding to improve the species, to originate a new strain, or even to originate an entirely new breed. But for thousands more, pleasure in their cats is contingent on security from their pets' reproducing. In crowded city areas, in small homes, among busy people, litters of kittens are out of the question. Whether you want to breed your catta or prevent her from breeding, you will want and need to know how her reproductive organs function.

Biologically speaking, the basic reason for the existence of any animal or plant is to pass along the germ plasm of which it is the custodian for the next generation. Everything about it which helps it to live in harmonious relationship with its environment is working toward that end. The creature is a bundle of tricks of nature to insure its perpetuation. One of the most interesting tricks or arrangements is the female mating cycle.

At maturity the female usually is said to come in heat or come in season. Most animals come in season in what are called mating cycles. The primary influence which causes different species to start their mating cycles is the length of the day. We do not understand how light accomplishes these changes which vary from one species to another. Dogs have a mating cycle summer and winter, and that is usually all. Cats have several mating cycles in succession in the summer and fall unless they mate—in which case the cycles stop. If the female is not mated she may repeat the cycle until she has been, or at least three or four consecutive cycles may occur.

As we have seen when we discussed body regulators, the pituitary gland initiates the mating cycle, the follicular hormone carries it through, and when the follicles rupture and discharge their eggs, the luteal hormone ends it. At the same time a rather complex series of changes is going on in the animal's body. The mating cycle of the cat is fairly typical. An understanding of this process will help you handle your pet intelligently—and may save you embarrassment if you own an unspayed catta.

Outwardly, the first signs of the season are the slight swelling of the vulva and increased appetite. The catta often becomes more affectionate. The first preacceptance period lasts several days.

Inside: The ovaries, which appeared smooth at the start, are showing the protrusion of the follicles as they enlarge. The uterus is growing longer and larger in diameter.

The second stage is initiated by a willingness on the part of the catta to copulate. The catta calls, rolls on the floor, becomes even more affectionate, sometimes even becomes a nuisance. This is considered the first day of the second, or acceptance, period.

Inside: The follicles are enlarging on the ovaries, and the uterus and blood vessels are greatly increased in size. The catta's follicles, each with its ovum (egg), do not rupture spontaneously as they do in the case of many other mammals. Copulation, with its stimulation and irritation to the vagina, is necessary; ovulation occurs shortly after. If copulation has occurred, the sperm from the male (thousands of them) will be waiting around the ovaries for the discharge of the eggs so one may fertilize each egg. Then the fertilized eggs move down the Fallopian tubes and eventually come to rest at fairly even spaces from each other.

As soon as ovulation has occurred, a blood plug forms in each follicle. This changes into the luteal body which secretes the hormone whose presence in the blood effectively stops the mating cycle and mating behavior. Luteal bodies remain throughout pregnancy. If they are dislodged, the catta aborts. After birth, the luteal bodies last for several months and their presence prevents another mating cycle.

If the catta does not mate, no ovulation occurs and no luteal body forms. No luteal body means no chemical influence to prevent recurrence of another heat period. Therefore, the pet may have two, three, or even four periods one after the other before she stops. Just what causes her to stop after the last one is not yet known.

Outside: During the copulatory, or acceptance, period the catta mates repeatedly, if allowed, but toward the end she "goes out" rather suddenly. As the luteal hormones take effect, her behavior changes. She may fight off willing males, and then just when the owner is sure the period is over she may play and be teased by a male until she accepts him. These late matings often result in large litters. Gestation is the time from fertilization of the eggs until birth.

MATING CHARACTERISTICS

Cats mate in such a haphazard manner that they must be considered genuinely polygamous. A female is often surrounded by a large ring of males; any of the males which leaps and catches hold of the back of her neck with his teeth may be the father of her litter. But she may mate many, many times with male after male in the barn or back yard. How a catta would act in the choice of mates if she were wild we are not sure. Some of the wild cat forms closely allied to the Egyptian cat are monogamous.

Under natural conditions, there is usually a fight when more than one male is courting a female. But it isn't always the winner which the female chooses. A pair of males may have a frightful contest of tooth and claw, and while this is going on a small male on the side lines may copulate with the female.

COPULATION

The cat's penis is unusual in that it is covered with small horns or barbs. When the female elevates her pelvis, the male thrusts the penis in, and while it stays, the female appears to feel no pain. Emission occurs, and then the male withdraws the distended penis quickly, with the result that the barbs on the penis tear the tissue lining of the vagina. The female then squalls characteristically, which often causes a person who is unaware of what is happening to think the cats are fighting. It is this irirtation which causes ovulation in the female. Considering the apparent pain to the female, it seems incredible that any animal goes through this ordeal as many times in one mating cycle as some cats do.

STERILITY

Sometimes successful matings do not result in offspring. Why? The catta's breasts may develop, her belly may increase in size. She has a much larger appetite, makes a nest, but produces no litter. This condition is called a pseudopregnancy—a perfectly natural phenomenon in all fertile animals which normally occurs when they are bred but fail to conceive.

Everyone who has bred an animal unsuccessfully wants to know why the female failed to conceive. There are several possible explanations.

The male may have been infertile at the time of the mating even though he was known to be fertile at other times. Overbreeding, infection in the genital tract, improper diet, sickness of a general nature— one or more of these and other less obvious conditions may cause his temporary sterility.

If males are too young they will produce sperm which are not virile enough to fertilize the ova.

To amplify some of the above points, overbreeding can easily render a male infertile. It has been found that a good "sperm swarm" is necessary to insure proper fertilization. At one service several million sperm are discharged to fertilize only half a dozen eggs. If only half a dozen sperm were present, there would be no offspring. Thousands surround an egg, yet only one enters to combine its germ plasm with that of the egg and start the new individual.

How often may a vigorous stud animal be bred? Cat fanciers allow three or four matings within two days. One copulation at the right time is enough, and cats, whose ovulation depends on copulation, should be allowed to copulate several times.

Among common misconceptions concerning breeding is the belief that if a female is bred to several males she will conceive from only one mating. This is not true. An animal can produce young in one litter which have been fathered by different males. Since the female produces a varying number of eggs or ova, it is possible for a sperm of the male with whom she has mated to fertilize one egg and for a sperm of another male to fertilize another. If a purebred female is bred to two males which vary greatly in type, it is easy to distinguish the young sired by each father. When mongrel cats mate with other mongrels, or when animals of like appearance mate, it is impossible to tell which male sired which offspring.

Infection of the genital tract is explained in Chapter 16.

Improper diet can cause sterility. Lack of vitamins, such as vitamin A and the B complex, lack of proper amino acids, minerals, and possibly certain fatty acids may produce sterility.

Undescended testicles are another cause of sterility. It is not advisable to breed to a male unless both testicles are in the scrotum, because this defect often runs in families.

Sickness of a general nature will debilitate a cat so that he will lose his vigor. Even though he can copulate, he will often be unable to produce virile sperm. Convalescing males are generally sterile. Severe worm infestations also decrease virility.

Cysts on ovaries are a common cause of female sterility. They may be removed surgically. Improperly developed reproductive tract, infection in the tract, tumors, or general debility due to disease all cause female sterility.

In rare instances females fail to come in heat because of juvenile reproductive organs. Nothing practical can be done with such animals. Hormone injections usually fail. Medications can bring the animal in heat, but she will not conceive.

Great quantities of vitamin E have been fed in the form of wheat-germ oil to produce fertility. Its value is questionable. Many wild animals eat nothing for three months before they copulate and still produce young successfully, even though their fat may be almost exhausted.

It is common for very old animals, which will still come in heat, to breed normally, conceive, and then to resorb their fetuses. One may feel the little lumps along the reproductive tract as they grow large, day by day, and then feel them grow smaller and softer until they disappear. One remedy for this is the female sex hormone in small doses. Your veterinarian can supply it in proper dosage for your female provided you are interested in breeding valuable old animals whose strain you want to perpetuate.

There are cases where animals are accidentally mated when pregnancy is most undesirable. Today your veterinarian can use either of two, or possibly three, hormones to terminate the pregnancy, usually without serious aftereffects. A series of injections is required, but the effect is generally achieved in from two to five days. There is no need for permitting fetuses to develop to full size and for pregnancy to continue to full term. If the young will be destroyed at birth, it is better to arrange for the mother to give premature birth while the fetuses are small, so that her task will be made easier.

BIRTH

After the catta's ova have been fertilized—that is, after each has become united with a sperm—they nest against the uterine wall. As they grow, each fetus is surrounded by amniotic fluid which is enclosed in an amniotic sac. Each has a placenta attached to the lining of the uterus from which nourishment is carried to the fetus, through the navel.

It is difficult to predict the size of a litter from the appearance of a pregnant animal. If she is very large, it may mean that she is carrying a small litter of large young or that she is carrying a large litter of small young. X-ray is the only dependable means of determining the number, and it is easily employed if advisable.

As the time of birth approaches, an animal will make a nest. If she is a house pet, she may fix a nest in a closet, on a bed, or out in the garden. As time of birth draws near, she will settle in her nest and appear to strain. The frequency and intensity of her uterine contractions increase.

The time of birth varies, according to the catta's condition, and the size and number of her young. Large animals take longer than small. And large litters take longer than small. A catta kittens in an average time of about two hours but may take as long as twelve hours. If her whelping lasts beyond twelve hours, she may need hormone injections to stimulate uterine contractions, or she may need a Caesarian operation.

The contractions of the uterus push the young animal out through the vagina. The kitten appears in one of several ways. It may still be in the amniotic sac. If so, the sac must be broken or the young will suffocate. If the mother doesn't do this, her attendant should do it for her. The kitten may still be in its sac, but the sac may have ruptured. Or the young may be born with the sac remaining inside the mother.

In this case the navel cord is still connecting it to the sac. The mother may chew this cord to break it, and the sac and placenta will be discharged later. But an attendant can wrap a cloth about the navel cord and pull gently until the sac comes out with the placenta.

If a placenta is not discharged from a catta she may develop peritonitis, a serious infection. It is essential for her health that every placenta be discharged shortly after the birth of a litter.

Normally a female will chew off the navel cord at varying distances from its socket, then eat the placenta and lick her young dry. This is unpleasant for most people to accept, but it is part of a natural function and there is no indication that interference is called for. However, it may be necessary to crush the navel cords with blunt scissors an inch from the body if the mother is unable to do it efficiently.

If you attend a mother catta during birth you will find that your assistance and affection is reassuring and that she will trust you with her young.

Two postparturition infections are common—uterine infections and infection of the breasts. Infection of the uterus is unlikely if no placentae remain in the uterus. Normally a female discharges from her uterus the lining to which the placentae were attached during pregnancy and through which the young were nourished. This takes the form of a dark red discharge and may last for ten or twelve days. Infected breasts are extremely serious to both a mother and her young. They require immediate attention.

The preparation of a nest has a great effect upon the success of a litter. Avoid using loose material that is likely to get into the mouths of the kittens and interfere with their nursing. Kittens are not much of a problem because their mothers will choose nesting places well padded with bedding.

The litter should be watched carefully to see that they are all getting enough milk. When they are a few days old they can starve in a very short time. They sometimes have to be helped so that they can find the teats or be fed artificially.

Before and after birth a mother needs an inclusive diet. The health of both the mother and young depends upon it. When the mother is carrying her young her food must not only keep her nourished, but must also build bones, blood, and bodies. She needs more fats, proteins, and minerals than usual. And a mother requires more water than usual while she is suckling her young, especially immediately following their birth.

Before the young are born, a long-haired catta should be prepared for suckling by having long hair cut away. It often prevents the young from reaching the teats.

Breasts often cake because a mother produces more milk than her young need. This is inevitable when her litter is small. Caked breasts are normal and disappear without medication.

Sometimes a mother dies during parturition or when her litter is very young. Although it is not easy to save the orphans, you can probably raise them successfully if you understand their needs. This means that you have to understand what their mother would supply if she were living.

Table V shows the composition of natural milk in the cow and catta. If you want to raise an orphan kitten, you can use cow's milk, since the composition of cow's and cat's milk is similar, except for the protein, which is much higher in catta's milk. Despite this difference, many kittens have been raised successfully on cow's milk.

People who are desperate to save an orphan often rush to buy goat's milk. Most people think there is something magical in it which will save the young of any species. Actually, goat's milk is very similar to cow's milk and much more expensive. It is richer in fat than most Holstein milk but not so rich as Jersey. About the only important difference is that in goat's milk the fat is broken up into much finer particles than in any cow's milk.

Table V—Composition of Milk in Cows and Cats

	FAT	PROTEIN	CARBOHYDRATE	ASH	WATER	TOTAL SOLID
Cow	4.0	3.8	4.9	0.7	86.2	13.8
Cat	5.0	7.0	5.0	0.6	82.0	18.0

Every year we see newspaper pictures of queer foster parents—adopted pet combinations—a cat nursing a young rat or tending a chicken, a mare pony caring for a puppy or a goat, a bitch nursing a kitten. Behavior of this sort is because of an excessive "mother complex." In the case of a catta that has not had kittens and has no milk a hormone (prolactin) can be injected which will make her into such a good mother that she will steal other catta's kittens in order to have something to love and protect. She'll curl up with them and accept them as her own.

Almost any female with enough prolactin in her blood will try to mother some animate thing. Perhaps it is a bitch mothering a duckling, or a rat mothering a young mouse. The trouble with getting a foster mother to adopt young not her own is generally that she already has got used to her own and then it is difficult to make the substitution. Most people have heard what pains a shepherd must take to get a ewe which has lost her lamb to accept an orphan.

The best way to encourage an adoption is to smear the orphan all over with vaginal fluids and milk from the foster mother. This makes the orphan smell like one of her own. She licks the fluids off and this licking tends to make her want it. There is no quicker way. Persistence will win over a foster mother even if she at first refuses an orphan. It may be necessary to hold it to her breast, remove it so she can't bury it or kill it, and bring it back at the next nursing. If you are there, she won't harm it, but if you are not, she may kill it. However, once a foster mother starts licking an orphan it is usually safe to leave them alone.

If no foster mother is available, the hardest thing in raising orphans is to arrange for a nipple of the right size. Kittens will seldom touch even the smallest baby nipple. Some people use medicine-dropper rubbers through which they punch holes. Others use children's doll nipples.

Many small orphans are killed through the careless use of medicine droppers. Unless you are very careful to put a drop at a time on the baby's tongue and see that he is swallowing it, his mouth may fill with the milk. Then he may cry or wheeze and inhale some of the milk. This often causes pneumonia, and from this the little thing dies. Few of those using medicine droppers know how much milk to give. A day-old kitten needs two to three dropperfuls six times a day; and day by day consumes more. The following table gives an approximation of the requirements for kittens by weights. As in humans, it varies with the individual.

Table VI

WEIGHT OF ORPHAN	AMOUNT OF MILK REQUIRED	FREQUENCY OF FEEDING*
2 oz.	2 c.c.†	Every 3 hours
3 oz.	3 c.c.	Every 3 hours
5 oz.	5 c.c.	Every 3 hours
8 oz.	½ oz.	Every 4 hours
12 oz.	1 oz.	Every 5 hours
1 lb.	1¼ oz.	Every 5 hours
2 lbs.	2 oz.	Every 6 hours
3 lbs.	2¾ oz.	Every 6 hours

SPAYING

For many years opinions about the results of spaying (not spading) a catta were bandied about by "experts" on a purely conjectural basis. Mr. James found his catta became obese; Mrs. Jones found hers did not change. Even veterinarians couldn't agree.

Considerable research now shows that spaying has little effect on the general characteristics of the animal.

This is true with one qualification: that the operation be done when the animal is nearly full grown or later. This is very important. Studies show that when animals are spayed very young there is a disharmony in their glandular development. If it is desirable to produce a chicken which will be large, awkward, lazy, and fat—a capon—the operation is

*All orphans under one week old do best on four-hour feedings or oftener.
†A c.c. (cubic centimeter) is ¼ teaspoonful.

not put off until the bird is full grown. If it were, the result would be merely a sterile rooster.

The fact that some spayed cattas get fat is not in itself a valid argument against spaying. Unspayed cattas, too, get fat. Some of the most grossly overweight cats I know are whole animals. They are overfed. If they had been spayed and placed in the hands of the same owner, his or her explanation for the overweight condition would have been that the catta had been spayed.

It is now believed that spaying has little effect upon a mature animal. The animal does not have mating cycles and the urges which they bring. This may have a very slight effect on weight and personality. Spaying in babyhood causes abnormal development. The only reason for spaying cattas young is to prevent the cattas of vicious strains from becoming dangerous as they get older. If they are spayed as kittens, they tend to remain gentle.

Actually, cats are often altered young to advantage. Ornamental cattas probably develop more handsomely if they are spayed before their third month. They grow to be larger, quieter, slower, and are more inclined to drape beautifully over the furniture. Usually the most beautiful cats are the ones which have been spayed early.

Spaying a catta has a number of definite advantages:
1. The animal is spared the risk attending birth.
2. The owner is spared raising or having to destroy unwanted animals.
3. The owner avoids the annoyance of males surrounding his home, killing shrubbery, spraying on his front or back doors.
4. The spayed female does not wander at certain seasons as the unspayed does.
5. The owner is saved perhaps forty dollars a year for boarding her pet twice a year.
6. Food is saved, since a pregnant, or lactating, mother consumes more food than a spayed one.
7. Considering the risks of pregnancy and birth, a female's chances for longer life are actually greater.

There is also a disadvantage in spaying:
An owner may someday regret that his catta can't reproduce.

CASTRATION

Much the same arguments hold for castration as for spaying. Generally it is done to make males stay home. Those which congregate around the abode of a catta come home punctured with tooth marks from the frequent fracases attending such meetings.

There are many other reasons for castrating. Cats of strains whose members tend to become vicious with age are often rendered gentle and lovable when castrated young. Castration also tends to prevent indiscriminate wetting the home and prevents obnoxious odors.

Tomcats which are of no use for breeding become stay-at-homes, and much expense in their care is saved. Uncastrated toms so often come home infected that the family has to face veterinary bills to cover treatment. If castrated after maturity, their ratting and mousing ability will not be impaired and in general they will be more satisfactory pets.

It seems to be the opinion of many that animals should not be spayed or castrated because copulation is essential to health. This is not the case. Any animal, whether whole, spayed, or castrated, is just as healthy if it is never bred as those which are used for breeding. Only a small percentage ever copulate in their whole lives. This is true of many species, not of our pet cats alone.

HOW TO TELL THE SEX OF A CAT

To the cat lover who has had considerable experience with animals it may seem strange that in a book of this sort it is necessary to discuss the ways of distinguishing sex. Actually the determination of sex is not always easy even for an old hand. When you realize that a certain few experts with exceptional powers of observation are paid large sums of money for their services in "sexing" baby chicks, that a few scientists in any university are often called upon to "sex" young laboratory rats and mice for others, you will realize that distinguishing the sex of many species is not so simple as you might have assumed.

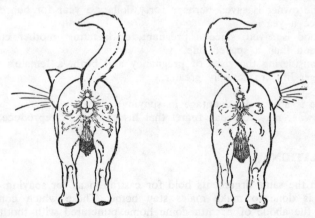

External sexual differences in male and female cats. Left, male; right, female.

Cat owners often make ludicrous mistakes. For a time I kept track of the cats brought to our clinic to be "spayed." I found that one out of every ten cats brought to us for spaying was a tomcat—which can only mean that at least 10 per cent of the cat owners can't tell the sex of such a commonplace animal as the cat. This fact is corroborated by the numbers of clients who bring their cats to the clinic to find out their sex. Some people are uncertain even about the sex of dogs. But what's so strange about that? If these facts surprise you, you might ask your physician to tell you some of the strange conceptions that people harbor about human sex, anatomy, and childbirth.

If you have any doubt about the sex of your cat, get a cat you think to be of the opposite sex and, holding the pair so that you can observe the organs, compare them.

Among the mammals there is one general characteristic of females which you have already learned in reading about anatomy: the anus and vulva are close together. The rectum, which terminates at the anus, and the vagina, which terminates at the vulva, emerge through the pelvis together. In females you will always find these two spots close together.

In a male you can feel the testicles, too, and even if your powers of observation are not sufficiently keen to tell the sex by looking, you can surely tell by feeling. Rarely is a cat a cryptorchid, but if it is, you may feel but one testicle or neither.

Many cat owners do not understand that all male animals have rudimentary teats. Finding them on a tomcat, they often become confused and may sometimes wonder if their pet is an intersex—a hermaphrodite. Or they may find one or two and ask if they are pimples caused by a skin disease. As a wit once remarked, these rudimentary teats are there "just in case a male animal ever should have babies." They illustrate the farsightedness of nature or something.

10. Sanitation and Hygiene

$\mathcal{Y}$OUR first concern as a cat owner must always be the maintenance of your pet's health and well-being. To be able to care for a pet in sickness is a necessary skill, but for many obvious economic and humanitarian reasons the prevention of disease is even more important.

The proper care of a cat requires that you have a fundamental knowledge of animal hygiene and sanitation, that you recognize the necessity of keeping the animal clean, that you provide quarters which are free not only of visible dirt and debris but also of disease-carrying agents. In short, it is essential that you have a thorough and realistic understanding of how to establish and maintain environmental and personal conditions which actively promote and preserve your pet's health.

Let us start first with the care of the animal itself and then consider its surroundings and how to manage them.

COAT CARE

When you think of an animal's coat condition, you must think both of his hair and of the skin under his hair.

The animal's skin, as we have seen, functions as an organ of the body, just as do the kidneys or liver. Its exposure subjects it to all kinds of abuse which better-protected organs never experience. In a healthy animal, glandular secretions of the skin keep the coat shiny. But a coat must be combed often. Dead hair must be removed and snarls untangled in all long-haired breeds. Only a comb and elbow grease will accomplish this. Burrs must be removed by hand. Hard mats have to be cut with scissors. To do this, push the scissors under the wad, pointing them away from the body, and cut the wad in half. Large wads may be cut into many sections which then comb out with the least pain to the cat. It is almost never necessary to do the easy thing—snip across the hair. With patience, all the dead hair can be separated from the wad, leaving a lovely coat.

Combing of long-haired cats should be done as frequently as necessary to keep the coat in good condition. Animals should be taught from kittenhood to stand or lie on a table and expect and enjoy combing.

Short-haired animals need less attention, but a fine comb, even for them, is more efficient than a brush. Some people take a hacksaw blade and drag it, like a comb, over the coat. The teeth catch loose hairs and pull them out. The bare hand, moistened and rubbed over a short-haired cat's coat, will pull out many loose hairs and leave the coat looking glossier.

Brushes should not be the mainstay of grooming. Running brushes over the outside of a long-haired animal's coat accomplishes little in the way of loose hair removal. It does sweep out some of the finest skin scales, accumulated dust, and a few loose hairs. There are many kinds of specialized brushes. Thousands of elaborate grooming brushes, with wire bristles on one side and fiber bristles on the other, are sold, but professionals do not use them. You can get along very well with: (1) a comb with very strong teeth, ten to fourteen to the inch, which can pull out snarls and do rough work; (2) a fine comb with twenty teeth to the inch; (3) a fine strong scrub brush; and (4) a pair of scissors.

If the animal to be groomed is a small, smooth-coated pet, a fine, strong comb plus a small scrub brush will suffice.

The skin of many species of animals, including the human, has large numbers of sweat glands. Cats, however, have them in restricted areas— under the tail, for instance, and fewer about the rest of the body. But if cats do not sweat, how is the skin cleaned? Cleaning is accomplished by the renewal of the outside layer, which is constantly being sloughed off by growth in the layers beneath, and by the shedding of the hair itself. There is always a fine scaling of skin going on, more at some times than at others. Healing skin often sheds large, flaky, dandrufflike scales which must be combed or brushed out of the hair. Sometimes the shed-off scales will stick to hairs and one may find little disks of skin clinging to them, an eighth of an inch out from the body.

Cats are equipped with another small pair of skin glands, the anal glands, which are situated at either side just under the anus. They discharge their contents through the anus via two ducts. Pressure on them will cause the expulsion of the contents. These glands are found in a great many related species and their purpose has not been fully explained. We do know, however, that the anal glands discharge automatically when the animal becomes terrified. Dogs, skunks, and weasels have them also, and each species is characterized by a distinctive odor. Everybody recognizes the penetrating odor of a skunk. Farmers are often able to detect the presence of a weasel by his odd musk. Many cat owners do not realize that their pets have these anal glands and that part of their body odor comes from them.

Because nerves are everywhere in the skin, it takes very little—only a fleabite, for example—for a pet to show his annoyance by scratching. With the other basic information necessary to care for an animal's coat properly, you should learn something about the nerve patterns in the skin. If you scratch your cat in certain places on the back, he will scratch, but he may not come within ten inches of scratching the spot where you are scratching him. I mention this reaction only because cat owners frequently do not realize that when their pet scratches his shoulder it is no indication that he is itchy there. He may have a sore spot at the base of his tail. A better indication in locating an itchy spot is to watch where he chews most.

NAILS

The nails are appendages of the skin. Each nail has a hard outer crust protecting it, while inside there is a blood and nerve supply. Nails, being organs of defense as well as being useful in holding food while the teeth tear it apart, are strongly attached to the toes—much more so than our nails. Cats' nails are retractable.

Cats like to have wood to wear their nails on and exercise their toes. If the animal fails to keep the nails short enough, long claws are easily trimmed by cutting off the transparent part.

SHEDDING

"Doctor," thousands of people ask of their veterinarians every year, "what makes my cat shed the year round?" The answer is—light. Nature intended animals to live without the benefit of electric lights. It has been

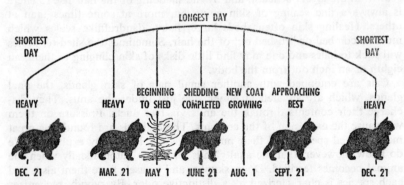

How the length of the day influences the shedding of the cat's coat when he is kept out of doors.

found that as the days get noticeably longer the influence of these length-ening days on the cat's body (probably via the eyes) causes the hair to stop growing and fall out. New hair replaces the old. If, now, the day is suddenly made much shorter, the new coat will grow faster and reach the acme of its beauty far sooner than if the days gradually shorten. Pets which are not subjected to the normal light cycle shed a little all the time and heavily in the late spring. Combing helps in removing the loose hair before it falls or is rubbed off on one's clothing, rugs, or furniture.

BATHING

Dogs and cats are the only pets ordinarily bathed, and they are bathed simply to remove dirt and odors. The odors disappear with the dirt. There is no best way to bathe a pet, and no way has yet been found to eliminate the need for "elbow grease." The human fingers surpass any mechanical device for efficiency in bathing.

Because the coats of cats are water-resistant, one needs the help of a chemical to wash a cat with ease. Soft or liquid soap is excellent and can be procured with either a 20 per cent or a 40 per cent coconut-oil base. You will save money by buying 40 per cent soap and adding an equal amount of water. A 20 per cent product is ideal. You can either add it to a bucket of warm water which will then wet the pet's coat easily or you can put some on the pet's back, pour on the warm water by the cupful, and mix the soap and water on the animal. Professionals use a tub and allow water to run onto the patient from a hose. Cake soap can be used instead of liquid, but it requires considerably more work.

By whatever method the soap and water are applied, the solution must be well worked into the coat and rubbed until the dirt has been loosened or dissolved. After the lathering, the soap must be thoroughly rinsed from the coat. This is best accomplished by working the fingers through the hair, just as one does in applying the soap solution. Usually one soaping and rinsing is enough, but if necessary, the process may be repeated.

There are soaps which contain vermin poisons. If one is used, no further medication is required. However, there are vermicidal dips and rinses available which are well worth using for topping off a bath on any pet. The solution is prepared just before the bathing starts. After the pet has been rinsed, the dip or special rinse is poured all over the coat, but this is not rinsed off. It is allowed to saturate the coat for a few minutes, the surplus is squeezed out with the hands, and the patient is dried.

A loosening of hair is generally a result of any bath. After the pet is dry, considerable combing is generally necessary to free the coat of the loosened hair and give it a sheen and tone.

Bathing cats may be accomplished by using a basin and towels. The whole animal may be dipped in the basin, leaving only the head out. The soiled water is allowed to run out and fresh water quickly drawn while the pet sits on a towel, waiting for the next immersion.

One of the questions about bathing most frequently asked is whether it is safe in winter. It is safe in winter provided the pet is well dried before being allowed outside in the cold air. For that reason many pet owners bathe their pets at night, knowing they are sure to be dry by morning.

Another common question is at what age it is safe to bathe a young animal. There is no rule about age. Small kittens which have become soiled and evil-smelling must be bathed if we are to keep them in a home. I have never seen a bath harm a pet provided it was properly dried. The fact is that kittens are frequent sufferers from parasites and diseases. When one gets sick shortly after being bathed, the bath is all too often assumed to be the cause. Most of the harm that has come from bathing has been of this nature: the pet was going to be sick anyway; the bath didn't cause it.

There are several dry shampoos available which are quite effective cleaning agents. These should be used according to directions, which vary with the type. Then there are also harmless detergents on the market which remove dirt without lathering.

REMOVAL OF ROAD TAR. Cats may run in newly tarred roads and return with a ball of tar and sand around each foot. Kerosene will dissolve the tar but it also irritates the skin. In most cases it will be necessary to rinse each foot in several washings of kerosene and quickly wash off the kerosene with strong soap and water each time. The discoloration of the tar is hard to eliminate completely but does no physical harm. Remember that it is as necessary to wash out the kerosene as it is to remove the tar.

REMOVAL OF PAINT. Paint removal is a frequent problem. Paint is not so poisonous as many people think—that is, white paint. Some of the paint pigments are poisonous, however, such as Paris green. If the cat comes home with fresh paint, still wet, on its coat, turpentine will remove it, if plenty is used without allowing too much to come in contact with the animal's skin. The turpentine must be removed by thorough washing with soap and water.

If the paint is dry, it will probably be necessary to clip the hair, even though it causes a temporary disfigurement. It will grow in again. Cats will fuss over coats which have been matted with paint and will often chew chunks of the paint out of their hair and eat it. Most cat owners promptly cut the paint out with scissors. There is often nothing else that can be done. Small amounts can be removed while still wet by mixing the paint with linseed oil and washing it out of the coat.

ANIMAL ODORS. The sources of animal odors, aside from those of excrements, are ear canker, anal-gland secretions, and the sebum from thousands of body glands. All of these can be eliminated—as already mentioned —by cleaning the ears, by expressing the anal-gland secretion, and by thorough bathing.

PARASITE CONTROL. Bathing in itself will not eliminate parasites, as many people seem to think, but preparations of excellent efficiency for use with the bath may be had for the purpose. Some are used as a rinse or dip following the bath, as described above; others are liquid soaps or soap cakes with insect killers added. Some manufacturers claim that their products will prevent fleas and lice from reinfesting dogs for several days after their use. Some claim their products will kill the eggs of lice (nits). In eliminating lice, it is necessary to apply the killing agent every eleven days, as this breaks the generation and so eliminates the lice.

The more effective way to control pests is to use a liquid dip, soap, or rinse to kill all the insect pests during the bath and then keep the cat well powdered with a nonpoisonous flea powder.

With the advent of government-supervised advertising, the banishment of dishonest claims and the insistence by the Federal Food and Drug Administration that ingredients be declared on bottles of drugs, any ingenious person can often make his own household remedies by reading the percentages of the contents of bottles he has bought. And it is amazing how much money he can save. This is especially true in the field of grooming. You will find mineral oil and pine oil mixed selling under a trade name at many times the cost of the ingredients, which can be bought in any drugstore. You will find derris root or cube root mixed with dried clay selling at high prices, recommended for flea powder. It is excellent flea powder, but you might just as well buy derris root or cube root and use less of it, undiluted.

THE MOUTH AND TEETH

A cat's unpleasant breath is often caused by dirty, broken, or infected teeth. Tartar is sometimes an eighth of an inch deep. Your veterinarian can snap it off and clean the teeth, which will do much to sweeten the breath. Cleaning an animal's teeth is not difficult. You can do it yourself with a tartar scraper which you can get from your dentist.

Examine your pet's teeth at least once a month. Look for tartar and loose or broken teeth. Animals fed soft foods have more tartar than those fed on hard foods. All animals enjoy chewing soft rib bones, which help to keep teeth clean and prevent tartar from building up. Animal teeth do not need brushing to keep them clean.

THE EYES

Our cats' eyes require very little attention. The only hygiene necessary is the removal of surplus hair that may curl inward and irritate the eyes, and the removal of exudate on the nasal side where the eye overflows in many breeds.

THE EARS

Ears are often troublesome in cats. Examine them occasionally under a good light. Dirty ears have a nasty odor which pervades the animal and may cause him to shake his head and dig constantly at the ear with his hind paw. If you see a pet moving his front paw over an ear as if it itched badly, he probably has canker or ear mites.

Drop a mixture of ether and alcohol in the ear to dissolve wax and dirt. Propylene glycol will serve as well. After the application swab out the ear carefully with cotton on the end of a toothpick. If a little alcohol and ether are left, they will evaporate.

COLLARS AND HARNESSES

An animal's health should be considered when collars and harnesses are bought. Salesmen do not always have this in mind in making recommendations. Round collars for long-haired cats, strap collars for short-haired cats, are usually most satisfactory. Harnesses are used for all cats. After all, a cat's collar is useful principally to hold an identification tag. Some owners hang bells on them to be able to know where the cats are or to frighten birds. For the latter purpose the bell is less protection to a bird than is commonly believed; a prominent ribbon which birds can see moving is more effective. Some persons take their cats walking on leashes; some tie them out part of the day, while others tie them up in the house. A harness is more comfortable for walking, but it must be quite tight or the cat can hold her front legs straight in front and back out of the harness. Some cats learn to reach down and chew the leather breast strap in two. There is no cruelty in a harness and often greater security.

Every collar or harness should be examined to see that no sharp points or rivets protrude to scratch the animal's skin or wear off the hair. It is most important not to get a lot of hardware on these accessories which can injure a cat's ears. When she shakes her head and her ears flap against a heavy buckle and license tags, the ears are often damaged. A cat that has worn a heavy combination of hardware sometimes has the hair entirely worn off his neck.

BEDS AND BEDDING

Bedding for cats is a problem. You may buy several different kinds of mattresses, canvas stretched across metal or wooden frames, and all sort of beds. You can make beds out of pieces of thick carpet or castoff mattresses cut down, or you can allow pets to sleep in old chairs.

Some people like the smell of cedar padding stuffed into cat mattresses or pillows, but stale cedar has an unpleasant aroma. After a while the smell pervades a whole house—even the clothing hanging in closets. If wood shavings or other wood products are desired for bedding, ordinary pine can be bought for a fraction of the cost of cedar. By sprinkling some flea powder in it a very much better flea and louse destroyer and repellent is made without the cedar smell.

Even though you may know cat owners who go to great lengths to provide shredded bedding and soft springy materials, don't try to follow their examples. Cats actually need no such soft cushions; many prefer bare boards to anything else—your mantelpiece, perhaps. Years ago when I was a farmer, I had four Maine "coon cats" which chose to climb the posts at the end of the horse stalls, curling up on top of the harness where it bent hanging over the big hook. The space was not much larger than a person's hand and yet those cats slept there every night without falling. A more uncomfortable place could scarcely have been found in the barn with its supply of soft hay.

SANITARY PROVISIONS FOR CATS

The type of pan, if any, that is furnished to a cat and the cleanliness with which the pan is kept are both highly important to health. This is chiefly because of worm infestation.

In deciding on the proportions of the pan or box and the material to be used in it, you must consider both the natural habits of all cats and any unusual habits your particular pet may have. A cat generally digs a hole, voids, then covers the excrement. When you place a flat piece of newspaper on the floor you should expect your cat to scratch it to shreds, deposit her feces on the floor, and then cover it with the bits of paper. Instead of getting angry, you should remember that the cat is merely following one of her hereditary behavior patterns. The tomcat sprays bushes standing up. That's his nature. His pungent urine isn't his fault either. To prevent the spraying and to tone down the urine odor, tomcats are frequently castrated.

If the pan furnished a house cat is shallow and small, you may expect the sand to be scattered all over the floor near the pan. If it is too large, you, being human, are likely to neglect changing it, realizing there is room for other deposits and because in winter sand is difficult to obtain. You must realize, however, that if you allow the pan to sit in the warm cellar or kitchen too long, the worm eggs in the stools will have time to incubate or pupate. Hookworms may have risen to the top of the sand to contaminate the cat's feet when she comes to the pan. Roundworm and whipworms will be in their infective stage. The sand in even a large pan should be changed every five days as a maximum.

Pans eighteen inches wide with sides four or five inches high make excellent cat pans. Large dishpans or old-fashioned icebox drip pans are ideal. Many prefer long, narrow pans. One cat fancier uses metal pans, six inches deep, seven inches wide, and eighteen inches long, and places two inches of sand in the bottom. She keeps many cats and finds that the narrow pans take less room in the cages. Pet stores sell various types. Whatever type of pan is used, it must be scrubbed regularly. Filthy pans repel cats and people alike, and certainly they breed parasites—worms and fleas.

The location of the pan is often an important factor in sanitation. If a tomcat stands in the pan and sprays the wall, the odor will last for weeks, and wallpaper can't always be washed. Frequently, moving the pan away from the wall will correct the cat's habits.

Opinions as to the best materials to use in pans vary. Sand, peat moss, ordinary garden soil, and paper, whole, shredded, or cut in strips, are the usual materials used. Sand has the advantages of being enjoyed by the cat, of being inexpensive, and of acting as an odor-absorbent. It has disadvantages too: it is not too easily obtained by city folks, it is sometimes difficult to dispose of, and it is likely to be tracked out onto the floor. For catteries it is excellent. Some people fill a barrel with new sand and keep an empty barrel outside into which they throw the used sand. Kittens broken to sand have some difficulty in learning to use newspaper in the homes of their new owners. A wise owner can first ascertain what the kitten is used to and use it. If the cat has been habituated to sand, then sand should be put in the new box, and if it is desirable to change to paper, strips of newspaper can be placed on top of the sand. By daily increasing the amount of paper, the sand may soon be dispensed with.

Paper is commonly used because it is cheap, it can be cut or torn quickly through many folds into inch-wide strips, it absorbs urine, and it can be gathered up and burned or wrapped in a whole sheet and disposed of. Cats learn to use it quickly. Shredded paper can be purchased in bales, and some cat owners prefer it. If too finely shredded, however, it may catch in the claws or long hair and be dragged out onto the floor.

Several pan litters are sold by mail and at pet stores and supermarkets. They are excellent, quite deodorizing, and do not track about the house to any extent. If you buy one, you will still need to change the litter often enough to prevent worm infestation, if not odors. Worm eggs are exceedingly resistant.

OUTDOOR ACCOMMODATIONS

Scientific studies on acclimatizing animals show that they should not be exposed to sudden changes in temperature. An animal which might die of exposure when taken suddenly from warm to cold can stand much lower temperatures if it is introduced to them gradually. One reason for this is that cold stimulates the growth of the coat, which in time becomes much thicker and so provides better protection. When southern cats are brought North, their coats are so much heavier in their second winter in the North that they look like different animals. An animal that has become accustomed to cold can stand a great deal.

Cats can stand far more cold than many people realize. I have treated cats which have been caught in traps during sub-zero nights and lived, without even frostbitten feet. Some cat owners have learned that cats, given snug shelters, can become hardy and beautiful without artificial heat.

There are many cat breeders who believe their cats do much better in outdoor pens. Some of the loveliest cats I treat are kept out of doors the year round. Of course, weathertight, well-bedded hutches, free from drafts, are provided.

We cannot consider the problem honestly without mentioning the feral cats and how they live. Many take up abodes in woodchuck burrows, deserted houses, under hen coops, and even in hollow trees. Their marvelous adaptability enables them to eke out a satisfactory existence and to cope with the cold as well as our pampered, overstuffed, pet cats cope with the other extreme of steam-heated apartment houses.

DISINFECTANTS

Disinfectants must be chosen with care. Cats and foxes cannot stand phenol derivatives. Their nest boxes, beds, and their coats should not be disinfected with these products. Some time ago, when an owner used a phenol disinfectant in fox nest boxes, many of the fox kittens were killed from the fumes long after the product had dried out or soaked into the wood of the boxes.

Odorless deodorizers are excellent and can be purchased reasonably. "Phenol coefficient" on a label may not mean a phenol product. It simply compares a product with phenol in germ-killing ability. Some of the odorless deodorizers do have high phenol ratings.

Some pet owners like the odor of pine oil; some prefer others, which often simply outsmell the odor to be removed. Good soap-and-water cleansing is usually adequate around pets, and if there is an odor left after scrubbing, it is a safe assumption that the spot or place is not clean. Disinfectants which give off chlorine are good but are also bleaches and must be used judiciously on that account.

PERIODIC HEALTH EXAMINATION

One of the best bits of advice a veterinarian can give to his clients is that they keep most careful track of the health of their cats, especially those that have passed middle age, by periodic physical checkups. If you have a competent veterinarian to whom you entrust your animals' health, he can make some tests which may be instrumental in prolonging their lives by many years.

He can determine the presence of some diseases by temperature readings and other signs. He can detect external parasites, intestinal parasites, heartworms, skin disease, ear canker, kidney disease, bad teeth, overweight and underweight conditions, eye defects, and deafness. These defects need correcting, if possible.

Any of these conditions can shorten an animal's life. When you take your cat to the veterinarian's for a periodic health examination, take along a small sample of stool and a urine specimen. Put new paper in your cat's pan and, as soon as he has urinated, before the urine has had time to soak into the paper, pour it into a container. If the cat has been trained to use only dirt or sawdust, however, you will be unable to obtain a sample of urine.

Let us consider how a periodic health examination can prolong the life of an animal. Suppose you know of nothing wrong. All you notice is that your cat hasn't the pep he used to have. You take his urine and feces and ask your veterinarian to examine him. But don't expect him to make an examination worth the name unless you have the urine and stool, because so many facts may be learned from them.

The veterinarian asks you whether the cat drinks more water than he used to. You have noticed that he has. So when he tests the albumin and learns that it shows XX, indicating kidney disease, he gives you medicine to administer at home and tells you not to feed any more meat, fish, liver, and just about everything your cat loves. He explains that the pet will learn to love his new diet as well when he gets accustomed to it.

He may see that your cat, who weighs twenty-five pounds, is thirteen pounds overweight, and show you how to reduce him. The number of diseases which can be uncovered in cats whose owners had no idea they were even sick, is legion. Fortunately the majority of them can either be eliminated or relieved by proper care and medication. A proper examination, which reveals many diseases in their early stages, when their treatment is most effective, is one of the surest ways to insure the health and longevity of your pet.

11. Health Hazards in Hospitalization, Boarding, and Shows

*C*AT owners sooner or later face the question: What shall I do with my cat when I have to leave him? There are a number of other questions closely related to this first one. If the pet becomes sick, shall I keep him at home or leave him in a veterinary hospital? Shall I exhibit my pet in a show? Is it safe to allow my cat free access to neighborhood animals?

Actually all of these general questions are part of a still larger one: To what extent shall I isolate my cat?

In order to answer these questions intelligently, there are certain basic facts you should know. Every proprietor of a veterinary hospital or a boarding kennel, every 'log warden and humane-society officer, knows these facts. If every pet owner knew them as well, sickness among pets might be greatly reduced. Omitting for the moment any consideration of the emotional side of the question, let us discuss only the purely physical factors, the health hazards which "mingling" entails.

Let's assume that every cat owner and every cat handler is honest, and that every person owning an animal he or she knows is sick will isolate it. Let's assume, too, that no Humane Society warden knowingly puts a sick cat in the pound. And last, but not least, let's assume that no veterinary hospital exists without isolation wards where cats with each kind of disease are separately segregated. It is obvious that none of these assumptions can be completely true. Pet owners are no more and no less ethical than other groups of people. Certainly not all of them are sufficiently concerned about the health of other people's pets to isolate their own when they know them to be sick.

But suppose that all these things were true. Could you even then be certain that your cat could be safely placed with a lot of other healthy animals and never contract a disease? You could not.

The average cat show probably furnishes the best example of the risk involved whenever animals are brought together, in spite of the fact that every cat exhibited is supposed to be a healthy animal. Although veterinarians examine all cats at the entrance gate and reject those which are sick, cat shows are still one of the prime means by which disease is spread.

Here is another example of the way disease is spread. The cattery owner accepts Mrs. Williams' pet in all good faith. The cat is placed in a room with many other cats. All of them appear to be in good health. After three days the cattery owner notices that Mrs. Williams' cat is sneezing. She isolates him in another room. But suppose your cat had been in a cage in the first room. Many of the cat diseases are spread by droplet infection. A day after you take your cat home he starts to sneeze. You telephone the cattery owner immediately and take your cat to her to cure. She tells you your cat was contented and well on its first visit. But the chances are she remembers Mrs. Williams' cat, and when two days later she finds that most of the cats in that room are sneezing, what is she to do? Whose fault is it? Is the cattery owner under obligation to take your cat back and keep it until it is cured or dies? Legally such an occurrence is considered along with lightning, wind, and fire as "an act of God." Pure slander! But lawyers have to have a pigeonhole for everything, and so cat diseases are blamed on God.

Perhaps your cat contracts feline distemper while being boarded, and when you return she is dead. The owner of the cattery has spent hours, half sick herself because of worry over what has happened, trying to nurse the cats under her care to health. You are hurt, indignant, and angry that your cat has been lost. Perhaps you refuse to pay even the board. Actually, considering the work and worry she has had, you owe the cattery owner far more than if nothing had happened.

Needless to say, no cattery owners ever *want* such things to happen. It hurts them every time it does. It causes worry, anguish, extra work, and loss of money. So what, then, should be one's attitude? Shall every pet owner say, "I left a well animal; now he's sick. You're to blame"? Or shall he look at it from a reasonable point of view, difficult as that may be when one's individual pet's health is involved?

It is impossible to assemble a large group of animals of any species and be 100 per cent certain that no one is infested with parasites or is incubating some disease. So long as this is true you can't board a pet and be 100 per cent sure the pet will be well, uninfested with parasites, and neither incubating a disease nor showing symptoms of it when you call for it.

The best and safest thing you can do is to leave your pet in a cattery where veterinary attention is given or where the owner knows diseases well enough to be able to recognize the first symptoms and is willing and able to treat them properly. It is, of course, essential that there be an isolation ward in conjunction with the boarding facilities.

If, when you call for your cat, he is sick or even dead, don't at once conclude that there has been some dirty business or blame the cattery owner. Be sorry for that person, knowing your animal has occasioned great inconvenience and, in the case of conscientious individuals, considerable mental pain. Loving animals as I myself do, I know that it is difficult to be wholly reasonable at such times, but this is the only fair attitude to take.

Far worse health hazards exist in allowing city cats to wander freely. Cats picked up by public agencies are usually destroyed at once, often in a carbon-monoxide gas chamber on the truck which transports them. If they are held, the chances are at least even that they will be placed in a large cage or room with other cats. One sick cat among the lot infects all the rest.

When your tomcat knows where a catta in heat lives, if he is healthy you may be sure he will be camped near her home, and so will all the other toms that know—another potent source for the spread of infection.

Unquestionably cats can contract diseases in veterinary hospitals. The most careful veterinarian, in the best of faith, accepts animals, apparently free from disease, for operations. Two days later those same animals may be sneezing and filling surgical wards with invisible virus-filled droplets. Even though ultraviolet lights and germ-killing vaporizers may have been installed, they are not 100 per cent guarantee that a few healthy cats will not be infected. I have never known a veterinarian to tell me that no disease was ever contracted in his hospital. But neither can the superintendent of a hospital for humans make that boast. Who doesn't know of at least one case of a patient in a hospital contracting virus pneumonia or some other of the contagious diseases? What of the diseases which sweep through the infant wards, or the women who even today are infected with "childbed fever"? I doubt that the risk of leaving a pet in a scrupulously clean veterinary hospital, complete with isolation wards, is any greater than the risk of contracting a disease yourself while in a hospital.

Remember that not everything that happens to your pet in a hospital or kennel happens *because* he is there. Many of these things are the result of normal health hazards; many are the direct result of the age, habits, idiosyncrasies, food, and appetite of your pet.

If you leave an old animal, remember that the older he is, the nearer he is to the end. If he should die of a heart attack or a kidney ailment, even though lawyers blame the death on God, be just enough to call it old age, remembering that he had to die sometime. And be grateful it wasn't in your arms. You were spared a heart-stopping anguish.

Most animals are boarded in the summertime. If your pet has died and been cremated or buried, don't feel animosity toward the cattery owner or the pet-shop proprietor in whose care he was left. The bodies of animals can't be preserved in summer. Those who have to see death and shield the rest from such unpleasantness know that. Those who never have seen death often find it difficult to understand.

You may have left a very fat pet and return to find him thin. You should be pleased that he has lost dangerous excess weight. Or a comfortably fat pet may have grown too fat by the time you call for him. A few days' attention to his diet will correct that.

Remember the characteristics of the breed and of the individual animal. If you know your Siamese will refuse the wholesome food of the institution where you leave him, then supply your own food. If you take him for frequent "vacations" he will have another home and may come to enjoy it.

If you own a lively cat, the first day after you take him home his stools will probably be quite loose. This does not necessarily mean he is sick. Excitement after confinement—not sickness—always causes loose stools. Your pet was probably in a small run or even a cage; at home he has the whole outdoors to run in and he jumps and frisks. Expect loose stools until he gets back into his old regime.

Most cats seem thirsty after leaving boarding establishments. They have had pans of water in their cages, but take them home and they seem thirsty. Expect this too.

Your cat may seem starved. This is not strange. He's been learning to know a new food and you take him back to the old one. Of course he enjoys it. It's like a newlywed husband going back home for Sunday dinner and Mother's cooking!

Try to be reasonable about the food and care you expect for your cat while he is being boarded. Too many owners seem to think to themselves, "Seventy-five cents a day! A lot of money!" Then they proceed to tell the cattery owner what to feed: six ounces of top round hamburg for the evening meal; this, that, and the other thing at stated intervals throughout the day. On such a menu the cost of the food alone may run to two dollars. No wonder the cattery owner smiles. His food cost can't be more than 25 per cent of the dollar or he'd have to go out of business. This is enough to buy adequate, wholesome food. If you want your cat fed fancy things, it is best that you supply them and pay seventy-five cents a day for the other expenses incidental to the care and maintenance of your pet. For the average pet, where the cost of everything is considered, the cattery owner is lucky to make twenty-five cents a day on the average cat when the charge is seventy-five cents a day. If you have boarded a cat for two weeks, the cattery owner actually got $3.50 for the care of the animal— not too large a fee for his services. Would you assume the responsibility of keeping a neighbor's cat for two weeks, feeding it, keeping it free of external or internal parasites to the best of your ability, changing its bedding every three days, cleaning its droppings twice a day, renewing its water twice or three times a day—all for $3.50? I doubt it.

The reason the cattery owner is willing to do this is because he is equipped to keep large numbers of cats. And this very fact throws a sick animal now and again next door to a well one. This is a normal and unavoidable condition which the pet owner must learn to accept.

Which brings us to this observation: If you find a boarding accommodation for your pet which suits you, keep using that establishment and don't shift around. In time your pet will become immune to any disease which may infest that place, and your troubles are over. Just as children in a certain school and community become immune and thereafter are glad they did have measles, mumps, and chicken pox so they don't have to have them later, so pet owners can be glad their pets were first protected against all the diseases they can be protected against by inoculation and then by having built up natural immunity to the others. This much is certain: Animals can't assemble in large numbers and remain free from disease any more than children can be expected not to contract the infectious diseases from their classmates in school.

One other factor or risk in boarding pets is escape. If your Persian cat suddenly bites the cattery assistant, jumps out of the cage while that person is recovering from the pain and surprise, and escapes out of a window, that is your responsibility and not the cattery owner's, unless you warned him that the animal was vicious.

The tendency of most human beings to blame the other fellow for their own shortcomings is evidenced to the fullest in their reactions to the loss of a pet in a boarding institution. If you will consider the facts as I have presented them, you will see the problem in a fairer light.

One precaution you can and should take: Consider the age of your pet. Kittens are far more likely to die than are grown cats, because they have less resistance. Intestinal parasites are more harmful to young animals than to older ones. Virus diseases go very much harder. One form of virus pneumonia will quickly kill 99 per cent of kittens but do little damage to old cats. Knowing these facts, you will be wise to keep your kittens isolated, so far as it is in your power to do so, until they are over a year old. Thereafter the ravages of diseases will be less severe.

After you have read this book you will be in a better position to judge where your pet contracted any disease, because knowledge of the incubation period will help you.

Nor can we neglect the viewpoint of the owner of the establishment where our pets are left, be it a boarding kennel or veterinary hospital. I think you would be amazed if you knew the number of times people who were aware that their cats were sick tried to leave them "to board" at our clinic. Every hospital owner has had the same experience. Kennel owners, too. Veterinarians with "weather eyes" out for such animals are not often fooled, but cattery owners often have diseases introduced by such unscrupulous cat owners because they fail to recognize the disease and are grateful to have another boarder.

One final thought: The risk to health where pets congregate or are congregated is unavoidable. It can be greatly reduced. Nothing does more to minimize the hazards than proper vaccination. If you neglect to take this simple precaution, you not only are not doing the sporting thing to the pets of others, but you are failing to take the most obvious step to protect the health of your own.

12. When the End Comes

*T*HE death of a pet is a very serious problem to a great many people. Too many otherwise intelligent pet owners simply can't bring themselves to realize that every life has a limit. When their conscientious veterinarian assures them it is time to say good-by to their pet, instead of taking his advice they say good-by to the veterinarian and take their pet to another who may prolong its miserable life to the advantage of no one, least of all to the patient.

It is interesting and helpful to consider the life expectancy of cats. If you know what to expect in advance, you will not be surprised at death, nor will you ask the impossible of your veterinarian.

In the table below, the average age at death means *from natural causes* in cats which have survived infanthood.

Table VII

BREED	AVERAGE AGE AT DEATH	OLDEST KNOWN TO THE AUTHOR
Egyptian (common)	12	22
Long-haired	12	16
Siamese	12	20
Manx	12	19

Unless our cat dies of heart failure or from violence, there comes a time when we must ask ourselves, what's best to do? Shall we let him die as a result of old age, general breakdown, a growth, kidney disease, or other causes? Or shall we bravely say, "He has led a good life, he's no longer enjoying what little is left of it, he's blind and deaf, he's in some pain; we'll have him put painlessly to sleep"?

It takes courage to make such a decision. To do so always makes us wish that our pet could live as long as we do. When the time comes for the owner to decide what to do with his aging pet, there are some general facts which he should know. They may make the decision easier for him.

There is no pain to euthanasia if properly administered. A humane veterinarian can inject a few c.c.s of an anesthetic into a cat's vein and the cat droops his eyes, nods his head, sighs as he feels release from pain, goes to sleep. He just never wakens.

An animal does not miss tomorrow. Suppose that you couldn't think ahead. If you had no imagination, you couldn't project yourself into the future. Mentally and physically you would live only in this moment—not even two seconds in the future. We can anticipate a fine dinner party and see images of it in our mind's eye. We can look forward in winter to next spring's flowers and thus make our winter more bearable. But an animal lives in the present alone, without any thought of the future. If he dies, his existence merely terminates. He is being deprived of nothing, for he has no conception of the future.

The death of a pet is not his loss so much as ours. The home will be empty without his presence. True, for the past year he probably hasn't been the friend we knew and loved; he's been ailing and not himself. But propinquity has endeared him to us and *we* see him as he used to be; we remember all the fine qualities he once had. When we hesitate to bring his life to an end, we are unconsciously thinking of ourselves. We may even allow him to suffer pain and discomfort because *we* don't want to lose him; we don't want our serene existence upset by no longer having our pet.

He's going to die someday. We must face this fact, even though we shrink from it. Isn't it better to stop his suffering by terminating his existence by our own volition than to allow him to linger in pain or extreme old age?

What might he say if he could think? He would probably say something like this: "I don't want to leave you any more than you want to be without me, but please give me comfort and freedom from misery. I can't see, so I bump into furniture. I can't hear you. I no longer enjoy the meals you prepare for me. I'm a burden to you, and certainly no good to myself. If I go outside, I might be crushed by an automobile. What good am I, anyway? Couldn't you be unselfish and grant me a blessed release?" And he might well add: "And if I gave you so much fun and companionship, get yourself another pet to fill my place, just as quickly as you can. Start giving him the attention you gave me when I was young. It will give you lots to think about and help to keep you young."

METHODS OF EUTHANASIA

The methods employed in euthanasia in the past—and, unfortunately, even today in some places—are largely responsible for the fact that so many people simply refused to consider ending a pet's life. They were shocking, inhumane, and often clumsy. Usually the animal was shot, gassed, or electrocuted. The drugs that were occasionally used were unsatisfactory: the injection of strychnine was certainly inferior even to shooting; ether and chloroform brought a kinder death, but even with these there was some struggle.

Today there are a number of drugs available which are both quick and painless. When you decide that it is best to terminate your pet's existence you have every right to insist that drugs of this type be administered. The best of these, in my opinion, are the barbiturates; and of them I prefer sodium pentobarbital. When injected into a vein or directly into the heart, its effects are almost instantaneous. A sudden sleep overpowers the animal and in a matter of seconds it is completely unconscious. The heartbeat and breathing cease; the end comes quietly and quickly. I have administered this drug to many pets in the presence of their owners, and without exception they have been tremendously impressed by the humane and painless death it has brought. The drug can be given by mouth in capsule form but it takes longer for the cat to die.

The lethal dose of sodium pentobarbital is usually considered to be one and a half times the amount required for anesthesia. In nearly every case such an injection is adequate, but I have known cases in which it produced only a prolonged deep sleep and a second injection was necessary. To eliminate even the possibility of such occurrences, I administer three grains for each five pounds of the animal's weight. A dose of this size is completely and immediately effective.

In spite of the fact that sodium pentobarbital is inexpensive and easily available to qualified persons, it has not been adopted so widely as it deserves to be for euthanasia. If your local humane society or dog warden is still using the methods of a decade or so ago, you will be doing a service to both the pets and pet owners in your community by discussing with the proper authorities the possibilities of using pentobarbital.

A saturate solution of magnesium sulfate (Epsom salts) is also satisfactory as an injection to produce euthanasia. It is now used by agents of many humane societies as well as by some veterinarians. The anesthesia which is its first effect is followed closely by death. Fairly large amounts must be administered, however. Doses of ten c.c.s are lethal to cats.

CARE OF THE REMAINS

Should you have your cat buried? If so, where? The back yard? This is illegal in many cities. In a cemetery for pets? A grave and perpetual care cost about sixty dollars in some communities. Should the animal be embalmed? Why? What happens after death, anyway? Slow oxidation is the answer. Oxidation is a chemical name for burning. Wood in a fire oxidizes with a visible flame. A decaying stump oxidizes slowly, with no such fanfare. An animal's body oxidizes slowly too. So it is actually a matter of deciding between quick or slow oxidation. Burial or cremation is the choice. I unhesitatingly recommend the latter. What matters if the oxidation be quick? Isn't it better to know it is over in a few minutes rather than slowly taking place in the cold ground over a period of years? Chemically, there's little difference; esthetically, choose cremation.

POST-MORTEMS

Sometimes the question arises: "Shall I permit a post-mortem examination?" A study made in a large hospital for humans to determine the percentage of persons who refused to allow free post-mortems on their loved ones showed that 26 per cent disdained the thought, refused permission. Even though the interviewing doctor could say, "The examination may be of help to you personally; such things run in families, you know," 26 per cent still refused. A similar study at the Whitney Veterinary Clinic revealed the astounding fact that 24.3 per cent refused to allow free examinations on their pet dogs after death. Many of the findings could have been of great help to other dogs, if not always to their owners. Had we kept track of the cat owners, doubtless the results would have been similar.

Occasionally cats die of diseases which are transmissible to their owners. If the veterinarian is willing to risk his health performing an autopsy, one would think the owner should acquiesce. The same applies when such an examination could help the veterinarian to help other cats, or when it would add to our knowledge of cancer, or parasites, or growth, or blood, or heredity.

When your doctor finds your pet's malady of sufficient interest to give his time to studying its body, you need an excellent reason to justify your refusing him permission. If you love pets, you love to see them well. You can hardly do less than to help the doctor to help other pets—and perhaps, incidentally, yourself.

Part Three

13. Cats and Their Food

$\mathcal{T}$ HERE are unknown millions of cats in the world today. In every age since the beginning of history, cats have shared man's food and shelter. And yet, in spite of all the opportunity there has been to observe and study the nature and habits of cats down through the centuries since ancient Egypt, we still know surprisingly little about them. The cat still walks by himself in a kind of mysterious and self-sufficient aloofness.

In the past too many of us, including cat owners, assumed there was little that could be learned about the cat. A cat was "just a cat"—one of those living, semi-automatic creations of nature which was put out at night and occasionally rewarded with a saucer of milk for catching a mouse. We settled back complacently and summed up the little we knew about cats in a few well-worn and contradictory adages: "A cat has nine lives," but "Nothing can be sicker than a sick cat." It is only in comparatively recent years that we have begun to replace these faulty casual observations with reliable scientific information.

There are several types of house cats, distinguished principally by the way they live. By studying each of these groups we have been able to collect a great deal of information useful to the pet owner.

Everyone knows that many cats living a domesticated life have become feral—gone wild. Not everyone realizes, however, that in a wild state cats thrive exceptionally well for the most part.

Actually there are two kinds of *wild* house cats. In one class belong the creatures which have fled human habitations and gone to live as wild animals in the wilderness. They are the ascetics of the cat family. They often fail to leave descendants, and their ranks must constantly be augmented by new converts to their cult. It is known that they frequently live to be quite old. Students of wild life, particularly game wardens who have captured large numbers of feral cats thought to be killing game birds, generally find that these wild animals are in excellent health and condition, a fact which attests to their rugged constitutions and unusual adaptability.

The second kind of wild cat is the rounder—more often a male—who goes from alley to alley in the city and from barn to barn in the country. He is a typical tramp—a scroungy, slinky, mangy, battle-scarred creature who has to elude dogs, dodge stones thrown by rascally boys, and live in spite of the putrescent food and rat poison he finds in garbage cans. He is an entirely different animal from the cat-gone-wild that stalks its prey in the woods. He is hardly admirable, yet one must at least respect his one outstanding characteristic—adaptability.

The comparison between the two wild classes demonstrates one thing clearly: that cats thrive best when they are quite well separated from other cats. The woods cat has less opportunity to contract diseases, virus, bacterial or parasitic, feeds on a diet composed principally of rodents, is less subject to accidents and violence.

Socially there are two general classes of well-*domesticated* cats: those kept for some useful purpose in barns or warehouses, where they save millions of dollars and prevent disease by holding the rodent population in check; and those kept as pets, some of which incidentally kill mice but whose primary purpose is companionship or even ornamentation. In the aggregate, pet cats probably outnumber all the rest.

Owners of the useful type seldom place any emotional value on them. To them a cat may be a wonderful ratter, but neighbors always have plenty of cats to give away or they may be had by the bushel from the Humane Society. What difference does it make if one or two die or disappear? I once made a call on a farmer who had fourteen sleek cats in his barn. When I called again two weeks later there was only one old tom left; all the rest had been wiped out by a disease. The farmer didn't care. The cats to him were not much more valuable than so many turnips; he'd get more as soon as he thought there was no infection left in the barn.

From all these four classes we can learn lessons, but the most useful ones come from those which live *without* the "loving care" of a mistress or master. Obviously we cannot duplicate the conditions under which the wild cats live. Some owners have to keep many cats together in a barn; others like to take their cats to shows; nearly everybody likes to put the cat out to exercise and relieve itself; and many people must board cats at vacation time. In short, we can't always isolate them. Nor can we provide a natural diet of rodents—and we wouldn't want to if we could. Imagine a city owner taking weekly trips to the country to trap field mice! What we can do is to provide food and attention which will keep our pet cats in top condition all the year round. Anything we can learn from observing wild cats or tame ones will help us to do it.

FEEDING

Many people, including some so-called experts, apparently feel that great variety is necessary in a cat's diet. They sometimes go to astonishing extremes, and if you were to follow their advice you would spend a good part of every day in obtaining, preparing, and storing the cat's daily rations. Fortunately most of their recommendations are based on personal opinion and preference and not on a scientific study of nutritional needs.

The fact that an elaborate diet is unnecessary to cats can be seen by studying the food of the feral cat, who thrives—and indeed stays in beautiful condition—by eating very few types of food. Several accurate studies have been made of the contents of the stomachs of wild cats trapped or shot by wardens. Some of the studies were made, incidentally, to determine the amount of damage done by cats to bird life, and the results seemed to indicate conclusively that cats destroyed far fewer birds than had been supposed.

One of the studies, which dealt with wild cats taken in Wisconsin, found that the contents of the stomachs were composed principally of remains of rodents, birds, and insects. The fifty stomachs examined contained fifty-nine rodents, nine birds, and five insects. A few of the cats had eaten garbage, and in their stomachs were found potatoes, string beans, apple, boiled rice, and custard pudding. Two had eaten ensilage.

In Oklahoma a study of the stomachs of eighty-four wild cats taken from several groups showed that 55 per cent contained mammals, mostly rodents; 26.5 per cent contained garbage; 12.5 per cent contained insects; and 4 per cent contained the remains of birds. In a small group of cats caught in residential districts 6.5 per cent showed evidence of having eaten birds. Other studies have shown that as much as 25 per cent of the contents of cats' stomachs was insects. Lizards also were found in some.

Our principal interest in these lists is not so much in the small number of items in the diet. More important is the fact that these studies all showed that whatever animal the cat fed on was eaten in its entirety. Very seldom do cats open their prey and eat only a single part of the animal, such as the liver or kidneys. Even bobcats—living chiefly on rabbits, hares, squirrels, mink, muskrats, mice, grouse, pheasant, bluejays, grass, insects—eat most of the body of their prey. Red and gray fox fur and meat has been found in their stomachs, and occasionally porcupine remains or venison. But who ever heard of a wild house cat eating only kidneys or liver of a mouse?

Cats do have some variety in their diet, but that variety is largely the result of their eating the complete animal. Rodents eat great quantities of vegetable matter, and when the cats eat the rodents they get a certain amount of this type of material contained in the stomachs and intestines of these animals. In all probability a cat could live indefinitely in excellent health on a diet consisting exclusively of mice. That single item would provide ample variety—muscles, bones, liver, intestines, brain, glands, *and* vegetable material in its digestive tract.

What was said in Chapter 1 about spoiling an animal by unconsciously training it to demand one particular type of food applies especially to cats. The number of cats which refuse all food but one kind of canned cat food, or kidneys, or liver, or halibut, or codfish, or horse meat, or lean beef, is myriad. The problem should be handled just as it is with other animals. It is best to pay no attention to a pet cat's likes and dislikes. Get her hungry enough to eat what is good for her and then see that she obtains in her daily meal the dietary essentials which can be obtained only through variety. But see that the variety is the same as that she obtains when she eats a mouse—variety in one meal. There is no harm, of course, in giving her tidbits as a *small* part of her diet.

Are there any foods which must be excluded? Is it true what some authors say about never feeding starches to cats? Must all their food be cooked? Must all pork be eliminated from their diets? And fat? Folklore notwithstanding, cats can digest starch. Science says they can, and very well, too, if the starch granules are cracked by cooking. How can authors logically condemn the feeding of starchy food and yet advise feeding kibbled food which may be 75 per cent baked starch? Yet they often do. Nor must *all* the food of cats be cooked. They digest raw meat as admirably as cooked meat. Fish *should* be cooked, since if it is fed raw in large amounts, it may cause paralysis. But canned fish has been cooked and is readily available in all food stores. If there is any meat which cats like less than another and tend to regurgitate more often, it is pork. But that is only because pork is a very fat meat. When fat and protein are fed alone, the cat's system does not tolerate it so well as when fat and carbohydrate are fed. If very fat beef is fed, the result is the same. People who advise against feeding pork or fat beef forget that if plenty of carbohydrate is fed along with either or both, the fat will be handled nicely and may safely be fed in reasonable amounts. They forget, too, that when a cat eats a mouse she may get as much as 30 per cent fat—but in that case there is sufficient carbohydrate to burn it up.

What should a cat be fed? There is no "best" diet. Here are several, any one of which is perfectly adequate. The decision should be made on the basis of convenience.

What you yourself eat, so well diced, mashed, or ground together that the cat can't pick out part and leave the rest. Cats will eat all items of human diet when trained to do so. They have even been known to eat olives.

Good canned cat food.

Two thirds dehydrated meal-type dog food, plus one third canned fish or cooked diced meal. Some of the larger catteries feed dog meal and mackerel with sufficient water or milk to produce a moist consistency, thinner than crumbly.

Fish—always cooked—mixed with bread, table scraps, et cetera.

Meat—beef, lamb, pork, horse—mixed with vegetable products.

Or variations and combinations of any of those listed above.

A well-fed cat is not a fat cat; a fat cat is a badly fed cat. Nor is the cat that is properly fed thin; a thin cat may be ravenous. A well-fed cat will eat what is set before it; it is hungry enough never to turn up its nose at wholesome food; it eats as though it enjoyed it. Mealtimes are the big events in a cat's life—mealtimes and the return home of the favorite family member. Both of these events can be made more enjoyable by proper training. There are few things that give the owner more pleasure than to see his pet eat the food he is given with evident enjoyment.

For some reason milk is the first food people think of giving to a cat. Some set a bowl of milk on the floor for the cat to drink instead of water —a great mistake. Milk is in many ways an unnatural food, if a good one. It is no more sensible to say a cat *must* have milk than that an adult human being *must* have it. It is true that cow's milk is much like cat's milk in composition. It is true, too, that the composition of milk acts as a sort of guide for deciding what the relative proportions of protein, carbohydrate, and fat in a diet should be. If this is true, then we should try to compound cat foods to be 85 per cent water, and of the solid materials (the solids in milk being our guide): protein, 27.5 per cent; carbohydrates, 37.2 per cent; fat, 27.5 per cent; ash, 6 per cent—all of which refutes those who tell cat owners not to feed fat. Liquid milk contains about three hundred and twenty calories per pint.

Milk is a fine food. Is it expensive? It costs about ten cents a pound, with three hundred and twenty calories, and 85 per cent is water, but of the remaining 15 per cent, which represents the solids, almost all is digested and absorbed. This is about thirty calories for one cent. Milk is in the category with canned foods, which contain four hundred and fifty calories in each pound and 70 to 75 per cent water, even though the food looks solid. Less of the solids in cat foods are digestible. The better grades cost about fourteen cents per pound (many cans now sold contain fourteen and one half ounces) and therefore give you about thirty calories for one cent.

We must never forget: milk is not water, even though it is fluid. If a cat has milk always before her and drinks a great deal, she needs very little other food. The average cat needs about three hundred and fifty calories a day, the amount contained in one pint of milk and no more. A cupful contains half her nutritional requirements, and many cats drink that much a day.

When you forget that milk is food and give your cat all she wants to drink, you will find it particularly difficult to alter her diet. If you are trying to change in order to get her to eat anything and everything that is good for her, take away the milk too. Don't coax her with special tempting food and don't feel sorry for her. Just offer her a little of the new food, and if she doesn't eat it, very little has been lost. Next day offer her more. She won't refuse it for more than four or five days. By that time she will be hungry enough to eat it, or at least some of it. There is no pain in starvation; the pain is in the owner's mind. It is not unusual for cats to fall in wells, be locked in vacant houses where only water is available, or even be locked out on a roof in a city, and live for thirty or even sixty days without any food whatever. One hates to think of it, yet we must be sensible and honest. There is certainly no cruelty in letting a cat fast long enough to accustom her to eating wholesome food that is good for her.

When a cat refuses food to which she is accustomed, she is either overfed or sick. Your thermometer can help you to determine whether she has a fever. Her actions may tell you whether she was poisoned; her appetite may tell you by evening she was overfed; a fecal examination can de‧termine if she has worms. She might have a mouth infection, a loose or broken tooth, but in those events she would probably act as if she were going to take a mouthful but stop just short of it. She needs veterinary attention. Here are some practical suggestions you may find useful in feeding your cat:

Warm all the food cats are fed. Cats dislike very cold food.

When you feed, place the food dish on an open newspaper on the floor or on a table. Cats like to drag food out of the bowl. The newspaper can be folded up with the crumbs and thrown away.

Remove any bones which might splinter—poultry and fish bones especially.

It pays to grind the cat's food. Enough for several days may be prepared ahead of time and kept frozen in the refrigerator. Grinding mixes the ingredients well too.

If meal-type foods are used, pour boiling water over them and then mix the additional ingredients.

Cats generally relish some green leafy vegetables well mixed in their food.

If a cat nibbles grass, it may make her vomit, but it does no harm other than sometimes sticking in her throat.

If a cat has a tendency to vomit but is otherwise well, feed her small amounts often.

Catnip.   The leaves and tops of an herb, *Nepeta cataria,* constitute for a cat one of the most alluring playthings any animal can be given. Cataria was once used medicinally as a drug to reduce gas in the intestinal tract. It is also known as a mild nerve stimulant. In cats it is regarded as something of an aphrodisiac.

When cats eat the leaves they do not digest them nor do they regurgitate them as they do grass, but it is necessary to consume a large amount for the drug to do any damage, and cats seldom eat enough for that.

The odor is what produces the antics, the rolling and playing when catnip is placed where cats can get close to it; they need not eat it at all.

14. Breeding and Raising Kittens

CATS give their owners less trouble in raising young than almost any other species. Show standards have not demanded abnormalities, as is the case for some dog breeds, and Caesarean operations are less often necessary. But unspayed females and unaltered males can cause ample trouble for an owner if he is unequipped to handle them during mating.

General preparations for breeding include deworming the female, if necessary, and making sure that she cannot pick up infestation while pregnant. Remove all external parasites and feed her well.

A catta comes in season several times a year and, as pointed out in Chapter 9, fails to ovulate unless she is mated. At each general mating season she comes in heat several times at about three-week intervals. At those times during the acceptance period she rolls about, often in front of her owner, "calls" in a different tone from any she customarily uses, and attracts males, which will use unorthodox methods to be with her, even crawling in through windows. If she goes out, she will be in the center of a circle of males, each facing toward her. First one and then another will mate with her. Males will have furious fights like knights of old jousting for the favor of a queen. Perhaps that is why cat breeders often use the word *queen* to designate a breeding catta.

Cats have phantom or pseudo-pregnancies, but the expectancy is not so great as in the case of bitches. Usually a cat's pseudo-pregnancy means that she was mated but that either the male was sterile or she resorbed her embryos.

Breeders usually allow a catta to call for two or three days and then put her with the male, allowing several matings. Since ovulation occurs only from the stimulation of having the vaginal wall scratched by the tom's penis, several matings provide a better chance for pregnancy than one; and, despite the screaming of the catta, she is willing and eager to mate again and again.

Cattas have been known to come in heat for the first time well before they are anatomically mature, to bear kittens, and to continue growing. A number of cases of cats breeding at four and a half months has been recorded. Five months is not an uncommon age, but most cats are seven months old before they copulate for the first time.

Males are usually fertile at seven months, but they often seem emotionally incapable of copulating so early. As they gain in age and experience, they become more reliable breeders.

To be sure that the catta is definitely bred after mating, feel through her abdominal wall for the lumps which constitute the developing fetuses and envelopes. The diagram shows how they feel at various stages. In palpating, use great care and gentleness. After thirty-three or thirty-five days of pregnancy, there is no longer any firmness. Do not again attempt palpation until the seventh or eighth week, when the kittens may be felt. When more than one kitten is developing within the catta, the abdomen will be obviously enlarged after six weeks. Also the catta's breasts become fuller than in the case of a pseudo-pregnancy.

About a day before the time of birth approaches, the catta shows signs of nervousness. She stays in or near her bed, usually refuses food, and all but tells the owner to let her alone.

When it is time for the kittens to arrive—about sixty-one or sixty-two days from the date of mating—careful palpation may reveal if a kitten is unable to pass out of the pelvis and if the mother must be saved by an operation. If the kitten has been in the birth canal for an hour or two and its face can be felt through deep palpation of the vulva, get the cat to your veterinarian. He may be able to deliver the kitten with a pair of special forceps, or he may have to resort to a Caesarean operation.

If the tail and hind legs of the kitten can be felt in palpation, take hold of them with a piece of cloth and pull gently but firmly; the first one—an

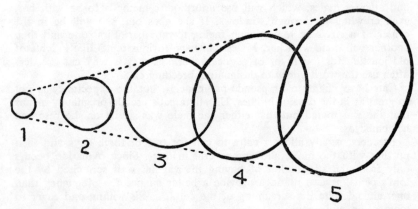

The size of the uterine lumps in a female cat at various stages of pregnancy: (1) 22 days, (2) 25 days, (3) 28 days, (4) 31 days, (5) 34 days.

oversize one—can thus be delivered, and the rest may be born easily for the mother. Give all help possible.

I am constantly amazed by clients who bring cattas to our hospital and say that "they have something the matter." A glance shows the dried front or hind end of a kitten which may have been stuck in the vagina for half a day or longer. There is indeed something the matter! A veterinarian's services are not needed—only common sense. If you find your pet in such a predicament, wrap a cloth about the half-born kitten and pull. If the mother strains and helps, so much the better. Out comes the kitten, and behind it comes a great deal of dark brown evil-smelling fluid and perhaps the placenta and membranes which enveloped the kitten in the uterus.

In cattas which have labored long trying to pass large kittens, the last one may stick because the mother suffers from sheer exhaustion. The longer the kitten stays in, the harder it is to expel, because of the dryness which develops. Help the mother in such a case. Nothing is likely to be hurt, and the kitten will probably be dead anyway.

A normal birth takes under two hours from first to last kitten. Occasionally a catta will produce four kittens in a leisurely manner over a six-hour period. Sometimes four will be born in less than thirty minutes. Forewarned is forearmed.

Always note the shape of the pelvis when exploring the vulva. Many a small kitten's pelvis has been broken and the kitten has grown up without the condition being noted. A mature catta's pelvis is often broken in an accident. The pelvis almost always sets in a partially collapsed shape. It may feel like a V instead of like an O. If the pelvis is abnormal, it is practically certain that an operation will be needed. Have the catta spayed after the kittens are weaned. If she is spayed at the time of the Caesarean operation, her milk will probably "dry up," although there have been cattas spayed at such a time who continued to give milk long enough to raise their kittens.

Palpation is again invaluable in telling when the catta has finished giving birth. It is very easy to feel all about the abdomen with thumb on one side and fingers on the other. If there is an unborn kitten still within the uterus, it will be felt. If your sense of touch is untrained, shut your eyes, feel a kitten that has already been born, and then feel through the abdominal wall of the catta from the last ribs to the pelvis. An unborn kitten feels quite large inside the mother.

After the last kitten has been born, the uterus shrinks rapidly. Palpation will reveal a retained placenta. A high douche sometimes aids in removing it. Let the water run in under a little pressure, with the douche bag two feet above the cat, and then let the water run out suddenly. A retained placenta can cause peritonitis. Even if she recovers, her milk is likely to dry up and leave the kittens to be bottle-fed.

Many cattas will start seeking a nest a week or more before the kittens are born. Some owners let them find a nest, learn where the nest has been chosen, and place a nest box of proper dimensions in that spot. It may be in the spare-room closet, in the attic, in the barn, in the woodshed, or under the porch. Others, the professional breeders especially, put the catta in a cage with the proper bed. She can have her kittens there as well as in a place of her own choosing. The difficulty lies in letting her out. If she is made to have her kittens in a spot selected by the owner, the first time she gets the opportunity she will almost certainly take them one at a time right to the place of her own selection. For that reason experienced cat breeders try to learn the location of the chosen nesting spot well in advance so that, if the kittens do disappear, they will know where to find them.

The bed can be a box eighteen inches square with sides about eight inches high. Since the kittens will have to stay in such a box until they are fairly large, the sides should be too high for them to climb.

The bedding can be of absorbent cloth, which should be changed after the birth of the kittens. It will become soiled again, however, because the mother continues to have a normal discharge from the vulva for a week or two following her delivery.

The mother cleans her kittens, consuming their evacuations and stimulating discharge of both urine and feces by lapping the external organs. After birth she consumes the fetal envelopes and placenta and laps as much of the amniotic fluid as she can.

Cattas are extraordinarily clever with their kittens. A mother cat is almost never clumsy enough to lie on a kitten, nor is she likely to lie down among her kittens with some behind her. She sees that they are all together and curls about them. If she is awkward with her first litter, however, she usually will be with every litter.

If kittens are lost and it becomes necessary to dry up the mother, just let her alone. Her breasts will cake, and in a short time the inflammation and discomfort will disappear. No massage or camphorated oil is necessary.

Cattas will often nurse their kittens for many months. It is not uncommon for a new litter to arrive before the mother has weaned the last. Pets brought to our hospital to be spayed frequently have several sections of breast functional, and the owners are amazed to learn that a new lot of partly developed fetuses has been found inside.

Raising orphan kittens or supplementing the milk of those whose mothers produce insufficient milk is easy but takes time and patience. If possible, leave the kittens with the mother, because she will take care of their elimination—a nuisance when the owner has to do it. If the mother is lost, killed, sick, or refuses to care for her kittens, gently rub the external genitals and anus with a piece of cotton and the kittens will be stimulated to urinate and evacuate. If they are not cared for, they will keep each other and their nests in a nasty condition. Tending to them each time they nurse will usually be sufficient.

Any kitten a few days old will take about seven to ten c.c.s of milk five times a day from a medicine dropper or a tiny doll's nipple. A full-size medicine dropper holds about one c.c.; a teaspoon, four c.c.s; and an ounce container, about thirty c.c.s.

As shown in the table of comparison of catta and cow's milk, there is not a great deal of difference between cow and cat milk, but there is a wide difference between cat and human milk. Yet many formulas for feeding kittens have been mistakenly modified in the direction of human milk. Lime water and glucose are wrongly advised as essential additions. Experience indicates that the additional protein in cow's milk is not detrimental.

Table VIII—Milk of

	CATTA	COW	HUMAN
Water	82.0	86.3	87.4
Protein	7.0	3.8	1.3
Sugar	5.0	4.7	7.0
Fat	5.0	4.0	3.5
Ash	0.6	0.7	0.2

At least half of all kittens which have not been dewormed will be found to harbor intestinal parasites. If they have hookworms, they will be anemic. Roundworms lead in the numbers found in kittens; and, while they are not so lethal to the hosts, they do produce toxins sufficient to cause fits, distended abdomens, and general unthriftiness. It pays to have stools tested for parasite eggs beginning at four weeks of age and to deworm the kittens as soon as eggs show up. Occasionally there will be an invasion of roundworm larvae so heavy that the kitten has verminous pneumonia. In post-mortems on some kittens enough roundworms have been found in the stomach and intestines to have caused death and yet not one worm old enough to lay eggs. Although such an infestation is not common, the fact that it can happen should make one alert to the possibility of parasites in a sickly young kitten even if a fecal examination is negative. Another examination the following week may reveal great numbers of eggs, because by then the worms will be old enough to lay.

No deworming of a kitten is complete unless done twice at two-week intervals. The first eliminates the worms in the bowels but will not kill the larvae in the blood. The second kills this lot when they have become intestinal inhabitants.

If kittens are not getting enough milk from either their mother or from supplementary feedings, they cry, become thin and woodeny to touch, and may suck on each other. Contented well-nourished kittens are hungry at the proper times but are generally quiet. Their thriftiness is shown by their plump little bellies.

Nearly everyone has seen mother cats teaching kittens to play with a mouse she has caught and partially numbed. When she eats it, she shares it with them—their first solid food. Soon she may be bringing them dead or nearly dead rodents, and even at a month of age they know the taste of blood, vegetable contents of the intestines and stomachs, and meat of the muscles and organs. This also helps to supply iron, in which their first nourishment, milk, is so low. It should be a lesson to every cat owner that milk alone is not the only food for kittens. Their milk diet should be supplemented by more substantial foods as soon as they will eat, generally by their fourth week. Some cat owners use human baby foods; others use special prepared foods such as Pampa for baby animals. Everyone to whom you sell or give a kitten will appreciate your having taught it to eat.

And one final word about a too often neglected precaution. By the fourth week the sharp nails of little kittens need cutting. If this is not done, one of the kittens may in play scratch another's eye and seriously injure or blind it.

15. General Diseases of Cats

VIRUS DISEASES

Feline Distemper. One of the great death-dealing diseases of cats is most often known by the name *feline distemper*. It has also been called *infectious enteritis, infectious gastroenteritis, feline agranulocytosis, infectious feline panleukopenia*. The reason for the several names is that the scientists who studied the disease at various times emphasized what seemed to them the outstanding symptoms or pathology of the disease.

Cats of every breed and all ages are susceptible. This has been reported from every place in the world where cats are kept. In this author's experience it comes close to being 100 per cent fatal to all cats under four months of age and at least 90 per cent fatal to those older. It sometimes destroys large numbers of cats in a single city neighborhood, or nearly the whole cat population of a farm area. Few diseases of pets are more devastating.

It is not a simple matter to look at a sick cat and say positively that it has feline distemper. Many diseases have similar features or produce similar symptoms. Poisoned cats often are thought to have distemper. Not infrequently police officials and humane officers receive calls from citizens complaining that someone is poisoning the cats. "Mrs. Owen's, Mrs. Johnson's, Mrs. Kelly's, and Mr. Wilson's cats all died in one day," they say. Investigation often reveals that there was no poisoner abroad, but that feline distemper was the cause. Cats severely infested with coccidiosis have almost identical symptoms and recover, and are often thought to have been victims of distemper. Later they may succumb to a real attack of distemper, much to the consternation of everyone concerned.

Do not expect your veterinarian to take a look and a temperature reading and tell you for sure what your cat has. He must make a stool examination and a white blood count to be anywhere near sure. But if he has already performed a post-mortem examination on a cat from your neighborhood to which yours may have been exposed, he can give you a better idea.

With mature cats distemper symptoms vary, but in general, after an incubation period of five or six days, the cat loses her appetite. The hair stands on end, there is no thought of cleanliness, no washing or licking the coat. The cat will seldom purr, wants to drink, and sits with its head over the water pan for long periods. Usually there are frequent spells of nausea. Seeing a cat with an oily look to the coat, sitting hunched up or lying on its belly with its legs stretched out, should make one suspect distemper.

A rapid loss in weight due to dehydration, a burning fever which seldom falls below 104° (except near the end), and diarrhea which is foul and often shows blood are all symptoms of feline distemper.

All this applies to older cats with some resistance. Kittens may die in less than twenty-four hours after the first signs of sickness. If you could look inside of such kittens, except for changes in the blood you might find what looked like a healthy cat. But the older cats would show reddened areas in the intestines as well as swollen lymph glands near by, and the bones, instead of showing nicely formed red blood marrow, would appear to be filled with red mush. Some cats will live long enough to give the infecting agent time to inflame the entire small intestine. There is often congestion of the liver, the kidneys, and the spleen.

The white-cell count is diagnostic and may be used by your veterinarian as a helpful laboratory test in reaching a verdict.

How do cats catch it? Apparently as easily as by sniffing the air another cat has breathed. The virus is found in urine, feces, nasal discharge. The sick cat infects everything it touches. Cat fanciers can tell you of having a single cat brought to their cattery, left in a cage in a large room, and isolated from the rest by many feet. The disease spread to the rest in spite of every precaution.

The virus is remarkably resistant. Even at room temperature it has been reported to live for three months. It is wise, therefore, not to bring a susceptible cat into the home for some time after another has been sick with distemper, unless the new cat has been previously immunized.

Once the disease breaks out in a neighborhood, there is no known medicinal agent which will save the cats. Sulfa drugs, streptomycin, penicillin, and others have no effect. Very valuable cats are sometimes given infusions to keep up the body fluids. Some claims are made for serum produced from the blood of hyperimmune cats. It may help if used in large amounts in the very early stage. Other than that, however, good nursing is the best treatment. Expect the cat to be sick—very sick—for a long while. Doses of penicillin to combat some of the secondary diseases are sometimes worth while.

Prevention is everything. Serum used to protect cats temporarily, when the disease is rampant in the neighborhood, probably is effective. Vaccine can be used as a preventive and so far has shown ability to give lifelong protection if fresh vaccine is given.

Anyone owning a cat suspected of being sick with feline distemper will, of course, inform all those with cats in the neighborhood to take special precautions. The warning may enable them to have their pets protected in time.

Rabies. Because of the many popular misconceptions concerning rabies, it seems advisable to consider a few general facts about the disease and its spread before taking up the specific symptoms.

CAUSE AND DISSEMINATION: Rabies is a virus disease, transmissible to almost all kinds of animals and many kinds of birds. Today, despite the fact that it could quite easily be eradicated, it is altogether too prevalent, and the dog is the principal agent of dissemination. This book is about cats, but even so, we have to consider dogs in this respect almost in the same sense as we do rabbits in the spread of tapeworm.

It is believed that if we were to apply what we know about vaccination and restraint, the disease would disappear in a few years. Needless to say, every effort should be made to eradicate rabies, because of its danger to humans, if for no other reason.

Not all dogs bitten by a rabid dog develop rabies. Only about 15 per cent of the humans who took no treatments to protect themselves after being bitten developed the disease. In the past, when rabid wolves bit humans, a higher percentage died. Of dogs bitten by rabid dogs, 40 per cent died; of horses, the rate is also 40 per cent; hogs, 30 per cent; cattle, 30 per cent. The percentage of cats is not known.

Statistics show that about seventeen times as many dogs as cats are detected with rabies. Of the 8,946 cases reported in animals in 1947, 6,949 were dogs and 393 were cats. This does not necessarily indicate that that is the actual ratio of infection, but may be close to it. Rabid dogs bite dogs, but they can't catch cats so easily. A rabid cat does not run about trying to bite other cats and dogs, although there are exceptional cases where they have been known to attack anything in sight—even cows. Rats may have rabies and infect the cats which kill them.

It is the saliva of the rabid dog which is dangerous. The bite drives the virus in the saliva deep into the tissues, where, being a neurotropic virus, it attaches itself to nerves and grows. It is not dangerous on the unbroken skin. When an animal is bitten, there is no certainty about how long the virus will take to progress along the nerves until it reaches the huge mass of nerve tissue represented by the brain. The position of the bite has some effect. If a cat is bitten on a back foot, the virus will have quite a distance to travel before it reaches the brain, while with a bite in the jaw the elapsed time would be much less. From 15 to 285 days are the extremes found in a study to determine how long it takes.

If the virus is able to attach itself to a nerve after the cat has been bitten, the cat has rabies. If his body is capable of destroying the virus, the cat does not have rabies. The time which elapses until the virus grows to the brain is not an incubation period in the true sense.

What we think of as rabies is merely the manifestation of brain inflammation—encephalitis—and the animal may exhibit any of several

typical forms of that malady. Thus present-day students of rabies have
come to hold concepts of the disease completely different from those of
our forefathers. Even the old name, hydrophobia, is no longer used. The
conceptions of dumb and furious rabies have been dropped because the
symptoms these terms describe are only two manifestations of encephalitis.
Once the symptoms appear, it is a downhill drag until death.

SYMPTOMS: The earliest sign may be what seems to be a perverse
appetite, but this may be due to hunger coupled with such a dimming of
the sense of taste that anything will be chewed and swallowed. A rabid
cat will usually hide. It will lose its normal voice and cry in a subdued,
hoarse voice indicative of paralysis of the larynx. Since it cannot drink, it
will soon show evidence of dehydration.

Complete character reversals are frequent. In its hiding place the seemingly timid animal may have a change of personality, springing out at
people, more often children, and inflicting scratch and fang wounds.
Children have had their faces disfigured by rabid cats, and adults, bending over to succor the cat which won't come out of a hiding place, have
sometimes suffered severe lacerations about their hands and arms.

In all forms of rabies, once the severe encephalitis symptoms appear,
death generally ensues in less than a week, sometimes in three days. Infected farm cats usually go into the woods and die, but if they are hiding
about the barn or in mangers, they may bite other animals. If one cat dies
in suspicious circumstances and a few weeks later another behaves in a
similar fashion, the owner should feel it incumbent upon him to report
the sick cat to the health authorities.

Diagnosis beyond the suspicion created by the symptoms is possible
only by microscopic and biologic means. In order to do this, the suspected
cat must be destroyed and a portion of the brain examined for inclusion
bodies.

PREVENTION AND CONTROL: Suppose you think your cat may be rabid,
what should you do? Confine him in a veterinary hospital or the pound.
Give him time to develop characteristic symptoms. If he does have rabies,
have him destroyed, have the brain examined, and put yourself in the
hands of your doctor.

The questions are often asked: Why don't veterinarians try to cure
animals with rabies? If they can't drink, why aren't they given water by
vein? Isn't there any serum for rabies? The answer to all these questions is
simple. Human beings do not want to handle rabid animals, so practically
nothing has been done in the way of cure.

Prevention is the keynote in rabies control. It can be made more effective by keeping all dogs, since they are the principal carriers, under super-
vision. Then, it can further be controlled by rigid enforcement of the
regulations requiring dog wardens to pick up all strays. The prevention
of rabies consists of the vaccination of all animals who might become
carriers. These vaccinations are very inexpensive in some states. In areas

completely free of the disease nothing need be done and this dread disease can be forgotten.

If there is any possibility that infected saliva or other excretion from a rabid dog has entered a cut or abrasion, a person can be given the famous Pasteur treatment. If taken in time, this treatment causes the human body to develop immunity in the blood, and the immune bodies in turn attack the virus growing on the nerves and destroy it.

Virus Pneumonia. From time to time scientists have suspected that humans could transmit an atypical kind of pneumonia to cats and vice versa. There are many cases, well authenticated, of the cats and members of the same household being sick at the same time, in much the same way. There have been a number of investigations into the nature of the disease which have made it possible to identify three distinct forms of virus pneumonia.

THE BAKER VIRUS: A highly contagious, debilitating disease of about a month's duration was the first to be described and isolated. Sneezing, coughing, discharging a thick putrid material from eyes and nose are the chief symptoms beyond the usual accompaniments of loss of appetite, fever, loss of any desire for affection. These symptoms, however, might at first make one suspect any one of several diseases, and in fact the disease is one not easily differentiated from many others.

If one cat of many affected dies or is sacrificed—say one of a barnful—and a post-mortem examination is made, the lungs will be found to be almost solidly filled in the front portions and grayish in color in these areas. This may seem strange in view of the fact that ordinary lung sounds characteristic of pneumonia are not obvious with a stethoscope.

Actually the positive diagnosis must be left to the pathologist, who can tell by mouse and egg inoculation. If mice have material from a sick cat sprayed into their noses they will be dead in three to five days. After the virus has passed through several animals, it will kill mice in two to three days. If it is inoculated into incubating eggs, the embryos will die in two to three days. There is very little bacterial contamination of the lungs.

Good nursing is the only practical treatment. Older cats usually recover; the disease is more severe in kittens.

THE YALE VIRUS: This virus was isolated from a group of cats, eight out of twelve of which had died and two of the remaining four were sick. Two members of the family were also sick with the same disease.

In this type of pneumonia the nose and eyes discharge thick purulent mucus. The throat and windpipe and bronchial tubes are inflamed, as is evidenced by coughing. The bowel movements are normal but scanty. The appetite is depressed. Pneumonia sounds are absent when a stethoscope is used. There is much similarity to the former disease as far as symptoms are concerned.

However, the disease differs from the Baker virus in several respects.

It affects the surface tissue of the bronchial tubes and lung spaces so that the tissue would have to regenerate in cats which live. The chest cavity shows no inflammation. The intestines appear normal. Kittens die quickly, having little resistance, but older cats have greater resistance.

That the disease is intercommunicable cannot be doubted. Human sputum remains infective to cats for three weeks. It is possible to transmit it from one cat to another. Unlike the Baker virus and ornithosis, the Yale virus is not transmissible to mice. This differentiates it nicely from the others. It also differs from the Baker virus in that there is always bacterial contamination in the lungs, commonly staphylococcus, streptococcus, and bacilli.

Good nursing and use of streptomycin or penicillin to destroy the bacteria are indicated. The virus itself is not affected by the drugs, but if the cat has sufficient resistance, it may survive.

CAUTION: If you suspect your cat of having virus pneumonia, isolate it in a veterinary hospital or some place away from the family and do not allow it to get close to the face of anyone.

PSITTACOSIS-ORNITHOSIS: While the name of the disease might seem to indicate that it is confined to birds, we know that humans and other animals can and do contract it occasionally. One group of cats is believed to have contracted it from pigeon droppings. When the virus is inoculated into mice, the mice contract the disease, which distinguishes this infection from the Yale virus. Mortality among older cats is low, and not all kittens succumb.

The disease lasts several weeks, and during that time the fever falls slowly. Relapses are common. The breathing appears normal, but a hacking, dry, irritating cough continues, frequently without raising phlegm. The cats are not physicked and may even be constipated. Indeed, there is little to distinguish the sickness from that caused by the Baker virus unless it is less discharge from eyes and nose, and considerable vomiting, which makes one suspect distemper.

One sometimes wonders how an infected cat can seem to feel so sick and yet show so few outward symptoms.

A post-mortem shows that the lungs are inflamed and the tiny air sacs filled with fluid, not solid as in Baker's disease. The fluid and the affected parts of the lungs are in the lobes rather than in the front parts.

The spleen swells with the ornithosis virus infection. In cats which I have studied these were the only unusual features. None of them had shown signs of pneumonia, and not until the first had died was the cause known with reasonable certainty. Mortality in cats infected with psittacosis is probably lowest of the three types of virus pneumonia.

Penicillin has proved effective in combating complicating bacteria which may develop where the virus has injured the lung tissue. Aureomycin shows great promise in treating the actual virus.

Among the cats which we have treated, there was no instance of the disease being transmitted to members of the household.

BACTERIAL DISEASES

Coryza. A disease, or diseases, of cats more closely resembling the human common cold than that contracted by any other species is coryza. As with humans, the set of symptoms may be the same manifestation of a multiplicity of infecting agents, virus and bacterial.

Some students have found a bacillus incriminated (*B. felisepticus*); others have found a streptococcal organism. Occasionally cats may develop a mouth inflammation along with the nasal symptoms. There have been epizootics among cats in which the disease has proved fatal to a large percentage of sufferers, but there is every reason to believe that in such cases there may have been complications of virus diseases.

However, there is one "common cold" or coryza of cats which is quickly cured by either penicillin or sulfathiazole. It is therefore bacterial in origin. The disease spreads as an epizootic, just as human colds spread as epidemics. It is not necessarily a cold weather disease. I have seen it spread in a few days throughout a cattery. Without treatment, it lasts ten or twelve days and seldom kills the cats.

Symptoms are sneezing, lack of appetite or a considerable diminution of desire for food, often a few days with soft stools but not diarrhea. Temperature seldom exceeds 103°.

Treatment has been mentioned. Your veterinarian will supply you with sulfathiazole, inject penicillin or give aureomycin by mouth.

Leptospirosis. Of spirochetal origin, the bacterial agent which produces this disease is spread to dogs most frequently by rat urine. Whole rat populations are affected at times. It is estimated that from 30 to 50 per cent of all mature rats are carriers. With cats' penchant for killing rats, it is amazing that more are not reported with this disease.

SYMPTOMS AND DIAGNOSIS: The disease appears in two forms, the *canicola,* which closely resembles distemper, and the *icterohemorrhagic* (jaundice-hemorrhages). The former is often inaccurately diagnosed since it presents particularly difficult diagnostic problems.

Both types produce a number of common symptoms which can be traced to the impairment of certain organs by the spirochetes. These are unsteady elevation of temperature, nausea, lassitude, loss of weight, loose stools, and stiffness. An almost constant symptom in both forms is the congestion of the tiny blood vessels in the whites of the eyes, which may be a coppery red. The canicola form shows a few additional symptoms. The urine may range in color from orange to chocolate brown and may at times contain blood. The cat is generally quite emaciated when it dies.

The second type (icterohemorrhagic) differs in the symptoms it produces in the manner implied by the name. There is bleeding in the intestines and gums, and sometimes tiny hemorrhages are scattered throughout the body. The vomitus often shows blood; the stools appear bloody.

A further diagnostic symptom is one which a disease of the liver would be expected to exhibit: namely, jaundice. The mucous membranes, skin, and whites of the eyes appear a more and more intense yellow as the disease progresses, until, at death, some tissues may be almost a canary yellow or orange. By the time the yellow has appeared, however, the disease has progressed so far that serious damage may have been done to the kidneys and liver. The difficulty of identifying the disease at an early stage makes it difficult to cure the first cat in an area to contract leptospirosis. By the time the diagnosis has been definitely established, there is usually little hope. Even if the cat should survive, the damage that was done before the treatment was started will often make him an invalid for the remainder of his life.

Leptospirosis in a cattery or in a pair of cats is a different matter. If one cat dies, diagnosis by post-mortem and bacterial examination is possible. Then, after the disease has been identified, treatment may be started immediately with those pets which have been infected a shorter time. When the disease is detected at an earlier stage, the cats may—and usually do—recover if proper treatment is given. Urine analyses can be made on all as a helpful indication. Every cat not entirely well, particularly those that show indications of a fever, can be treated. If the temperature fluctuates markedly from very high to almost normal, it may add to one's suspicions, for leptospirosis does not cause a uniformly high fever even at the beginning.

TREATMENT: Penicillin has been found to be useful when given in heavy doses, but it should be administered as early as possible. The mortality is high, but some cats do recover with no aftereffects. Laboratory tests with the serum from infected cats, mixed with colored spirochetes, cause clumping of the bacteria and show whether or not a cat has recovered. From my own experience, it would seem that the difficulty in diagnosing this disease and the harmlessness of penicillin injections warrant their use whenever suspicion points to the possibility of leptospirosis.

Tetanus (Lockjaw).   Cats can become infected with tetanus but, despite the vast number of abscesses which cats have, they seldom do. Tetanus germs cannot grow in air; they do best in mixed infections where the other germs use up the oxygen when they begin to grow. Whether because the staphylococcus germs which are most commonly found in cat abscesses inhibit their growth or because the abscesses break before the tetanus gets a start, I have never seen a cat develop lockjaw because of external abscesses. I have known deep, penetrating wounds that caused tetanus.

Symptoms are those typical of tetanus in other animals: the cat slowly stiffens, even the tail standing out straight with its end hanging from the weight. Indications of hunger and thirst but inability to chew and swallow, cessation of defecation and urination, often a pitiful moaning. Finally, dehydration and death.

Tuberculosis. When cats have tuberculosis it is more often the bovine, or cow, form. Barn cats which live in close proximity to cattle and often drink unpasteurized milk are most often infected. In Europe it is estimated that 2 per cent of the cats are tubercular. In America the percentage is far less. Attempts to infect cats with the human form of tuberculosis have failed.

The most frequent sites of lesions are lungs, liver, and kidneys. The lungs may become so heavily infected that areas of tissue may die and a tuberculous pneumonia occur.

So far we have no proven case of a cat having infected a human with T.B. They have been incriminated in spreading it to cattle, but there is always the possibility of birds also spreading it. If a T.B. test demonstrates that a cat is infected, it is best to destroy her as quickly as possible because of the ever-present possibility of infection.

Bacterial Pneumonia. Inflammation of the lungs with bacteria of several types causes difficult breathing, high temperature—104° and over—prostration, loss of appetite, moderate thirst, and the rasping sound one hears if he holds his ear to the cat's chest. It is hard to mistake the symptoms of bacterial pneumonia.

Pneumonia follows exposures. Cats caught in traps or for any reason forced to remain cold and wet for any length of time are fit subjects. Such exposure in some way reduces the strength of the cat's bodily defenses, and pneumonia starts. Cats seldom live through it without drug administration.

The cat with pneumonia should be kept dry and warm, and for good measure and for good reason a pneumonia jacket should be put on. No attempt should be made to reduce her temperature, which is her body's way of helping to discourage the growth of the germs. Get the veterinarian to confirm or disaffirm your diagnosis and give you the sulfa drugs you need to treat her—a dose at least five times a day—or let him give daily injections of penicillin. More often than not, such treatment will save her.

Treating pneumonia is not the whole story. Pleurisy may follow, with the lungs being stuck to the lining of the chest cavity. Areas of the lungs may break so as to form pockets and the cat be left with what in a horse would be heaves—emphysema. In that event the cat will no longer have the capacity for a long, fast frolic. She will become out of breath far too quickly, and her breathing may have a wheeze characteristic of this affliction. There is no cure.

16. The Reproductive and Urinary Systems

KIDNEY DISEASE

*D*ESPITE the large amounts of meat and organs consumed by cats, kidney disease, even kidney stones, is rare in any except old cats. It does occur, of course, as a result of infections, poisonings, and injuries. Abnormal thirst is one of the first signs of the disease. Urine analysis, by boiling a little urine to which a few drops of acetic acid have been added, will also show the cloudiness or flakiness indicative of albumin.

Taken in the early stages, infective kidney disease is often curable. One should not delay in taking the cat to the veterinarian for treatment at the first sign of loss of appetite and a sharply increased thirst. In chronic incurable cases there is dehydration and a smell of urine on the breath. Antibiotics such as penicillin may be injected if the cat finds it impossible to keep sulfa drugs in the stomach.

Feeding ice cubes, which the pet can lap, often overcomes the thirst, and absorption of the water from the body cavities can still be encouraged. Withholding of meat is imperative, and, as you have seen in the section on feeding, cats can be fed low protein diets and still thrive. Very little meat, organs, fish, skim milk, cheese, eggs may be fed to a cat with kidney disease. Cereals, vegetables, and fats must be the mainstay of the diet. After you think the animal is cured, a visit to the doctor for another urine analysis is necessary to determine whether a higher protein diet is safe.

Stones may develop in the kidneys. Their presence can be determined only by X-ray. Small gravelly stones which move from the kidneys down the ureters to the bladder cause pain to the cat as they do to humans.

The kidney pelvis may be inflamed, even when the bladder is not. Stones often dam up the urine and cause a larger pocket to develop in the kidneys. Bladder inflammation may be spread forward to the kidney, and when this occurs the cat may suffer pain under the loin, run a fever, void urine containing blood and pus, and even have diarrhea. If the inflammation is not treated, it may in time result in enlargement of the kidneys.

Kidneys long infected lose their ability to function and shrink so that a chronic condition is produced.

One result of malfunction of the kidneys is dropsy. The abdomen distends and the tissue along the belly and the legs stocks up with blood plasma. Quite often heart weakness is associated with this disease.

BLADDER TROUBLES

Many cats have bladder trouble. Almost everyone has known of a tomcat which couldn't urinate, despite his best efforts, or a female which was pained so much by the effort that she cried out.

Most tomcat urinary retention is due to fine gravel which irritates the urethra so greatly that inflammation at length closes the passage. The bladder becomes distended and very firm. The cat makes unsuccessful attempts to urinate and finally sits around most mournfully and unhappily. If not relieved, he goes into a coma and dies of uremia.

By patient efforts a veterinarian can sometimes pass a fine tomcat catheter, moving the gravel out of the way. Occasionally he may successfully massage some of these little stones out, and the urine may then flow unrestricted. But frequently it becomes necessary to tap the bladder through the abdominal wall. It is important that a needle of the proper size be used in this operation. If it is too large, the opening through the bladder left after the needle's withdrawal may be large enough to permit the urine to pass out into the peritoneal cavity. When this happens the cat dies within a few hours.

URINARY INCONTINENCE

Incontinence occurs in spayed females on rare occasions due to the removal of the ovaries, with the consequent loss of tone of the bladder sphincter muscle. The condition is usually easily corrected by giving stilbestrol—one milligram or even one half milligram every other day until the condition is corrected, and then less until the minimum amount which will hold the gain is determined.

UTERINE INFECTIONS

It is not uncommon for female cats to develop infections in the uterus (metritis) which can be treated only by removal of the organs. If that is done, it is advisable to remove the ovaries also, since there is no point in having a female cat repeatedly coming in season and attracting males if she can no longer produce kittens. Such a cat usually leaks a sweet-smelling pus from the cervix which keeps her soiled about the vulva and backs of her legs. Her abdomen, in a severe case, is distended sufficiently to make the owner suspect pregnancy. She has a fever.

At birth kittens are sometimes too large to pass through the pelvis, and at such times, if action is not taken to help the delivery, all the kittens may die, causing decomposition and rupture of the uterus.

CRYPTORCHIDISM

In males, next to urinary retention, the failure of the testicles to descend constitutes the most common defect of the genitourinary tract. The cryptorchid (animal with hidden testicles) needs attention. He may be a monorchid (one testicle hidden) or a complete cryptorchid. It is better for cats to have hidden testicles removed.

NEUTERING

It is the consensus of opinion among cat fanciers that the altered male and female make far more satisfactory pets. I have heard many of our clients with wide experience in handling cats say bluntly that breeding cats are definitely unsatisfactory. Some people think otherwise.

Generally speaking, the altered cat requires much less care. It stays home, is more carefree and affectionate, is safer to handle, costs less to keep, lives longer actuarially speaking, and seldom is made useless as a mouser as so many believe.

The males specifically lose their potent and—to most people—obnoxious odor, stop spraying and use their pans or boxes, and stop howling, fighting, and staying out all night. If castrated at an early age, they never develop these undesirable traits and tend to grow larger than their whole brothers.

Cattas, after the spaying operation, attract no more males and cause no more cat concerts outside the house. In addition, the neighbors cannot blame the spayed female if their tomcat must be taken to the veterinarian for wound treatment. The cattas stop calling and rolling, a type of behavior abhorrent to many owners. They use their food to better advantage, have no periodical weight losses, and have no kittens with the occasional complications and nuisance this entails. To many owners, just the task of having to find homes for unwanted kittens is reason enough for spaying a cat.

One should think ahead and ask, at the time of taking in a kitten, "Do I want a breeder, or do I want a pet?" If the answer is a pet, then neutering is the ready-made solution.

17. The Digestive Tract

THE MOUTH

*T*HE mouth, which is properly considered as part of the digestive tract, is perhaps more exposed to infection than any other part of the body. Although the tissue is particularly resistant to infection, the several parts of the oral cavity are subject to a number of diseases.

Lips. Where the long upper "canine" teeth rub on the sides of the lower lips there occasionally develops an irritation which produces a sickening odor. The lips develop sore spots and the cat drools copiously. Even a few drops of the saliva which the cat drops is sufficiently odorous to make a whole room unpleasant. Though the putrescent odor might lead one to think that the animal is about to die, actually the condition is easily cured with a few drops of tincture of iodine, full strength, daubed on the infected spots with a small cotton swab. Sometimes two treatments on consecutive days may be necessary to do the trick. A weak silver-nitrate solution is also effective.

Injuries to the lips commonly cause difficulty. Sometimes an upper lip becomes impaled on an upper canine tooth. It must be removed, and this often requires considerable manipulation. The upper lip may ulcerate along its lower border from a cut, until a long area has a cheesy growth in it and has become greatly thickened. The only cure for this condition is surgery. The veterinarian must remove the dead tissue and suture the inner and outer lip surfaces together.

Stomatitis. Stomatitis is infection of the mouth. It is thought by some that it may be indirectly due to a vitamin G (niacin) deficiency, although the one vitamin that cats usually have in ample amounts is niacin. Whatever the cause, cats' mouths often develop infection of this sort, and injections of niacin do help greatly in relieving the condition. The spirochete of Vincent's angina (trench mouth) is present with the infection, but whether it is the primary cause of stomatitis has not been determined, since the mouths of normal cats frequently harbor this spirochete. It is probable that infection more or less destroys the victim's sense of taste and causes pain whenever food is eaten.

Treating a cat with an infected mouth is difficult. Sodium perborate can be obtained in any drugstore and used as per directions for humans. But the cat will soon learn to fight off attempts to swab her mouth. When she does, it is best to soak a ball of cotton in the solution and hold it so she bites it. The squeezing of her jaws will swab her mouth thoroughly. Medication should be continued twice a day until the infection is cleared up. It is not difficult to tell when the patient is cured, for when the pain and soreness has passed, the cat will stop looking wistfully at her food and really eat it with a voracious appetite.

Diseases of the Teeth and Gums. Although cats' teeth are generally uncommonly sound up until old age, they do sometimes have minor dental ailments. Occasionally a tooth will be broken. The most frequent malady is tartar accumulation. As much as an eighth of an inch must sometimes be removed from the back teeth of a cat. The accumulating tartar slowly builds up a thick coating on the teeth until it pushes back the gums, food packs around it, the gums become painful, and the cat no longer has any desire to crunch on hard food. Since it is not at all difficult to snap tartar off the teeth, it is surprising that all cat owners do not learn to keep their cats' teeth clean. By occasionally removing the tartar, the owner can prevent an annoying accumulation. When the deposit is heavy, however, cats often object so strenuously to its removal that considerable restraint is needed and expert's dental tools must be used.

Cats on deficient diets often lose their teeth in their youth. Those which got off to a poor start frequently develop such poor teeth that they have to be extracted by the time the cat is eight years old. One warden tells of examining the teeth of over four hundred wild cats killed while preying on a pheasant ranch far out in the country. Not a cat among them had a missing tooth, and none had an excessive amount of tartar. Apparently cats on natural complete diets have beautiful teeth, in contrast to the pampered house pet which is so often given meat, meat, and only meat. The owner usually shrugs and says, "That's all he will eat." The cats-gone-wild prove otherwise.

It is only humane to have all loose teeth extracted, even if it means the cat must be fed mush the rest of its life. Many canned cat foods are excellent and all of them are mushy in consistency so that a cat can thrive on them.

THE GULLET

Troublesome conditions in the esophagus are chiefly the result of burns from poisons; injuries by foreign bodies such as bones, pins, needles, and wood splinters; and inflammation caused by infections.

Symptoms are cessation of eating and vomiting, sometimes with blood in the vomitus. The cat may sit with her head and neck stretched out. She may drool and gag. If you press her throat, she may resent it by pushing your fingers away with a paw.

Removal of foreign bodies necessitates anesthesia and veterinary treatment. Injuries may so nearly close the gullet by the inflammation they cause that only passage of a soft stomach tube, or intravenous medication, can save her.

THE STOMACH

Inflammation of the Stomach. In humans we speak of dyspepsia. Cats have its equivalent in a simple inflammation of the stomach which interferes with digestion. It may be caused by accidents, such as a kick or blow when the stomach is filled; by distention of the stomach wall from overeating; by too coarse or indigestible foods; by poisons, including food poisoning; by foreign objects such as chips of broken glass, tiny sharp bones, or porcupine quills; by parasites and diseases.

In poisoning, the stomach lining reddens, thickens, and may even slough off in areas. The inflammation often extends through the entire wall. A doctor performing a post-mortem examination may see the normally white stomach wall, with great red blotches, usually along the lower curve where food settles and where most of the damage is done.

One of the earliest symptoms is nausea. Loss of appetite is to be expected also. Temperature is a poor index, because, while disease may raise it, poisons or toxins may depress it. In many cases the cat will let out agonizing cries easily recognizable as expressions of pain. Depending on the cause, the bowel movements may be normal or of a diarrhea consistency. Since stomach inflammation associated with disease ordinarily affects the whole intestine as well, diarrhea is usually present.

Treatment depends upon the cause. Some objects can be removed with peroxide (page 132). In most cases, however, the problem is best left to your veterinarian, who can remove the cause and give you drugs to relieve the cat's pain.

Hair Balls. Actually these are usually not balls at all. It would probably be more accurate to call them hair strings. I have removed several surgically where the hair accumulation had taken a spherical shape. One had a sort of handle which protruded up the gullet, and the lump itself was as large as a tennis ball. In most cases there is a large clump in the stomach and attached to it there is a hairy rope which may extend several feet along the intestine. Cats normally rid themselves of hair in the stomach by vomiting it, if it does not pass out of the pylorus—the exit valve of the stomach. But when the lump becomes so large that it can't be regurgitated it causes serious difficulty.

There are two facts to be remembered about hair balls. The first one is that nature's way of eliminating hair in the intestinal tract is by decomposition. The lump fills with myriads of bacteria which in time decompose it so that it can be sloughed off. While this is going on—the process may last a month or more—the cat is absorbing the bacterial toxins. She gets thin, and in many cases shows a definite rise in temperature as a result of autointoxication. As soon as the lump has decomposed and passed out in sections, the cat becomes ravenous and recovery is rapid and complete.

The second fact to remember is that there is never any reason to allow the hair to accumulate. It should be a matter of prevention—and prevention is such a simple thing! It consists of administering mineral oil once a week, or giving the cat some edible oil in amounts too large to be digested. Some people add mineral oil to the food, but it is not so effective this way as when given on an empty stomach. Others open a can of sardines, eat the fish, and set the can with the fishy oil on the floor and let the cat lap it on an empty stomach. This is an excellent method of preventing hair balls.

A bile-salt pill can also be given once a week to prevent hair balls. There are several proprietary mixtures, containing laxatives and oils, which are very effective preventives.

Once sizable hair balls have developed, difficult and complicated procedures are sometimes necessary for their removal. Surgery may have to be employed. Your veterinarian will usually decide to operate only when he can palpate a lump too large ever to be eliminated by drugs or natural means. Such a step is much better than doing nothing, on the assumption that the cat can live long enough without nourishment for the lump to decompose. This starvation treatment is inhumane, even though many cat owners, through inertia and thoughtlessness, allow it to go on.

Decomposition can be used sensibly as an ally. If drugs are given which kill the bacteria in the hair lump, the cat may feel better but the lump will be even harder to dislodge. It is usually wise, therefore, to give oils or drugs that cause a slimy mass in the stomach, in which the tangled hairs will gradually disintegrate. Sometimes a dose of hydrogen peroxide (page 132) will bring up a large-sized hair lump. This treatment is most likely to be successful after oil has been given for a long enough time to thoroughly disentangle the mass in the stomach.

Veterinarians often give oil and, while it is still in the stomach, an injection of a drug such as Lentin or Peristaltin, to speed up the intestinal motility. Arecolene pills frequently are extremely effective. Bile-salt pills can also sometimes be used to rid cats of large accumulations. If one pill is given every four or five hours until three have been given, a single series may move the hair which is causing the cat's sickness. However, it is usually advisable to repeat the treatment after a few days.

In some cases the veterinarian may be able to pass a small tube into the gullet of an anesthetized cat, insert instruments which tangle in the hair, and pull it out. There are other methods which may prove feasible in certain cases. If your cat does not respond to home treatment within a reasonable time, it would be best to seek professional help.

Whatever method is used to eliminate the hair balls, it is unnecessary to see the cat starve during treatments. Her appetite may be nil, but in this case forced feeding will have a considerable sustaining effect even if nothing more than corn syrup is given. A few tablespoonfuls during a day are very helpful. It must be thinned somewhat to pour. If powdered dextrose is used, it must be made into a solution thin enough to be swallowed easily. A small amount of yeast mixed with it furnishes B-complex vitamins, or a syrup containing vitamins and minerals is a worth-while addition.

Foreign Bodies in the Stomach. Aside from hair—and occasionally grass—it is rare to find other foreign bodies lodged in the stomachs of cats. In my experience the most common cause of digestive difficulty has been bugs. Large meals of crickets or grasshoppers may gather into balls with the legs of the bugs intertwined and the sharp points of the mass scratching the tender stomach walls. This results in severe discomfort until the skeletons have been softened by long exposure to digestive fluids. In some areas Japanese bettles are particularly troublesome to cats eager to eat bugs. If you will look at a beetle's legs with a magnifying glass, you will understand the danger of allowing a cat to eat too many. Obviously a cat may eat a few insects of any kind along with other food without harm. The indigestible residue is mixed with the other material and thrown off in the feces. When too many are eaten, however, it may be necessary to dose the cat with mineral oil to help move the crusty insects along the digestive tract.

String and even thread with needles on the end are sometimes swallowed. There is something about ordinary dry string which seems to entrance a cat. Generally the interest which starts with play ends in swallowing. Strings two or more feet long have been pulled out of cats while others pass unnoticed with the feces. Nevertheless, the sight of a foot-long piece of butcher string dragging after a cat quite naturally causes the owner alarm. It need not. It is a simple matter to catch hold of the string and pull it out.

No matter in what part of the cat's body a needle is ultimately found, it is safe to assume that it originally found its way into the mouth on the end of a piece of thread. If you attempt to pull a thread out of the cat's anus and it refuses to budge, veterinary attention is called for. The needle on the end of the thread may be crosswise of the rectum. The same applies to a regurgitated thread which is found hanging out of a cat's mouth; it is probably attached to a needle embedded in the tissue of the throat.

Whether treatment will save a cat with gastritis depends on the cause. Large foreign objects can be surgically removed. Ground glass is not so dangerous, and if the pieces are small enough to be swallowed they will usually be found in the feces. Hair can be helped out slowly, as we have just explained. Porcupine quills work themselves out, and whether they will kill the cat is a matter of the direction they take after leaving the stomach. Sometimes administering stomach sedatives, which a veterinarian can give you, helps greatly. Since rectifying the injured stomach is simply a matter of removing the damaging agent and waiting until the body heals itself, there is always the danger that the owner will lose patience. If any kind of treatment requires patience, this is surely it—this waiting for the slow regeneration of injured tissue. There is no quick cure, but in the long run the waiting pays.

Ulcers.   In cats ulcers are produced in a number of ways, the most common being the administration of excessive amounts of drugs, such as aspirin or caffeine. Aside from such external causes, ulcers also seem to develop spontaneously. Regardless of what causes ulcers, they are always difficult to diagnose. Usually they are discovered only on post-mortem examination. They might be suspected if a cat eats very little, loses weight, occasionally passes blood in the feces, and shows pain when examined in the vicinity of the stomach. Perforating ulcers cause incurable peritonitis.

THE INTESTINES

Diseases of the Intestines.   Much of what has been said of the common ailments of the gullet and stomach applies equally to the intestines. They are exposed to the same organisms which are carried on to them. Parasites do more damage to the intestines than to the stomach. Hookworms attach themselves to the intestines and suck blood; the larvae of both the hookworm and the roundworm bore through the intestines; and in the intestinal walls coccidia live. Tapeworms hold to it and whipworms sew their whiplashes under its lining. Rough, coarse material may chafe the delicate villi and cause diarrhea. But aside from these special conditions, the ailments of the intestines are largely extensions and complications of those arising elsewhere.

THE LIVER

Jaundice is seen occasionally in cats. When it appears, it may indicate that any one of several things is wrong with the liver, or with the gall bladder—the storage reservoir for the bile that the liver makes.

Leptospirosis.   This disease is a common cause of jaundice in cats. It is discussed on page 209.

Bile Duct Obstruction.   The ducts leading from the liver to the gall bladder may be closed by infection, inflammation, or stones; or the duct from the gall bladder into the duodenum may be plugged. The bile distends the gall bladder, the surplus is picked up by the blood, carried about the body, and deposited in the tissues in sufficient quantities to turn them yellow in time.

Sometimes a good meal with considerable fat in it will cause the empty-ing of the gall bladder, but when an infection such as distemper is the basic cause of the jaundice, very little can be done.

Cirrhosis of the Liver.   Cirrhosis occurs only rarely in cats. It is due to disease which thickens parts of the liver. These parts later contract, leav-ing a shrunken organ mottled with yellow spots. Nothing can be done for this condition.

Enlargement.   Liver enlargement is produced by an excess of toxins. A continued kidney condition which throws urine into the blood is a com-mon cause. Tumors in the liver result in considerable enlargement, both because of their own additional bulk and because the pressure they fre-quently exert on the great veins makes the liver itself enlarge to compen-sate. Nearly always the cat slowly loses weight. Emaciation is the end result.

Poisons.   Jaundice has been seen following poisoning—metallic, food, or gas—and sometimes appears even after snake bites. The poisons pro-duce jaundice by causing red-cell destruction and a resultant formation of bile pigment which settles in the tissues.

In most forms of liver upsets, where bile is not poured into the duo-denum to split the fats and alkalize the food coming from the stomach, the stools are grayish or clay-colored and of a sticky consistency. Con-stipation may be evident. Cats with the common forms of liver trouble usually run abnormal temperatures—from 102° to 104°. Vomiting often accompanies the appearance of jaundice but is not a constant symptom. First signs may be an undue pigmentation of the urine with deep yellow.

If there is any suspicion of jaundice first evidenced by the deep yellow urine, it is wise to give a meal of fat or, if the cat refuses food, to give a dose of Epsom salts (one half teaspoonful). Magnesium, like fat, tends to cause emptying of the gall bladder. And in most liver troubles large doses of glucose (corn syrup or dextrose) can be given to advantage. Several teaspoonfuls a day will usually be welcome. But since any jaundice might be an evidence of leptospirosis, which is contagious to man, the best place for a yellowing cat is in the veterinarian's hands.

18. Other Ailments of Cats

PARASITES

*F*OR the treatment of all intestinal parasites see Chapter 4, for the life histories of the parasites and Chapter 5 for drug dosage. Additional information is given below.

Roundworms. One of the best indications of roundworm infestation is the lifting of the "third eyelid"—nictitating membrane—over the eyes. Although it can be an indication of other stomach and intestinal troubles, it is far more likely to indicate roundworms. In kittens, these worms cause potbellies, unthriftiness, diarrhea, anemia, often subnormal temperature, dull coat. When only a few worms are harbored, the symptoms are, of course, less noticeable and may consist only of a general unthriftiness, in spite of a fair appetite. In older cats, their ravages are much less severe. Perhaps the most serious injury done by roundworms is to the lungs. Cats may develop verminous pneumonia as a result of the damage inflicted by large numbers of larvae boring from the blood vessels to the air sacs and causing irritation as they work up the bronchi and trachea to the throat.

Prevention consists of deworming the catta before breeding, keeping her off soil and out of quarters which are contaminated with roundworm eggs, and washing her teats before the kittens nurse if there is any chance that she has been where roundworm eggs are present. Food which can be dragged around in filth is a common source of infestation. When the kittens start to walk, they too must be kept out of infested quarters.

With kittens, a fecal examination should always be made before treatment. If worms are present, the kittens should be put on absolute starvation for twenty hours and then dosed with tetrachlorethylene in capsule form, using one tenth c.c. to each pound of the weight of the kitten. An hour later milk of magnesia may be given, and food two hours after that.

Let me again stress the *necessity* of a twenty-four-hour starvation period. If the kittens have even a teaspoonful of milk in their stomachs or intestines, the drug may kill them. In spite of the obvious danger involved, I have found that for small kittens tetrachlorethylene is much safer than either N butyl chloride or wormseed oil.

In adult cats, N butyl chloride is safe and effective but has no advantage over tetrachlorethylene, except that it is less toxic if food has been taken unknown to the cat's owner. Dosages are given on page 110. The drug can be followed by any safe physic.

The treatment had best be repeated in two weeks to destroy the worms which have arrived in the intestinal tract from the lungs. Obviously those in the blood won't be reached by the drug.

Here is a trick which often comes in handy if you are deworming a number of individual animals: smell the breath of every cat half an hour after dosing to be sure he has retained the capsules containing the drug. An etherlike odor should be plainly detectable in the breath. If you find a capsule on the floor of a cage in which the, say, five kittens you have just dewormed are confined, all you need do to ascertain which kitten lost the capsule is to smell their breaths.

Occasionally kittens are so filled with roundworms that even tetrachlorethylene prostrates them. If that happens, you should keep them warm until the physic has moved the worms down into the colon. Then, administer a mild enema with a bulb syringe. This will usually bring relief.

Hookworms. The principal damage done by hookworms is the anemia they produce in young cats and kittens. As cats grow older and are subjected to repeated infestations, they develop partial immunity.

Infested kittens will first suffer from lung damage similar to that caused by roundworms. This is followed by anemia. One glance at the gums will reveal the kitten's condition. There are many other variable symptoms. The kitten may have fits; diarrhea may become persistent and the appetite picky; sometimes the legs will swell. He may moan; usually he remains lying down, as if even standing were an effort. He will lose weight, breathe more rapidly than a normal kitten, and an acrid odor can be noted because of the water discharge which coats his anus and the surrounding hair together with part of his tail.

Older cats may have fits when they first become heavily infested. They, too, lose their appetites, develop anemia, become sluggish, and develop a generally unthrifty look. If proper food is not provided, even older cats may die—because the best efforts of their red-blood-cell-building mechanism are insufficient to make up for the loss caused by the hookworm infestation.

Prevention is the same as that indicated for roundworms, but in the case of hookworms, diet is more important. A diet rich in iron and copper is essential, and the protein food fed to the cat must be of good quality.

Treatment for hookworms is the same as for roundworms, so far as drugs are concerned, but supportive treatment is advisable. Food of high quality helps the cat to recover quickly. Transfusions often work wonders, once the worms are gone, or even before, in very anemic cats.

Cat breeders sometimes say it is better to build up an infested cat before he is dewormed. This seems to me to be a great mistake. In my experience, a cat can't be built up as fast as his blood is being thinned by the worms, except by transfusion. When getting rid of worms, the promptest possible action is best if the cat is to be saved.

After you have rid the cat of his worms, you should provide a diet rich in iron and copper. Meat and liver are excellent sources of both. A small pinch of ferrous sulphate or ferric and ammonium citrate added to the diet daily will cause the redness to come back into the gums and the cat's energy to return more quickly.

One treatment is not enough to completely rid a cat of hookworms any more than it would be enough to eliminate all roundworms. A second treatment two weeks after the first will kill the worms which were blood-living larvae when the first treatment was given. If the cat picks up another infestation, it will be much less severe than the first, and each subsequent infestation will build up a degree of immunity.

Whipworms. These worms live in the intestine. Since most cats have been dewormed, however, and ordinary worm medicines will also kill whipworms, cats are not too much troubled with this parasite. In dogs whipworms lodge in the cecum (blind gut), escaping the effects of drugs intended for other parasites, but cats have no such structure which the worms can use as a hiding place.

A mild infestation of whipworms produces no more indication of its presence than alternating soft and firm stools. Severe infestations may produce fits even in old cats. Although the worms do not suck blood as do hookworms, they produce toxins which cause anemia. Loss of appetite, unthrifty coat, and some eye discharge are additional symptoms.

Prevention consists of promptly removing all feces from the pans of house cats so that the animals have no opportunity to come into contact with whipworm eggs.

Treatment is the same as for roundworms and hookworms.

Tapeworms. Tapeworm infestation, also called teniasis, is a disease just as is any one of the ailments caused by bacteria, though its effects need not be serious.

In small numbers tapeworms produce few ill effects, but when large numbers infest a cat they can make him a very sick animal. He will show symptoms of nervousness, restlessness, and sometimes irritability. Because human beings are thought to have an increased appetite when they harbor tapeworms (it is doubtful if they really do), cats also are generally expected to be hungrier. They are not. Actually cats usually lose their desire for food to some extent when they are infested with tapeworms.

Tapeworms can cause such loss of condition that the cat has convulsions; his coat may become thin, his digestion be disturbed. There is often a marked tendency to vomit small amounts—enough to be a source of worry to the cat's owner as well as a nuisance in a house pet. Occasionally, segments of the worms lodge in the anal glands and cause irritation, so that the cat pulls himself along on his rear quarters.

Dectection of segments of tapeworms in the cat's stool is the most certain method of determining the presence of the pest. A fecal examination may be made, but in the case of the flea-host tapeworm it is not conclusive even when done by a thoroughly competent technician. They tend to retain their eggs, and the examination of any particular stool may not show evidence of infestation even when the worms are present.

While it is obviously impossible to avoid all contact between a cat and any potential tapeworm host, try to reduce such contact to a minimum. It is wise to see that all beef, pork, and lake fish fed to the cat is well cooked. Whenever possible he should be prevented from catching and eating rabbits. Both the cat and his quarters should be well dusted with flea powder in order to reduce to a minimum his chances of catching and swallowing an insect host. If a cat has been infested, the rugs and furniture in the rooms where he has been should be thoroughly gone over with an efficient vacuum cleaner to remove all dried worm segments. For a time it is also necessary to burn or bury the feces to eliminate the chance of reinfestation.

Arecolene hydrobromide, the drug most frequently used to eliminate tapeworms, is available in any drugstore, or your veterinarian may supply you with it. He may also give you Nemural or Teneathane or some newer drug. Correct dosages are given on page 108. Be sure the cat is starved for fifteen to eighteen hours before dosing. If he vomits in less than fifteen minutes after dosing, you should assume that he retained some of the drug because arecolene is quite quickly absorbed. Wait seven to ten minutes and give half the dose again. The effect is unusually rapid, and generally a cat will have passed all of his tapeworms within forty-five minutes.

Coccidiosis. This disease (pronounced cock-sid-e-osis) affects cats of all ages. It is self-limiting and the cat usually recovers without treatment just about as quickly as with any treatment which has been devised to date. Any cat, once recovered, will never again have the disease caused by that particular species of coccidium. He can, however, be infested by one of the other species. It takes about four weeks for the cat to become immune to the disease.

Kittens are usually quite severely affected, but mature cats may show no symptoms other than impairment of appetite and loose stools. Symptoms to be watched for are loose stools, often with bloody color, maturating eyes, elevated temperature, loss of appetite, general unthriftiness. In severe cases, weakness and depression are apparent, as well as emaciation.

When nursing kittens are infected with coccidiosis they seem to have only a light case of it. If it strikes them after they have been weaned the infection is much more severe. Whether this is the result of changing from a diet rich in fat to one with a very low fat content, whether the mother's milk possesses some antibody, or the kittens possess some maternal immunity, we cannot say positively. It is known, however, that kittens weaned onto a high fat diet come through the disease with less loss of condition and weight than those on a low fat diet.

Kittens can contract the disease from their mothers' breasts or pick it up from infected quarters. Because of the latter, coccidiosis has been called the "pet-shop disease." Where kittens are placed together indiscriminately one or more is likely to be infected, and, not being housebroken, they drop stools into which other kittens are bound to walk. Infection is a certainty in that case. When direct contact is not responsible for infection, flies are usually the carriers. Even in catteries where the environment is immaculate and kittens are raised in wire-bottomed cages, coccidiosis occurs regularly because other cats in the cattery are infected, and recovered cats become carriers.

PREVENTION: It is possible to raise kittens and to keep them free from the disease. You can only do this by thoroughly screening the pens and cages and by thoroughly cleaning your hands and shoes every time you enter the cattery or handle an infected animal. It is difficult to realize that even though you can't see the organisms they may be present since they are only a few sizes larger than bacteria.

We are now faced with the question: Is it essential to raise kittens free from the disease? Most parents are not greatly disturbed when their children contract one of the so-called children's diseases. They feel that it is best that the children be immunized early rather than be subject to these diseases later, when they may be more difficult to overcome. Similarly, it is a good thing when kittens have coccidiosis and recover. They will, in all probability, contract it sooner or later anyway, so perhaps we should not complain of the loose stools indicative of the disease. The only danger is that the kittens might have more than coccidiosis. When several diseases strike at once, kittens may not be able to recover. If they have to have it, it is better for them to have passed the young kitten stage, for when they are a little older they will throw off coccidiosis quite easily.

From a study of the life history of the infecting organism (page 91), it becomes obvious that in order for a kitten or cat to have only a light case of the disease it is essential that he get as few infections as possible. If every day he is exposed to new eggs in large numbers he has far less chance of recovery.

The use of a wire-bottomed pen is the best possible insurance against heavy reinfection. The outside of the pen should be covered with fine screening that reaches to the ground so that flies cannot continue to carry eggs from feces to food dishes or lips.

TREATMENT: The whole duration of the disease is only about three weeks and almost all cases of coccidiosis are already on the way to recovery when treatment is begun. Let us assume your kitten shows definite signs of sickness. His eyes maturate; he has a fever of 103°; his stools are watery. You may reasonably think he has coccidiosis and when your veterinarian makes a fecal examination he finds thousands of coccidia eggs. The kitten is then at the height of the disease. If you now give him brick dust, cobwebs, sulfa drugs, vinegar and molasses, or any of the other remedies, he will probably recover. He will start to recover not because of the treatment but because he is getting well anyway.

Every so often a new cure is reported but usually the investigation has been made without untreated controls for comparison. As one scientist has said, "Coccidiosis is the disease about which more foolish cures have been reported than any other disease of animals." However, some promising treatments are now under scientific investigation and your veterinarian will tell you about them if they prove satisfactory.

A rich diet is important in the treatment of coccidiosis. At least 25 per cent of the kitten's diet should consist of fatty foods such as rich milk, cream, and fatty fish. The diet can further be improved by adding bone ash to the food. Bone ash is *not* bone meal or steamed bone; it is an entirely different product obtainable through your veterinarian or druggist.

Immaculate cleanliness is as important as any medicine. If the kitten uses paper for defecating purposes, destroy the stool before he can walk in it. Prevent reinfestation, and his chance of recovery is better than 90 per cent.

Fleas. Use a good flea powder, preferably one containing rotenone. Bathe and use a dip or rinse with not over 2 per cent DDT. Use a liquid soap containing a small amount of DDT or benzene hexachloride.

Lice. Use the same treatment. Repeat every ten days to break the generations.

Ticks. Pull ticks off with a pair of tweezers. The tick remedies are dangerous to cats. There is some indication that benzene hexachloride may be safe, but it is still uncertain. It will kill fleas at a low concentration, but ticks require a solution so strong as to be dangerous to cats.

Ox Warble. This large grub is found under the skin, often on the cheek, or the neck or back. The usual practice is to open the skin and pop it out. Flush the cavity with an antiseptic daily until it is healed.

Mange. When your veterinarian is certain of his diagnosis, after having demonstrated the mite in his microscope, he will prescribe a remedy. Apply it religiously. Whether the cat has sarcoptic or red mange, be sure the infected areas are kept saturated. And watch your own skin. If you notice a suspicious rash, tell your doctor what your veterinarian found in your cat. It may help him to treat you successfully.

Ear Mites (page 235). Mites are exceedingly easy to eliminate if a little rotenone is used, especially if the rotenone is mixed with a good wax solvent such as propylene glycol. But there are usually some mites on the hairs around the ear waiting to reinfest the cat or spread to others. Almost invariably some mites are shaken out of the ears in the dry crumbly scabs and wax; if they are about the house, the cat may be reinfested by them. It is therefore necessary to treat the animal again in two weeks after the first cure is effected.

AILMENTS AFFECTING THE NERVOUS SYSTEM

Convulsions. There is actually no *disease* called fits or convulsions, as so many people think. They are a condition brought about by a variety of causes affecting the nervous system. Fits in cats are alarming, but most of them can be eliminated and prevented. They are caused by brain disease, worms, anemia, severe fright, autointoxication, coccidiosis, poisons, and other causes.

Encephalitis—inflammation of the brain—may follow some as yet unidentified virus disease. There are indications that it does. No cure has yet been discovered for encephalitis, but fortunately fits resulting from it are comparatively rare in cats.

Fits following heavy roundworm infestations are common, especially in kittens. Eradication of the worms eliminates the fits. The same applies to tapeworm infestations in cats of all ages.

Coccidiosis is often an unsuspected cause of fits in cats. In rabbits it has been reported much more frequently as a direct cause when the organisms gain entrance to the blood and lodge in the brain. I have seen many kittens exhibit fits during severe attacks of the *I. rivolta* form of coccidiosis but never during the *I. felis* form. In my experience coccidiosis fits have generally been fatal to cats.

Anemia can be caused by hookworms, and anemia causes fits. Even after the hookworms have been eradicated the fits may continue for a considerable time unless some iron-bearing foods are fed in addition to the usual milk, which has so little. Liver is excellent in these cases. Hookworms cause toxins too, sometimes in sufficient quantities to cause fits. I have also known cases in which tapeworms produced the same effects.

Very sensitive cats, even when in the best of health, have been known to have fits when unduly excited. When taken for their first car ride, cats may become so terrified they rush wildly about and froth at the mouth. Owners occasionally report that cats attending their first cat shows have had fits. Whether there are other contributing causes or whether the excitement alone brings on the fits remains to be demonstrated, but certainly cats which have never had fits before or since have had violent ones under the stimulus of excitement.

Autointoxication from constipation and the self-poisoning which comes from urine in the blood when cats have kidney ailments predispose them to fits too. Poisons such as strychnine and arsenic will cause protracted convulsions which end in death unless radical treatment is given. Eclampsia—lack of calcium in the case of pregnant or nursing females—causes a trembling which gives the appearance of a long convulsion or fit.

Treatment for fits is seldom symptomatic; rather it consists in finding the basic cause and eliminating it. An injection of calcium gluconate into the blood stream quickly stops eclampsia; Nembutal is used to counteract strychnine poisoning; constipation may be relieved by means of enemas and by a change in diet. Do not attempt to "cure" the fits themselves. Concentrate on finding out what causes them and eliminate it.

HEREDITARY ANOMALIES

Cats which hop like rabbits are not born that way because their mothers were frightened by rabbits, but because of a hereditary factor which deforms their pelves and affects the nerves in such a way as to cause this common defect.

Cats with bobtails are called "Manx" by most laymen, as if this were a virtue. True Manx cats are a distinct breed, produced by breeding for certain "show points" and the bobtail. Indeed, not a few cats are "Manxed" with a knife when small kittens. You can tell which is which by feeling of the last bone in the tail. In a true Manx the final bone is pointed, but in the cat whose tail has been "Manxed" it is always a blunt stub.

On the other hand, cats with crooked tails inherit them. This used to be considered a virtue by Siamese-cat fanciers, who also favored cats which were cross-eyed, another hereditary anomaly. Today fanciers are trying to eliminate these oddities.

Extra toes are an abnormality. Such cats are freaks—not, as some people insist, better ratters than cats with normal feet. Many of them have claws which tend to grow into their toes, necessitating frequent clipping. Occasionally infection sets in and requires treatment. The extra toes are inherited as a Mendelian dominant characteristic.

Tortoise-shell cats are nearly always females. Some people think they must be three-colored with considerable white showing, but this is not so. The bicolored, mottled-black or red-and-yellow tiger cats are also tricolored—and, incidentally, are usually females too.

NUTRITIONAL DEFICIENCIES

Cats can suffer from the same deficiency diseases as other animals, but these diseases rarely occur, because house cats, in spite of being pampered, usually get a reasonably complete diet. Think how seldom rickets is seen in cats! Vitamin A deficiency is almost unheard of, because cats commonly are given fish and milk. Cats probably need no vitamin C. Meats and milk are rich in the vitamin-B complex. Even those cats which seem almost on the point of starvation as a result of hair balls in their stomachs —and they have been known to go for a month or more without food before the hair is finally eliminated—develop a robust appetite as soon as the mass is moved and become fat again. Anemia, except for the hookworm sort, is rare too. In my experience the only deficiency disease which occurs with any frequency is eclampsia. Mothers producing a lot of milk, yet receiving only muscle meat to eat, often develop the shivering, trembling symptoms. These are relieved, as has been pointed out earlier in this chapter, by an injection of calcium gluconate.

Although the layman seldom sees deficiencies in his pets, cats used by scientists in food studies have exhibited the same symptoms as dogs, including those of blacktongue. These studies showed that the cures were the same as for any other species—supplying the short essentials.

HEART AILMENTS

The diagnosis of heart disease in cats isn't easy even for experts. The veterinarian is trained to weigh the symptoms carefully. He listens to the heart for leaky valves and for rapidity, which he can also feel in the pulse, easily taken on the inside of the hind legs. He may watch for rapid, shallow breathing, for swelling of the legs and filling of the abdomen with blood plasma. He notices whether the pulse is feeble and thready or full and bounding. With a stethoscope he can tell if the heart is enlarged, and with an X ray he can check any findings about which he is in doubt. The layman cannot be expected to develop all these skills, of course, but he can learn to recognize some of the outward symptoms of heart disease so that he can get expert advice before the condition has progressed too far.

Enlargement. It is a simple matter to feel a cat's heart. If you place your hand beneath the cat with the fingers on one side of the chest and the thumb on the other, the pumping heart can be felt clearly, its location determined, and some idea gained of its size. If you do not know how large the heart should seem, find a sound cat for comparison. It is not unusual to find the heart enlarged to twice its normal size when the walls have become thinned. The pulse then feels weak and feeble even though the contraction is strong, because the heart muscle has not the power and resiliency it needs. Leaky valves can sometimes be felt as well as heard when the ear is pressed against the chest over the heart.

These facts are about all that the owner can learn by direct examination of his cat's heart. Beyond this he must depend upon observation of general symptoms.

Dropsy. In dropsy, the legs stock and the abdomen fills with fluid, sometimes becoming so distended that the cat may seem to be pregnant. In some cases only the abdomen fills; the legs remain normal. Frequently the cat has an abnormal thirst, in which case kidney complications can be suspected and some acidified urine boiled to test for kidney trouble. If it turns cloudy or a white precipitate forms and settles out, the prognosis is unfavorable. Such indications mean that the heart does not have the force to pump the blood through the circulatory system and back to itself. The fluid part which is left stranded in the tissues settles in the easiest places—the lower extremities and the abdomen. The red cells stay in the vessels.

The water which the cat drinks to satisfy its excessive thirst provides the system with more fluid than it needs. If the cat is allowed only small amounts of fluids, however, the tissue fluid will be resorbed into the blood and the cat will become quite normal in appearance and will feel less sluggish. Once adjusted, she must be kept on a normal fluid ration, for as soon as she has more than the body actually requires, the surplus will again produce dropsy.

Caffeine is sometimes administered as a heart stimulant, but since it has been found that caffeine tends to produce stomach ulcers in cats, it must be given sparingly. Digitalis is a good drug for the purpose. Your veterinarian or druggist can supply you with powdered digitalis or pills.

Heart Infections. Cats often develop infections which produce leaky valves. Sometimes fluids accumulate in the space between the heart and its covering (the pericardium). Such infections may eventually produce adhesions of the pericardium to the heart. In other cases infections may inflame the lining of the inside of the heart (the endocardium), with resulting rapid heartbeat and shortness of breath. Quite often this condition is associated with stiffness, indicating a joint inflammation or rheumatism. If either part of the heart is infected, the cat's temperature rises considerably and it pains her to be pressed in the region of the heart. These diseases call for professional treatment, penicillin, sulfa drugs, and patient care.

Age itself takes its toll of cats, and its effects are often seen on the heart. One has to expect very old cats to become feeble. Their hearts simply are not able to stand the strain of the activities of young cats, and as they grow older they should be treated accordingly.

RESPIRATORY AILMENTS

We have already read about the pneumonias and coryza of cats. These are the most frequent ailments of the respiratory organs. But cats do have others and, rarely, tuberculosis of the lungs (page 211).

Edema of the Lungs. Edema develops when the body is stocked with dropsical fluid and the lungs also fill up with the fluid. Shortness of breath is an important symptom of this condition. In addition to the pressure from abdominal distention, the fluid in the lungs puts a burden on the respiratory system. The fluids must be drastically withdrawn from the body with drugs like caffeine (see Dropsy). It is also imperative that water be withheld from the sufferer until most of the surplus fluid has been withdrawn from the tissues.

Emphysema. As an aftermath of diseases of the lungs—and from other unknown causes—sections of the honeycomb lung tissue break down, allowing large pockets to form. These pockets often collect mucus. When many such pockets are present, a great deal of the lung tissue is useless and the cat has to breathe faster and deeper to aerate his blood.

There is no cure for this condition, but temporary alleviation of the symptoms is possible. Doses of Fowler's solution and belladonna will often relieve a cat for a few hours. The atropine in belladonna dries up the fluid in the pockets, and the arsenic in the Fowler's solution acts as a stimulant. This treatment, however, should never be considered more than temporary relief; it is certainly not a cure.

Pleurisy. During pneumonia infection, when bacteria may have worked through the pleura or coating of the lungs, infection may pass across the chest cavity to the pleura on the rib side. In such cases the two surfaces may adhere to each other in spots when healing is completed. While the inflammation is present, an exceedingly painful pleurisy can result.

Areas of the chest cavity may become filled with fluid which the veterinarian will have to tap and draw off. Certain areas of fluid may prevent heart and lung sounds from passing clearly. When these areas are tapped with the fingers, a dull thud is heard instead of a hollow, healthy resonance. In "dry" pleurisy a sharp, sandpapery, grating sound is produced with every breath. The treatment for pleurisy is the same as for pneumonia.

Hydrothorax. Hydrothorax, or fluid in the chest cavity, follows lung infections, growths, or accidents. The cat is unable to obtain sufficient oxygen and shows symptoms of shallow breathing and, frequently, bluing of the tongue and gums. Treatment is a task for the veterinarian, who can draw off the fluid by tapping.

Tumors. Tumors in the chest cavity are not uncommon. They are difficult to diagnose but may be suspected when the cat loses weight too rapidly, has shortness of breath, and develops an abnormal spring of ribs. Tumors sometimes occur in the lungs themselves. This kind often sends out buds (metastases) which grow in other parts of the body. The conscientious cat owner should have every growth examined in a competent laboratory as soon as discovered.

EYE AILMENTS

Enlargement of the Nictitating Membrane. This is a condition, not a disease, and is usually a manifestation of other troubles. As you remember (page 47), this membrane—which is sometimes called the third eyelid—seems to rise from behind the lower lid. In a normal eye this membrane often cannot be seen at all, and when it rises up prominently, even though it is apparently not red and inflamed, it can be taken as a signal that the cat is not in perfect health. In extreme cases these "third eyelids" may rise so high as to completely cover the eye proper. More often, however, they just peek over the lower lid.

A cat with many roundworms nearly always has prominent nictitating membranes. The same is true for a cat with indigestion or constipation and for one with hair in the digestive tract. For once those who tell you this symptom is a sure sign of worms may be right—but they are not always right. If the membranes are distended with blood, swollen and unlike their normal appearance, and if the rest of the tissue inside the lids and around the eye is also red and inflamed, the cat has conjunctivitis. It may affect only one eye. Pull down the lid. It is possible that the eye has been scratched, or there may be a foreign object behind one of the lids. Have you been applying sulfur, either in dust or in liquid suspension, and allowed some to get into her eyes? Sulfur will produce just such symptoms. Has a mischievous boy with an ammonia pistol squirted some of the liquid in her face? Has a sudden blast of fresh exhaust from a car sprayed her and fumes of carbon dust and gasoline burned her? All these things happen, and they are but a few of those which could be named, beside bacteria, which commonly produce conjunctivitis.

When a cat's eyes burn, she seeks dimly lighted places. She may rub her eyes so constantly as to irritate them more. If the trouble is in only one eye, a scratch or foreign body is usually the cause.

TREATMENT: Remove the cause. If only the nictitating membranes are enlarged, have a fecal examination made and deworm the cat if necessary. It may be necessary to treat the animal for hair impaction or autointoxication. Medicines applied to the eye will not reduce enlarged nictitating membranes.

If, however, the conjunctivae are infected, scratched, or irritated, and if no veterinarian is available, apply some ophthalmic ointment, which the druggist will sell you (sulfa eye ointments are prescription drugs), and apply it to bring relief. Butyn sulfate and metaphen is an excellent remedy because, being a local anesthetic as well as bacteriostatic, it acts in two ways. Its slippery consistency lubricates the lids and helps the tears to wash out the dust or bacteria.

On rare occasions cats have one or both of the ducts which lead from the eye to the nose infected and plugged. Tears overflow the lid and moisten and soil the nose. Here again ophthalmic ointments may help to unplug the duct, but it is necessary to use them for several days and several times a day.

Corneal Diseases. Any injury, however slight, sustained by the cornea —the transparent outer front of the eyeball proper—usually causes an opacity or bluing. This is the result of the white blood cells invading the cornea, trying to protect it from disease and setting off the process of healing. The white cells, and with them the blueness, disappear as surely as they came, but not until healing is accomplished. Before whiteness begins, if you know the eye is injured by its watering, look closely for thorns, metal chips, or any tiny object penetrating the cornea. Have it removed if you can find it.

When the cornea of your cat's eye turns white, she cannot see, but she does not have a cataract. A cataract is in or on the lens and is seen only through the pupil. How long a cat will remain blind in the injured eye depends on how long healing takes. If a deep wound has filled in, the cat will generally carry the scar all through life. Whether it is in a location outside the line of vision determines whether it interferes with the cat's sight. The only treatment is applying an antiseptic eye ointment or argyrol in 5 per cent solution and waiting for the wound to heal.

Since all these afflictions cause pain, the cat should be kept out of strong light. She may manifest her pain by refusing food and hiding, pawing at her eye, and so on. A "boxing glove" can well be applied to the paw she uses.

Infections in the cornea may cause abscesses—very serious affairs which need expert attention. The whole eye may become infected and have to be removed. Or it may ulcerate because of bacterial invasion, and day by day you can watch the ulcer growing larger unless its spread is checked by drugs.

When the opacity refuses to leave, a veterinarian can often help greatly by injecting specially prepared sterile milk intramuscularly at regular intervals.

Even after healing, it is not uncommon to find the healed areas filled with pigmented cells—usually black—which remain during the cat's life. I have seen them in eyes of cats which have had only superficial corneal injuries.

Inflammation of the Eyeball. The entire eyeball may become infected. Remember what an excellent culture medium it is for certain bacteria! When it is infected, the cornea usually becomes cloudy white and enlarges, or an opening may develop so that the pus runs out and the eye collapses. Treatment usually is of little avail, although recent tests indicate that penicillin may be of value.

Glaucoma. This disease, which so far as is known is not inherited in cats, produces slow swelling until the eye bulges. The lens may drop down from the window behind which it normally lies. The internal pressure becomes greater and greater. A similar condition, called hydrophthalmus, is difficult to differentiate from glaucoma, as is an abscess which may have formed behind the eyeball, pushing it forward. In any of these conditions the cornea may appear blue. Treatment usually involves surgical removal of the eyeball.

Protruding Eyes. This condition should not be confused with the naturally prominent eyes which some cats show. In certain cases one or both eyes may be pushed forward abnormally. Such a displacement occurs when the bony arch over the eye is fractured. A tumor in the orbit behind the eyeball can also push it out. Then, too, as a result of accidents, fights, or bites, the eyeball may be knocked or pulled outside of the lids. Because of the inflammation which sets in quickly, the eye cannot be squeezed back into place. If you find a cat in this condition, smear the eyeball with vaseline or an ophthalmic ointment and rush her to the doctor, who can slit the eyelid, drop the eye in place, and suture his incision. If the muscles and optic nerve are not injured, the cat may see again.

Cross Eyes. Siamese cats are considered acceptable specimens if they have "casts" in their vision, but ordinary cats have casts or are cross-eyed only from accidents which tear eye muscles. If a protruding eye has been replaced surgically, there may have been a broken muscle, in which case the injured eye may be looking in an entirely different direction from the uninjured member.

Eyelid Maladies. Lacerations are the most frequent ailments of the lids, and those made by other cats are most common. Any sharp object which is hooked under a lid may tear it so that it must be sutured. Every such wound should have attention. The natural healing process may close the tear, but the lid will usually have a notched, uneven edge. The result will be an ugly, jagged scar which will greatly detract from the cat's appearance.

General inflammation of the lid is seen occasionally. It is caused by fungus infection, sarcoptic mange mites, bacteria, or scratches. Appropriate treatment for each will bring about a prompt cure if the cat will leave her eyes alone. If she insists on rubbing them, it may be necessary to apply an Elizabethan collar.

EAR AILMENTS

Canker and Ear Mites. Canker is a term covering many ear infections which manifest themselves by the accumulation of excess waxy secretions. It may be due to dirt or irritation caused by bacterial growth. Canker can be recognized by a cheesy odor, a gummy wax in the ear, and frequent scratching. Ear mites, which cause the same symptoms, usually produce a drier, grayer, crumbly wax with less or no odor. By their irritation, which often drives a cat frantic, they cause symptoms or general sickness, with loss of appetite, loss of weight, and frequently hematomas in the ear flap, from the batting and bruising of the ear when the cat scratches it.

The mites are easily distinguished through a reading glass. If a little of the crumbly wax is mixed in some mineral oil and spread on a piece of glass it can be examined with the reading glass. Even a magnification of eight times will enlarge the mites sufficiently to make them visible as moving dust particles. A veterinarian can diagnose them at 140 magnifications so that they look like crabs, and their eggs, too, are visible. Often when mites are not found in profusion the eggs alone are sufficient for diagnosis.

Canker can generally be cured by flushing out the wax with alcohol and ether and applying a sulfa-drug solution in propylene glycol into the ear canal; some veterinarians prefer an oily base with an antiseptic.

To cure mite infestation the ear may be flushed with peroxide, or a mixture of ether and alcohol, to dissolve the wax. This should be followed by an oily solution, or propylene glycol (also an excellent wax solvent) containing an insecticide such as rotenone or luidance. The mites are usually killed with one application, but a few may still be on the hair around the ear flap. These mites can crawl back inside the ear after the insecticide has been eliminated and start the infestation again. Treatment once a week for three weeks will effect a cure, but the cat must be watched so that companion cats will not reinfest the cured one.

If the cat's ear flap itches, it may have skin disease, the outer edge may be crusted, and a thickened fluid-filled lump (hematoma) may develop in it. These must all be treated by a veterinarian. Hematomas require prompt treatment or they may cause a cauliflower ear.

If water runs into the ears of the cat during bathing, it will not cause canker. The ear has a lining of wax which helps to protect it.

To cure persistent canker, the chronic, seemingly incurable kind, an operation has been devised which consists of opening the ear canal to its lowest point on the side of the face and suturing the skin to the skin lining of this canal. A V-shaped opening is thus left, from which the discharge can drain and into which air can penetrate. The surgeon may find that irritation has continued for so long that the canal is solid and the cartilage may have turned to bone. The owner will at least have access to the area and can flush it daily so that the infection itself can be eliminated.

Hematomas. Hematomas—blood tumors—are common in cats' ear flaps. Causes have been discussed above, and treatment is described on page 145.

SKIN AILMENTS

Your veterinarian should be able to give you a remedy to be applied externally for the control and cure of both forms of eczema, unless complications such as we have mentioned have set in.

Ringworm. This skin ailment is easy to detect because it grows in such neat areas with well-defined boundaries. Many persons believe that it grows in a perfect circle. It may, in fact, be quite irregular, but tends to grow in an oval. When it reaches a certain size, the infection stops spreading, the hair falls out, and the area becomes cured automatically.

Soon after it appears in a new place. In severe infections the areas may run together into one large spot. Frequently, the first noticeable spots are under the short hair of the face, but it may appear anywhere on the body. Short-haired cats are more susceptible to ringworm than long-haired breeds.

Another way to find out if the cat's infection is caused by ringworm organisms is to examine the members of the family. It has been my experience that in most cases the cat has contracted ringworm from a person. They spread it, too, to other cats, to dogs, and to children and adults as well. Ringworm is caused by a definite fungus and is easy to cure. Iodine and glycerine is an old familiar remedy which stops the growth of the fungus. The only difficulty in treating ringworm is in trying to prevent new spots from forming. Fungicides, when applied liberally, can be quite effective in preventing any further spread. Powders containing fungicides can be used liberally and are the simplest method of ending the infection. These can be bought in nearly any pet shop or drug store.

Sarcoptic Mange. This is a skin disease which quite definitely is transmitted back and forth from man to cat. (For the life history of the causative mite see page 83.) After World War II many soldiers came home with the itchy patches on their arms or legs and frequently their cats contracted it from them. It is now becoming less and less common.

At first glance, without a microscopic study, sarcoptic mange resembles dry eczema. The hair falls out, leaving bald areas which become inflamed from the irritation and itch intensely, often forming small scales. Experienced cat breeders and even veterinarians have difficulty in telling these two ailments apart. Because of the similarity of symptoms in the two diseases, the diagnosis should not be considered complete before a careful microscopic study has been made.

Finding the mites for the microscopic test is not an easy matter. The following procedure should be followed: a fold of skin in the infected area should be squeezed and a sharp scalpel or knife scraped across it. This scurfskin should be discarded. The fold should then be pinched harder until serum exudes, and scraped again. This material should be saved on a microscope slide. This whole process should be repeated in several places. The accumulated substance should then be mixed on the slide with a few drops of mineral oil. The mixture is spread thin and studied under the microscope for mites. If none is found, it is sometimes profitable to try again. Sarcoptic mange mites are much more difficult to find than the mites causing red mange, which will be considered next.

Once it has been diagnosed, there are few skin diseases easier to cure than sarcoptic mange. Lard and sulphur was one of the old remedies. Even axle grease and finely powdered sulphur will effect a cure. Every drug store carries several effective sarcoptic mange remedies.

Eczema. Actually eczema, in the true sense of the word, does not exist. The word "eczema" is derived from the Greek "to boil out," and the old idea was that food somehow heated the blood, causing the blood to boil and come through the skin as a rash. We still hear the absurd phrase used in describing certain foods, "they are too heatening to the blood." It is strange that even today it is necessary to repeat: Blood does not overheat; it does not boil out.

There is a skin disease, however, that is characterized by *moist* discharges which scale over. These cause itching, and the cat constantly scratches and chews at the affected area. This disease is generally called eczema, even though the name is inappropriate. In other cases a condition of dryness (as contrasted with the moist form) occurs and causes itching. It spreads rapidly and the hair falls out. This condition is often called dry eczema—again badly named.

Both dry and moist eczema are found on cats of all breeds. They occur most often in the warm, damp days of summer, just when fleas are starting to be most prevalent. For this reason it has been thought that the eczema is caused by insect bites which irritate the skin areas. When the cat chews these areas they become even moister. In these spots the fungus spores find a perfect place to incubate and are the principal cause of the disease. This seems to be proved by the fact that fungicides generally cure the infection quite simply, and insecticides combined with fungicides seem to help greatly in preventing the infections from starting. The whole story of the cause of exzema is not yet known. Possibly many organisms are responsible for eczema, and even viruses may yet be found among them.

Red Mange. This is a serious disease. Up to only a few years ago the appearance or a spot of any size was sufficient reason for destroying the animal. Veterinarians would sometimes cut the spots out like cancer and hope that no mites were left. Many animals were killed to prevent the spread of the disease, but with the discovery of effective modern remedies, the disease has lost its terror.

Red mange (demodectic or follicular mange) starts so innocuously that the cat owner pays very little attention to it. In our hospital we show the newly infected areas to the owners far more frequently than they show them to us. We usually discover them when the cats have been brought in for some other ailment.

Red mange nearly always starts with a baldish spot on the face or forelegs, though exceptions are numerous. The spot spreads and the hair comes off. Other spots of irregular shape appear and form large areas. The skin begins to itch; the scratching and the mites cause inflammation. The skin thickens and reddens, finally becoming raw. The name red mange fits it perfectly at this stage. Until this point is reached, however, owners can scarcely believe their cats have it.

Red mange is a strange malady. Cattas who have only a mild case will sometimes pass the infection on to their kittens. I told the owner of one catta to cure such a mild case before he bred his pet. He did nothing about it and only two of the six kittens contracted it. Even they died needlessly, though. They would not have been infected if their mother had been cured.

Can people catch red mange? Dermatologists say that they can. The infection starts on the cheeks next to the nose. How long can the mites live away from the cat? Probably not for more than three days, so it is certainly safe to bring a new cat into a home where a cat previously had red mange a week after the first cat has gone.

Diagnosis with a microscope is simple. Follow the same procedure as for the miscroscopic test for sarcoptic mange. The cigar-shaped insects are easily visible at 100 magnifications.

Curing the disease is relatively simple now that we have rotenone, DDT, and lindane. If any one of these drugs is mixed with a good penetrating oil or a salve, it will kill the mites in the follicles. It is a little difficult to discover the new areas. Some new data seems to indicate that a heavy dusting with a good flea powder containing rotenone will keep new areas from becoming infested while the known areas of infestation are being treated.

Dandruff. This is a term used to designate constant flaking of the skin. All cats, like all human beings, are constantly shedding off the outer layer of the skin which is being replaced as the skin grows outward. Some cat owners are concerned when they find even a small number of scales. It appears to be a normal occurrence and a good brushing with a coarse brush will very often rid the hair of flakes. If the cat is scratching, however, it is another matter, and an infection such as we have considered is probably the cause. Often cat owners are advised to feed cod-liver oil, wheat-germ oil, and raw eggs, and told not to feed starchy foods. Vitamins are concerned with skin health, to be sure, but special food supplements seldom effect cures. Some of the unsaturated fatty acids, certain building blocks of fat, are necessary for skin health in rats and children, but whether these food ingredients help coat health in cats remains to be proved.

Dandruff seems to be seasonal with some cats, causing them to shed skin scales at certain times of the year and not at others. You may read that the use of crude caustic soaps or the dry atmosphere of a heated room will produce dandruff. Yet cats treated with the daintiest soaps may be the worst offenders. Again it is said that the dry atmosphere of a heated house is conducive to dandruff; yet it is seen in outdoor cats which are seldom in heated rooms. It appears to be a normal occurrence, and, as we have seen, it can be helped by hard, vigorous brushing.

In treating cats for any skin disease, remember that they are inclined to lick themselves. By all means cut an Elizabethan collar from two pieces of stiff cardboard and apply it so that the cat cannot reach the medicated areas with her tongue. If she does manage to get a little on her paws she will suffer no ill effects from what she licks and the medicine will have an opportunity to do its work unmolested. A mixture of olive or cottonseed oil and finely ground sulphur often cures a cat of fungus diseases in a week. Many proprietary mixtures can be obtained in pet and drug stores. Be sure you read the label. You may read on the label that a medicine called "Mange Remedy" is effective only in treating sarcoptic mange and may have no efficacy whatever in the treatment of fungus disease. Other remedies may be indicated as valuable in the treatment of fungus or at least may contain a fungicide. The latter is preferable. Better still, let your veterinarian prescribe. He will probably save you money, time, and needless worry.

Anal Gland Involvement. If your cat twitches or chews on his tail, appears unnecessarily nervous, sometimes jumping up suddenly and running across the room for no good reason, or licks under his tail, investigate to determine if the anal glands may not be infected. These two small glands are part of the skin and are situated just under the anus, one on each side. Their secretions are passed out of the body through ducts which discharge into the mouth of the anus. The normal secretion of the glands is yellowish and oily looking, but when bacteria cause infection, the glands may become filled with nasty, purulent, blackish, brownish, or bloody material.

To relieve the cat of this infection, use the following method: Place him on a table and have an assistant hold his head and shoulders tightly against the table. With your left hand lift the tail straight up, holding it close to the base. With a piece of cotton held in your right hand, squeeze just below the anus. The contents of the glands will be expelled into the piece of cotton. This should be repeated once a week until no more infected matter can be expressed.

GROWTHS

Cats are subject to many kinds of growths, but probably to not such a variety as affects dogs. For example, my own experience indicates that the incidence of cancer in cats is far below that in dogs or mice.

Enlargement of glands and formation of salivary cysts is common, goiter is occasionally seen, and hernias are no rarity, especially hernias due to injuries and wounds inflicted by dogs. Abscesses which swell and burst, liberating creamy or bloody pus, occur after cat fights with considerable frequency. All these maladies can be easily recognized. Only the last should be treated by the home veterinarian. The hair is clipped off the area to be incised—the top of the abscess where the skin is thinnest—a sharp knife blade is inserted, and the incision slit long enough to permit its being kept open.

The pus is squeezed out and the abscess then flushed with a good antiseptic. Hydrogen peroxide will serve the purpose. It had best be flushed daily until healing is complete. The central opening is not allowed to heal until last.

19. What You Can and Cannot Catch from Your Cat

*N*EARLY every cat owner wonders, at some time during his or her cat ownership, whether there is any danger that cats can transmit diseases. The answer is yes, they can. I think, though, that the danger to cats from human contact is even greater. I have seen cats infected by their owners with ringworm and sarcoptic mange more often than the reverse.

By combing the medical literature for reports of authentic instances where cats have infected human beings, you can find an impressive list. The list can also be quite frightening if you forget that in most cases the diseases are extremely rare. It was nearly always quite a surprise to find that the person had the disease and even more of a surprise to find that he "caught it" from a cat. The following diseases can be contagious: tularemia, rabies, rat bite fever, cat scratch fever, virus pneumonia, ornathosis, diphtheria, tuberculosis, brucellosis, typhus, pasteurellosis, ringworm, scabies, creeping eruption, favus, amebiasis, salmonellosis, trypanosomiasis, leishmaniasis, dog tapeworm infestation, fish tapeworm, liver fluke, episthorchiasis, schistosomiasis, strongyloidosis, scrub typhus, leptospirosis.

We also find other cases in which cats are suspected of having infected human beings. The suspicion in each case is based on the fact that cat and man were in close contact and both had the same disease: leptospirosis, plague, or histoplasmosis.

Are there any diseases in the above list which you, as a cat owner, really know anything about? Have you ever, among all of your acquaintances, known of a single person having contracted a disease from his or her cat? Let us consider several of these diseases whose transmission has been determined possible.

On the basis of my own experience with thousands of cats and their owners, the following, from the impressive list of possibly transmissible diseases, represent those to be watched for: rabies, tuberculosis, virus pneumonia, scabies, ringworm, and cat scratch fever. In Chapter 4 you will find these diseases—except cat scratch fever—described as they affect cats. Here we consider their danger to human beings.

RABIES

Rabies contracted from rabid cats is unknown in many sections of the world but the disease is a real danger where rabies is prevalent. If you live in a section where rabies is often found, and your cat begins to act abnormally, hides and sulks, take the necessary precautions. Put the cat in a room by itself and watch it carefully. Do not handle it. Perhaps it is only coincidence, but in cases in which human beings contracted the disease from cats, every one was bitten by a cat which previously had become asocial and wanted to hide. Possibly it was under the sofa and the cat charged suddenly and bit the person's leg. Possibly it was in the tall grass behind the house and, as the person walked near where the sick cat was hiding, it sprang, bit and scratched the person's calf or ankle.

TUBERCULOSIS

Tuberculosis definitely can be contracted from cats but usually it is the bovine form, not the human. Cats living in contact with cattle, walking in their mangers, breathing their breath, drinking raw milk from cattle whose udders have tubercular lesions, can transmit the disease to humans. Cats which unaccountably cough or grow thin can be tuberculin tested. If they test positive, they should be destroyed mercifully. In fact, when they are a public danger, they should be eliminated just as the United States government destroys every cow which proves to be a "reactor."

VIRUS PNEUMONIA

Virus pneumonia may be a far greater danger than has been realized to date. Since there is more than one form of the disease no cat which is sick with virus pneumonia—the Baker, the Yale, or ornithosis form—should be kept where a human being might contract it. However, we need not destroy the cat since aureomycin now does such an excellent job of curing many of the cases and renders the pet safe to have around.

CAT SCRATCH FEVER

Cat scratch fever had a great deal of publicity in the newspapers in 1951 and 1952. Again it makes news because it is so unusual—the commonplace things never do. It is a case of "man bites dog." Cat scratch fever is probably a virus disease, although as yet—in 1953—the virus has not been isolated.

The symptoms of cat scratch fever in a human being begin with a painless swelling in the lymphatic glands near the scratch a few days after the scratch is received. These glands are located in many places both inside and outside of the body cavity. Those under the skin can be felt in the throat, the neck, under the arms, and in the groin. The infection often spreads to all the lymph glands. The body temperature rises and there is general ill feeling. Sometimes the glands break down and suppurate and the skin may show pustular eruptions. The person recovers spontaneously and, according to one investigator, administration of aureomycin hastens recovery.

One of the strange facts about cat scratch fever is that cats themselves cannot be infected with the virus, but seem to be merely bearers of it. Every cat whose scratch has infected a man or woman was found to be healthy.

SARCOPTIC MANGE

After World War II many returning soldiers brought with them the sarcoptic mange mite which causes scabies. This brought about an outbreak of mange among cats which took some years to diminish. There was no question that this was a case where man infected cats. It was so common that it made no news. It happens occasionally today that infected cats spread the disease to human beings, the infection usually appearing on the arms or neck as itchy red areas. When such areas do appear the cat should be carefully examined. If he scratches himself, look for areas where the hair appears thin and the skin slightly thickened with little scabs on its surface which may be felt through the hair. If you find these symptoms, then look out: Have your cat's skin examined by your veterinarian. That may tell you why you too have itchy spots.

It is now easy to cure scabies in humans but not in cats. A hot bath followed by an application of Lindane in a vanishing cream base cures it. This must be ruled out as a treatment for cats because they lick the Lindane and become sickened.

RINGWORM

By all odds, the most commonly transmissible disease from cat to man is ringworm. Many a cat shows no evidence of the disease, yet passes it on to every member of the family. This is especially true in the case of long-haired cats. If ringworm suddenly starts with its reddish round or oval spots, and your physician is sure of his diagnosis, then examine the cats with meticulous care. Even if you did not contract it from them, you are almost certain to transmit it to them and, even after you are cured, they will continue to infect you.

Ringworm is easy to cure on man and cats if the proper mixture of drugs is used. In fact, a large number of our clients have, on their own responsibility, used the remedy which was given them at the Whitney Veterinary Clinic for their cats and speedily cured themselves and children as well as the cats.

LEPTOSPIROSIS

This is one of the few diseases, probably rare in cats, which we may contract from our pets. You will hear much more about it in the future. At present it is being studied and appears to be of small concern to cat owners because its effects on cats are not severe and it is quite probable that cats have the disease and recover without their owners realizing that their pets are sick.

Leptospirosis is caused by a spiral-shaped bacterium which may enter the body through the mouth or the genital organs. It is being recognized as a much more common disease of cattle than had been suspected and is transmitted via milk or urine. Cats drinking unpasteurized milk can contract it; barn cats are often exposed to the disease.

Cases severe enough to be recognized generally show jaundice. Although two forms of the disease are recognized—the jaundice-hemorrhage and the canicola—they are difficult to distinguish. They have not as yet been sufficiently studied in cats for us to be able to state which form is more prevalent. In human beings the canicola form of the disease often passes for influenza.

Of all the other diseases in the transmissible list, tularemia is a good illustration of how little we have to worry about. Although it is considered primarily a rabbit disease, yet only three cases of tularemia were diagnosed in the State Health Laboratory in Connecticut—all in cats. Three cats out of the thousands in that state is indeed a very small percentage.

Actually then, we have little to fear from our cats so far as the transmission of diseases is concerned.

20. Heredity in Cats

*J*UDGING by the few breeds of cats to be found in the world today, the average cat fancier in the past has known and cared little about heredity. It has, of course, been difficult to know much about their heredity because of the elusive habits of cats during the mating period. Today, however, cat breeders are clamoring to know how to improve their strains. They want to be able to tell in advance the outcome of proposed matings. No doubt, cat shows should be credited with stimulating some of this desire for information. Pride in ownership also has a lot to do with it, as does the financial aspect of cat breeding. Cat breeders know that certain colors are more popular than others in certain sections and they want to be sure to produce the most popular colors. Many persons, too, prefer to breed for specific forms of cats such as Manx cats and cats with extra toes.

A number of highly unfactual ideas about heredity have been bequeathed to us by our fathers, and some of them are still widely revered as scientific facts. To understand the essentials of the science of genetics, we must first rid our minds of these ideas and, secondly, we must adopt the scientific method of thinking.

The scientist is a doubter. The fact that a self-constituted "authority" said or wrote in the past that a given statement was true means nothing to him. He knows that having written it doesn't make it true unless facts substantiate what has been written. *Truth is opinion which has been verified by test to conform to nature.*

Another difficult but necessary step for the layman is to rid his mind of the false idea that, because one event follows another, the first was necessarily the cause of the second. Simple minds are nourished on that kind of reasoning. Someone sits in a draft and a day or two later develops a cold; therefore, the draft caused the cold. We forget that millions of people sit in drafts every day without developing colds.

The scientist keeps accurate, usually mathematical, records, and that

helps him with his work. Keeping records is particularly important in un-
covering the facts of heredity. The scientist formulates a hypothesis and
then assembles all the facts *on both sides*—those which show it to be true
and those which show it to be wrong. When he has all his facts, he says,
"My data seem to show such and such to be the case." The scientist never
rationalizes—that is, tries to show that what he wants to believe is true.

Remembering this, let us consider the wrong ideas about heredity which
were bequeathed to us. These are the discarded, erstwhile "facts" on which
to place no reliance; each of them illustrates fallacious reasoning; they
failed, when tested, to correspond with nature. If you still firmly believe
in one or more of these ideas, you had probably best study the facts a
little more.

1. Birthmarking. If a cat who has been raised in a room with a colony
of rabbits gives birth to a litter of kittens that hop like rabbits, it does not
mean that constantly seeing the rabbits caused her to mark her embryonic
kittens. Nor was she mated with a buck rabbit, as some theorists have
insisted. Her kittens are not "cabbits," a name coined by those who mistakenly believe that a cat and a rabbit can mate. The frights or other
experiences of the mother during pregnancy are not transmitted to the
offspring. Disregard these ideas.

2. Prenatal influence. The belief is still widespread that if a pregnant
cat is taught many tricks or is starved so that she will become an excellent
ratter or mouser, she will tend to impress her kittens through the exercise
of these learned abilities, and they will be more easily taught tricks or will
be better ratters. Books have been written on this subject to prove the idea,
but when scientists, by scientific methods, began to test it, they soon
learned that all the effort spent by animal owners who believed in this
false principle was completely wasted. All it did was to help in the selection of more vigorous animals.

3. Telegony. The fact that cattas produce great variation among kittens
has often been said to be the result of earlier matings to a male of a different breed or to a mongrel whose influence was said to carry over to the
later ones. Literally, millions of worthwhile brood females have been unnecessarily destroyed because of such accidental matings. Perhaps this
antiquated idea has made owners more careful in the choice of mates for
their catta, but it has also done tremendous damage. There isn't a word
of truth in it, as far as science can demonstrate.

4. Blooded inheritance. Nearly all breeders still talk about pure-blooded
cats, blue-blooded cats, cats with the blood of some famous cat ancestor
coursing through their veins. We have come to use the word *blood* to
mean heredity, and, because it gives us such a completely erroneous picture, it would seem best to discontinue its use in this respect. We know
today that blood has nothing to do with heredity; its only function is to
nourish and protect the embryo. Even the blood with which a kitten is
born is lost in a few months and a new supply manufactured, a process
continual throughout life. A pure-blooded cat is one with clean blood.

When we want to talk about heredity, we should say the cat is purebred, not pure-blooded.

GERM PLASM

The complete heritage of the offspring is contained within the sperm cell of the male and the egg or ovum of the female; from here on let us consider some of the essentials modern science has uncovered to help you understand better the complicated process of hereditary transmission of characteristics.

As long as man has been able to observe, he has noted that certain characteristics seem to skip a generation, but he couldn't explain how or why. He invented strange theories, some of which seem logical but which, we have seen, were not borne out by facts. What we know today makes us realize that the *germ plasm* contained in the male's testicles and the female's ovaries is the basic reason for the animal's existence. He lives in order to perpetuate his heredity. The germ plasm is an endless stream of life that goes on from generation to generation, regardless of the appearance of the individuals which carry it.

The germ plasm usually goes on for generations without changing at all or only in the very slightest degree. The sudden changes such as taillessness or extra toes are called mutations. When such a change proves to be hereditary (a change in the germ plasm), fits the environment, and helps the animal or, at least, does not hinder it, the change in the germ plasm will be perpetuated. However, mankind has seized upon these mutations, often curiosities which are detrimental to the cat under natural conditions, and by selective breeding has incorporated them into the strain. A good illustration is the Pekingese face which one finds in some Persian strains, or the blue-eyed white cat—both of which mankind perpetuates as a fancy, not for any particular value to himself or the cat.

GENES AND CHROMOSOMES

Every hereditary characteristic is determined by a pair of *genes*—certain little packets of chemicals in the germ plasm. If you will keep this fact in mind, it will help you to understand heredity. At certain times during division of the cells, the genes congregate into strings called *chromosomes;* these, too, are in pairs. When the sperm are formed in the male testicle, each sperm has half the number of chromosomes required for the new offspring. That is the male's part in heredity. The female egg also contributes half the necessary number of chromosomes. When the two join, therefore, the new embryo has the total number—getting half its characteristics from each parent.

Why then, you may ask, does he seem to favor one parent more than the other? This is because certain of the genes are dominant over others.

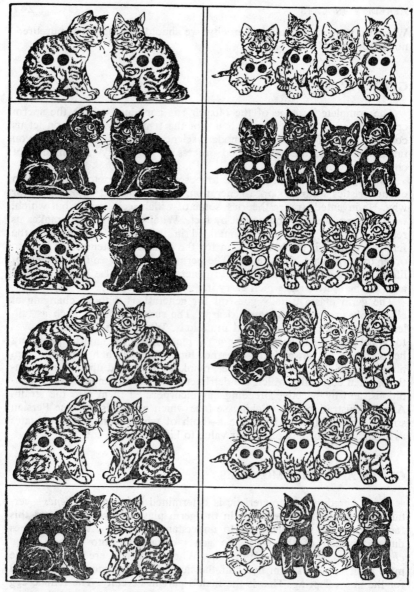

The six possible ways in which individual characteristics may be inherited. Black dots (genes) represent dominant characteristics (in this case tabby color); white dots represent recessive genes. Cats with either one or both black dots appear as tabby. The recessive (black) must have a pair of white dots. A cat having one white and one black is a hybrid and capable of transmitting the recessive character if it mates with another carrying the recessive.

Suppose we mate a pure black cat, that is, one with two genes for black, with a pure tiger cat, that is, one with two genes for tiger. The kittens will have one gene for tiger and one for black and will be tiger cats because the banded hair is dominant over black. Now suppose two of these tigers, each of which carries a black gene in its germ plasm, are mated. What the kittens will look like is just a matter of chance.

You can conduct a little experiment to see the results for yourself. Place in a container twelve black marbles, representing the tiger pattern, and twelve white marbles, representing the black pattern. Without looking, reach in and pick out two marbles. Keep picking, two at a time, until there are none left. Keep a record of what you got each time. The expectancy is three pairs of blacks, three pairs of whites, and six pairs of white and black.

You may not get these results in one experiment, but if you will try it ten or twelve times you have large enough numbers to find that you have definitely realized this expectancy.

The results of the marbles test are what you can expect in breeding the cats we have been discussing—three purebred black kittens, three purebred tiger kittens, and six tiger kittens carrying a recessive gene for black. Obviously you can't tell what you will get unless you have a record of which characters are dominant and which recessive.

The subject of genetics becomes a little more complicated when we consider two characteristics instead of one. We know that short hair is dominant over long hair. Suppose we mate a pure black, long-haired cat with a pure tiger-striped, short-haired cat. Tiger, being dominant, is represented by T; black, being recessive, by t. We represent short hair by L and long hair by l for the same reason. To predict the results of the mating, we have to compute, on the basis of chance, all the combinations of these two traits in the germ plasm.

One cat is LT, that is, short-haired and tiger-striped; the other is lt—long-haired and black. The progeny will have one of each of these genes, so they will be LlTt.

Now, let's theoretically mate two of these kittens when they grow up. What can we expect: Again, this is a matter of mathematical chance. What will the sperm and eggs carry in the way of genes for these four characteristics that we are considering? Each will carry the following assortment of genes: LT-Lt-lT-lt. The simplest way to see what will happen is to make a checkerboard like that shown below, putting the genes of the sperm along the top and the genes of the egg along the side, and then filling in the squares where the two cross. Altogether, we have sixteen possibilities. These represent the chances for each kitten carrying the four genes.

We find that we have nine possibilities which are represented by the two dominants LT, three by Lt, three by lT, and one by lt. Our two hybrid kittens, therefore, can produce kittens in the following expectancy—nine short-haired tiger-striped, three short-haired black, three long-haired

tiger-striped, and one long-haired black. Because we know which traits
are dominant and which recessive we know what we can expect.

In the same way you can determine the expectancy where three characteristics are considered simultaneously, but this makes a table of sixty-
four squares, and the ratio on the basis of appearance works out twenty-

Sperm Genes

		LT	Lt	lT	lt
Egg Genes	**LT**	LT LT	Lt LT	lT LT	lt LT
	Lt	LT Lt	Lt Lt	lT Lt	lt Lt
	lT	LT lT	Lt lT	lT lT	lt lT
	lt	LT lt	Lt lt	lT lt	lt lt

seven, nine, nine, nine, three, three, three, one. If you are interested in
mathematics, you will enjoy such computation.

This method also shows how traits appear to skip a generation. The
dominant traits always mask the recessive. When in the next generation
the individual has two recessive genes, he shows the recessive trait and
thus takes after one of his grandparents. The trait, therefore, seems to
skip a generation.

WHAT DETERMINES SEX—SEX LINKAGE

The chromosomes determine sex as well as other characteristics but in
quite a different way. Among the many pairs of chromosomes in the individual there is one pair which contains the sex-determining chromosomes. In the male these two chromosomes are unlike. Geneticists call one
chromosome X; the other Y. In the female they are always alike—the
catta always has a pair of Y chromosomes. Therefore, the sex chromosomes of the male are XY, of the female YY.

Remember that each sperm has only one chromosome of a pair. Half
the sperms will have an X chromosome and the other half will have a Y
chromosome. Since the female has two Y chromosomes, all the female
eggs will have Y. There is a 50–50 chance that an egg will unite with an
X bearing sperm. If the X bearing sperm unites with an egg, the kitten
will be male; if a Y bearing sperm unites with the egg it will be a female.

The sex chromosomes also contain genes that determine other characteristics. One of these, borne on the Y chromosome, is for orange color.

A recent theory to explain tortoiseshell seems to be the best; when a tom has a gene for orange, the black-producing gene is masked. When a catta has two genes for orange, the black is also masked. But when a catta has one gene for orange on a Y chromosome, the black is not masked entirely and the result is a tortoiseshell.

For those who want to go a little more deeply into the genetics of cats, the following information should prove helpful. First keep in mind what a wild-type cat looks like. It is a tiger-striped animal (tabby) with yellow as well as gray in the banded hairs. But it is not the banding alone which makes the stripes, for if you will inspect a tabby, you will find some black-tipped hairs in the light stripes.

COLOR CLASSIFICATION

We will need to know what the colors are and how they are classified before we can see how they are inherited.

The Tabby Cat. Tabbies are found to be of three basic types:

1. Stripes narrow, close, clear. Hairs are banded with gray and black. This pattern is often called the Abyssinian, although Abyssinian is also the name of a breed. The genetic symbol is T^1.

2. Medium wide striped with fairly clear, black stripes. The genetic symbol is T^2.

3. Blotched, stripes few, broken up. The genetic symbol is T^3. Tabbies may be black, blue, orange, or cream.

The Black Cat. As mutations of the germ plasm occurred and bred true, cats showed different coloration. Black, for instance, is simply a loss of the hair banding. Genetic symbol is t.

The Orange and the Tortoiseshell Cats. A good show-type tortoiseshell has clear, distinct spots of red and black. A tortoise-and-white is black and red, with white spots—the famous "three-color cat." If the cat carries the tabby gene, it will be tabby striped (one without the tabby gene would be black). If it carries the dilution gene, it can be blue tabby and cream and still be a tortoiseshell.

The orange cat is one which came from another mutation. Orange cats are black cats with the black masked or repressed by orange-producing genes. They are often called yellow cats and may be tabby or nontabby.

The Blue and the Cream Cats. In the germ plasm there is a pair of genes which determine whether the color shall be full expression or be diluted. The black and orange cats show the full expression of their color (D). But if they carry a pair of dilution genes (dd), these cats will be

Major coat colors of short-haired cats. Except for the white spotting, these same colors are found in long-hairs.

Left to right, top row: blotched tabby; wide-striped tabby; narrow-striped tabby. Second row: black; blue. Third row: black with small white spot; black with white collar; mostly white tabby. Bottom row: chinchilla; smoke.

Left to right, top row: blotched red tabby; wide stripe red tabby; narrow stripe red tabby. Second row: solid red; solid cream. Third row: tortoise with small white spot; tortoise with white collar; mostly white tortoise. Bottom row: seal point Siamese; blue point Siamese; Burmese.

respectively blue (Maltese) or cream. These dilution genes apply equally to cats with or without tabby stripes. A tabby with the dilution genes will be blue striped instead of black; and the orange will become cream striped. This must not be confused with silver, which is produced by an altogether different pair of genes.

The "Siamese"-Colored Cat.   We are not going to consider the breed—just a color (c^h)—because that color can be, by breeding, transferred to any breed. Long-haired cats with typical Siamese markings are already in existence.

Students of heredity consider the Siamese to be part of an albino series —imperfect albinos. The cat with albino genes has no color. The Siamese has weakened color-producing genes, but not total absence. The Burmese (c^H) has more color. The silver is a light tabby.

The Siamese and Burmese have light bodies and modified black ears, nose, feet, and tail. When a pair of dilution genes are also present, the points of the Siamese become blue. This explains the *seal-point* and the *blue-point* patterns. How can we explain the *orange-point* Siamese? The very fact that such cats have been deliberately created shows that the Siamese is a color pattern. If, by selective breeding, the orange color has been substituted for the imperfect black (seal), then the cat is an orange Siamese. Those so far produced do not yet all look like pure Siamese in body shape or hair texture, but it will not be long before such cats can be typical Siamese, if breeders want them.

A Siamese crossed with a black cat appears black but the undercoat is grayish. This is an important fact to know because it can help to determine the paternity of a cat.

The Smoke Cat.   This is a silver (C^{ch}) lacking the tabby gene. The smoke color in a short-haired cat lacks the typical appearance of the long hair. The blending effect of long hairs which become intertwined produce the true smokey effect.

The White Cat.   We have three kinds of white cats:

1. The pink-eyed albino (c) (very rare). This is a cat with absence of color.

2. The white cat with pigmented eyes. The genetic symbol is W. In this group we find blue- and green-eyed cats and, not infrequently, cats with one green and one blue eye. I personally have known of six such cats. Blue-eyed whites are frequently deaf. Some students consider them partial albinos. True albino cats, however, are not deaf.

3. The white-spotted cat. White spotting is produced by a distinct gene or group of genes whose genetic symbol is S. We recognize three types of spotting (actually it is difficult to find a cat without at least one white hair): The cat with a white spot on the chest (S^1). The general white collar pattern, consisting of a band of white over the neck, white on the chest and about half way up each leg, a white tip on the tail, and a white

blaze on the face has the genetic symbol of S^2. Lastly, we have the pattern of large areas of white which produce the effect of pigmented areas appearing as color spots on a white background (S^3).

GENETIC SYMBOLS

Some geneticists use the symbol A for tabby, and the lack of it a. The a then stands for black. Others use T for tabby hair banding and t for the lack of hair banding. We shall use T for tabby because there are orange tabbies with lines as distinct as those on black and gray tabbies. Then too, there are orange cats with no tabby markings. You will see how easy it is to use symbols in predicting the outcome of any mating. The dominant character or gene is always represented by a capital; the recessive by a small letter.

> T—tabby banded hairs
> t—lack of tabby (black, blue, red, and cream)
>
> > Dominant in this order:
> > T^1—blotched
> > T^2—wide striped
> > T^3—narrow striped
>
> W—white (dominant)
> w—pigmented
>
> Y—orange (or yellow)
> y—not orange
>
> D—natural expression of color
> d—dilute
>
> C—full color
> C^{ch}—silver
> c—albino
> c^h—Siamese
> c^H—Burmese
>
> White spotting series—dominant in this order:
> > S^1—small amount
> > S^2—moderate amount
> > S^3—large amount
>
> H—normal hair
> h—hairlessness

L—short hair
l—long hair

P—polydactyl (extra toes)
p—normal

R—normal eye
r—ruby eye

The table of symbols tells us what to expect from any mating. The explanation of what the symbols represent will be found in the description of coat characteristics on pages 251–255. Now let us make practical application of this seemingly theoretical material.

COLOR INHERITANCE

The tabby and the black constitute a series. The banded hairs and striped effect, as we saw, constitute the natural color (TT), but when the cat inherits a pair of genes for the loss of banding (tt), he or she is a black. The chart on page 248 clearly shows the six possible ways in which this pair of characteristics can be inherited.

When a pair of dilution genes (dd) are put with the tabby or black, the kittens will be blues (Maltese).

When the catta has a pair of genes for orange, it will mask the black, when she has one, she will be a tortoiseshell. If the tom has even one gene for orange it will produce orange kittens or, in rare instances, tortoiseshell.

The tortoiseshell toms, when fertile, seem to produce kittens of orange color rather than tortoise. One such tom sired 56 kittens. Of the progeny from his matings with a black catta, 13 were black toms, 14 tortoiseshell cattas, and 1 black catta. Matings to a yellow catta produced 9 yellow toms, 8 yellow cattas, and 1 yellow with black spots. Matings with another tortoiseshell produced 1 black tom, 2 yellow toms, 5 yellow cattas, and 2 tortoiseshell cattas.

A Siamese mated to a black produces black kittens with grayish undercoat showing the black to be almost dominant over the Siamese. Two of these kittens, when mated, can produce the Siamese color in 25 per cent of their kittens.

Black is dominant over every color but tabby, red, or the dominant white.

Dominant white is dominant over all other colors.

The lesser amount of white on white-spotted cats is dominant over the greater amount. S^1 is dominant over S^2 or S^3. S^2 is dominant over S^3. A pair of S^3 cats have kittens which are mostly white. A pair of S^1 cats, if not pure S^1 parents (if they carry S^2 or S^3 genes), may have part white or nearly all white kittens.

Normal color intensity is dominant over Silver, Burmese, or Siamese. Silver is dominant over Burmese and Siamese, and Burmese is dominant over Siamese. All are dominant over albinism (white with pink eyes).

HAIR LENGTH

Short hair (L) is dominant over long hair (l). That is why a pair of Short Hairs so often have long-haired kittens but two Long Hairs never produce short-haired kittens.

When considering the length of a cat's hairs, remember that a castrated male tends to grow longer hair. At the clinic I have noticed that clients will often, when showing me a castrated male, mention that he must be half long-haired cat. Later I sometimes see cats from the same litter with definitely short hair. It is quite obvious that, while there are intermediate hair lengths in cats, allowances must be made for the effects of castration.

TAILLESSNESS

Although the tailless condition of the Manx is due to a dominant gene, it is only imperfectly dominant. When we study the same condition in other species as well as in cats, we are forced to admit that it is actually a deformity. When two pure Manx cats are mated, the kittens sometimes are cripples. This condition is also found in the offspring of other tailless species—rabbits or dogs, for instance.

When we study the mode of inheritance of the short tail we find that it is practically impossible to predict the outcome. Parents with natural bobtails about two inches long may have kittens with no tail vertebrae, with little short stubs which do not show through the skin, or with tails three quarters of normal length. Sometimes a pure Manx mated with a cat with a normal tail produces all tailless kittens.

EYE COLOR

Unfortunately, the mode of inheritance of eye color has been studied very little. The students who have reported on coat color inheritance have not mentioned the eye colors in enough instances to give us the needed information which would enable us to breed the eye colors to order, or predict eye colors in kittens when we know the eye color of the parents.

However, the rarest eye characteristic—the capacity which some cats have to reflect red rather than the golden-yellow color—has been studied. If, when driving, you have seen red cats' eyes reflected in the glare of your headlights, you have seen one of these cats. The ruby eye color has been found in combination with nine different coat colors, proving there is no linkage as there is with blue eyes and white color. The characteristic may appear in any breed. I have seen it in Long Hairs and Maine Coon Cats, and several cases in Siamese have been reported.

HAIRLESSNESS

This is decidedly an undesirable characteristic in cats. Some specimens are completely hairless and others have a transitory fuzz. Strains have been established that breed true with either condition being recessive to the normal hair length. This accounts for the fact that hairless cats are sometimes born to normal parents. They are not necessarily mutations but the result of the recessive trait having been carried, masked, often for generations, waiting only for another gene in another cat with which it can combine to produce a hairless kitten.

DEAFNESS

So far as can be learned, deafness is usually associated with blue eyes, although it does not follow that all blue-eyed cats are deaf. One report lists a blue-eyed cat with normal hearing, a cat with one green and one blue eye, completely deaf, and an albino with the usual pink eyes with normal hearing.

POLYDACTYLISM (Extra Toes)

This is a characteristic determined by a dominant gene. A cat with a pair of these genes will produce only kittens with extra toes. One with one gene mated to a normal-toed cat will put extra toes on half the kittens. A pair of cats with extra toes, each having only one gene for the trait, may produce 25 per cent of their kittens with normal feet.

Suppose that you wanted to write out the genetic composition of, let us say, a long-haired tabby, half of whose body was white, and whose feet had extra toes. You would first look at the table and set down the symbols. Tabby (T), white (S^3), long hair (l), extra toes (P). You would need a pair of each of the symbols. Since you could not tell whether or not the cat carried genes for recessive traits, you could only determine the secondary genes by breeding. She could be TT, $S^3 S^3$, ll, PP, or Tt, $S^3 S^3$, ll, Pp.

Suppose you decide that, from your newly acquired knowledge, you were going to breed a blue-pointed, Siamese-colored, long-haired cat. How could you accomplish it? There are several ways. One would be to breed a blue Long Hair with a blue-point Siamese. The kittens would be blue short-haired cats. You would then mate a pair of these and you could expect one out of sixteen kittens to be just what you want.

BEHAVIOR PATTERNS

As yet we know but little about inherited behavior patterns of cats. Every farmer who has had much experience with cats will tell you that certain strains will be good ratters, while some refuse ever to catch a rat, even when hungry. The tendency for viciousness to run in cat families is very marked. Some of the best show males have produced large percentages of kittens which turned out to be completely untrustworthy unless they were spayed or castrated early in their lives.

The tendency of some cat families to sleep on high places has also been noted. I have already mentioned this characteristic in certain so-called Maine Coon Cats. One cat family of which I know could not be kept in the house because they insisted on climbing the window curtains. The mode of inheritance of the characteristic has not been determined.

INBREEDING AND LINE BREEDING

Some mental characteristics, like viciousness, are often attributed to inbreeding. We are told that such and such a family produces such cats because they are too closely inbred. This means virtually nothing and is only an excuse for sloppy breeding. Inbreeding, of course, does tend to purify the strain. If a certain stud cat is known to be vicious and his progeny are mated together, the greater part of the offspring will eventually also come to be vicious, if the viciousness is hereditary. Inbreeding simply tends to make a strain pure for characteristics, good and bad.

The closest inbreeding is brother and sister. If brother-to-sister mating continues, bringing together only the finest characteristics and eliminating all inferior characteristics by refusal to breed their possessors, inbreeding can definitely improve a strain just as fast as it can impair it. It is true that close inbreeding tends to make the offspring somewhat smaller than the original. A certain amount of outbreeding is necessary for size and vigor. However, laboratory animals are bred brother to sister for many generations with no harm. In short, it is not the inbreeding that is bad; it is the lack of proper selection on the part of the breeders.

Line breeding is usually considered to be the mating of animals farther removed by heredity than first cousinship. Mating first cousins is generally considered inbreeding, but mating second cousins is considered line breed‐ing.

SELECTIVE BREEDING

In the final analysis, it is most important for the average cat breeder to know the dominant and recessive traits and what to avoid. Beyond that, breed improvement consists of mating to the best according to the standards of what is considered best. All too many cat fanciers do the easiest thing and mate their cattas to the most accessible male, usually one of their own. The careful breeder, however, looks around and obtains the use of studs which are noted for producing high-quality offspring.

If you have a choice between two studs, one of which is excellent and one of which is fair, look into their hereditary background. It will tell what you can expect much more than you can tell from their individual appearance because you must always keep in mind their recessive characteristics.

There is a Norwegian proverb at least 2,500 years old which says, "If you would have good children, marry not the maid who is the only good maid in the clan." Applying the proverb to the problem we have just been discussing, suppose that the excellent cat is one which just appeared in an otherwise poor family of cats, and the fairly good cat is the poorest one of the best family of cats which you know about. The latter would be the one to use as a stud because all the kittens will tend to be better than he is, whereas the progeny from the former will tend to be poorer than he is. This is not theory; it actually works out in practice. If you have already had experience in breeding cats, no doubt you yourself can testify to its truth.

21. Fifty Questions
Frequently Asked by Cat Owners

1. Q. How can oil be given a cat which fights and refuses to swallow it?
   A. Smear it on her feet and she will lick it off.

2. Q. How early may a cat be spayed?
   A. Any time after birth, but it is better to wait until she is three months old.

3. Q. How early must she be spayed to avoid her first heat?
   A. Before she is five months old.

4. Q. How early can a male be castrated?
   A. At two or three months of age.

5. Q. Can a female be spayed safely after she has had a litter?
   A. Yes, at any time. However, more careful surgery is required.

6. Q. Can a tom be castrated safely after he is a year old?
   A. Yes.

7. Q. Do cats have asthma?
   A. Yes. Something very much like the human variety.

8. Q. Are cats strictly carnivorous?
   A. Zoologically speaking, yes, but they eat vegetable foods and thrive on them in addition to meat.

9. Q. Is beef the natural food of cats?
   A. Studies of cats gone wild indicate that rodents are the natural food of cats.

10. Q. Is a brush best for grooming a cat?
    A. A comb with strong teeth spaced twelve to the inch serves best.

11. Q. Are cats' nutritional requirements the same as for other pets?
    A. Very similar, with exceptions. Unlike a guinea pig, a cat makes her own vitamin C; unlike a rat, she needs little, if any, vitamin E.

12. Q. Is catnip the best tonic for a cat?
    A. Its odor serves as a mental tonic. If eaten, it is a weak nerve stimulant.

13. Q. Does a cat come in season only once a year?
    A. She may have one season follow another in rapid succession if not bred. Another series may occur in four or five months.

14. Q. Can a cat become pregnant while she is nursing a litter?
    A. Yes. She often does. Cats have been known to attempt to nurse two consecutive litters at one time.

15. Q. Must a cat touch another with distemper to become infected?
    A. Being in the same room may cause infection, because the virus is small enough to live in the minute droplets of moisture floating in the air.

16. Q. Is virus pneumonia in cats caused by only one virus?
    A. Three different viruses have been implicated.

17. Q. How can a cat be made to stop clawing furniture, wallpaper, et cetera?
    A. Keep her claws trimmed. As a last resort, your veterinarian can operate on two toes in each foot and cut a little tendon.

18. Q. Can cats have tuberculosis?
    A. Yes. Two per cent of European cats were found to have the cattle form.

19. Q. Do cats have convulsions from eating meat?
    A. Only indirectly, if they become constipated. Toxins such as those from food-poisoning organisms and worms, or certain poisons, cause fits.

20. Q. Are blue-eyed cats always deaf?
    A. No, but many are.

21. Q. Are tortoiseshell and tortoiseshell-and-white cats ever of the male sex?

    A.   This color is inherited as a sex-linked characteristic. Very few tortoise males have been reported.

22.   Q.   Does diarrhea come only from improper feeding?
    A.   It comes more often as the result of disease—distemper, coccidiosis, et cetera.

23.   Q.   Are phenol disinfectants safe around cats?
    A.   No. Never use them or phenol derivatives in cat medications.

24.   Q.   Are cat distemper and dog distemper one and the same disease?
    A.   They are caused by totally different viruses.

25.   Q.   What makes a cat's breath bad?
    A.   Bad teeth, infected mouth and lips, kidney disease, poisoning, to name a few causes.

26.   Q.   Is ear canker the same as ear-mite infestation?
    A.   No. Mites are small insects which produce a dry, crumbly wax; canker is a bacterial infection which generally produces a dark brown sticky wax.

27.   Q.   When a lactating female develops violent trembling and becomes prostrate, is it a sign of poisoning?
    A.   It is probably eclampsia, caused by inadequate amounts of calcium in her diet.

28.   Q.   How can one make a cat eat what's good for her instead of only beef kidneys?
    A.   Make her hungry enough by starvation.

29.   Q.   Is DDT flea powder safe for cats?
    A.   No. It may be safe used in a rinse, but not in powder. Rotenone or benzene hexachloride are quite safe if the cat is not placed in a closed container when they are applied.

30.   Q.   Can an orphan kitten be raised on cow's milk?
    A.   Yes. It is similar to cat's milk in composition.

31.   Q.   How does one pick up an ugly cat to avoid being scratched?
    A.   Usually holding him by a large handful of skin on top of the neck is painless and makes the cat curl up like a little kitten.

32.   Q.   Should cats be inoculated?
    A.   Against distemper—by all means.

33. Q. Does mineral oil, when given every day in the food, help constipation?
    A. It is much better to feed laxative diets. Mineral oil tends to absorb the fat-soluble vitamins so that they become wasted on the cat.

34. Q. Is it wise to add lime water to cat food?
    A. Very foolish. The cat needs all the acid in her stomach juices to digest her food. Lime water tends to neutralize it.

35. Q. How do mange and eczema differ?
    A. Mange is caused by a mite; "eczema" is due to an infection, either bacterial or fungicidal.

36. Q. Does it pay to grind cat food?
    A. Very well. You can incorporate all the things that are good for your cat in one mixture.

37. Q. Do well-cared-for cats live longer than those which fend for themselves?
    A. No one knows. Overfat cats may not live so long as leaner ones, but the age of feral cats is not accurately known.

38. Q. What are the chief advantages in castrating a male cat?
    A. He stays home, has few fights, urinates sitting down, and his urine loses its acrid unpleasantness.

39. Q. How long should a cat take to deliver a litter of kittens?
    A. A few hours. However, normal deliveries lasting twenty-four hours are not uncommon.

40. Q. Can cats have rabies?
    A. They can and occasionally do.

41. Q. What does a ringworm look like? Can people catch the disease?
    A. It is not a worm but a fungus infection with produces bald patches of ring or oval shape, with quite clearly defined margins. Yes, we can catch it from cats and also spread it to them.

42. Q. How many common intestinal parasites are found in cats?
    A. Several species of tapeworm, several species of coccidiosis, roundworm, hookworm, whipworm.

43. Q. How much water does a cat drink a day?
    A. There is no standard amount. If she has much milk, she'll want very little water. If she has salty fish. she will drink a lot.

44. Q. Do cats change their teeth as they get older?
    A. Only to lose their baby teeth, from between three to five months of age.

45. Q. Can cats be washed safely?
    A. Yes, if they are dried and not exposed to cold.

46. Q. At what age should kittens be weaned?
    A. Start at six weeks and be finished at eight or nine.

47. Q. Can cats digest vegetables?
    A. Very well, if the starch granules have been cracked by cooking.

48. Q. Is thirty pounds a good weight for a cat?
    A. Certainly not. A human being proportionately heavy would be a circus curiosity. It is a very bad weight.

49. Q. Can cats be raised in outdoor cages safely?
    A. Most can, but cats often love to sit out in the rain and may develop pneumonia.

50. Q. How many litters of kittens can a female have?
    A. Many have had twenty litters in a lifetime.

Acknowledgments

Abyssinian, Double Champion Raby Nefertari, imported by Mrs. Blanche Warren, Casa Gatos Cattery, Idyllwild, California: *jacket*

Short-haired tabby, owned by Mr. Arthur Brunkhart: *jacket*

White Persian, Blue Acres Doll Baby of Les Cygnes, owned by Mr. and Mrs. Paul Swan, Les Cygnes Cattery, Independence, Missouri: *facing page 126*

Short-haired black. International News Photo: *jacket and facing page 126*

Russian Blue, imported from England by Mrs. Blanche Warren, Casa Gatos Cattery, Idyllwild, California: *jacket and facing page 126*

Peke-faced red tabby, Pineland's Pepper Pat, owned by Mr. and Mrs. Robert B. Treat, Jr. and Robert Treat 3rd, Callavorn Cattery, Porter Hill, Middlebury, Connecticut: *facing page 126*

Siamese. International News Photo: *jacket and facing page 126*

Abyssinian, Double Champion Chirn Sa-hai Ani, owned by Mrs. Richard O'Donovan, Chirn Sa-hai Cattery, Tarrytown, New York: *facing page 126*

Smoke Persian kittens, owned by Mrs. H. N. Bellows, Bellows Falls, Vermont: *facing page 127*

Manx, Grand Champion Guthred of Manx of Glen Orry, bred and owned by Misses Ruth and Ellen Carlson, Glen Orry Cattery, West Chicago, Illinois: *jacket and facing page 127*

Blue Persian, Grand Champion Purri-Isle's Bobadil, owned by Mr. and Mrs. L. I. Olsen, Purri-Isle Cattery, West Palm Beach, Florida: *facing page 127*

Tortoise calico cat, owned by Mrs. Mollie Brennan, New Haven, Connecticut: *facing page 127*

Black Persian, Double Grand Champion Hermscrest Natajha, owned by Mrs. Frances M. Herms, Hermscrest Cattery, Tarrytown, New York: *facing page 127*

Burmese, owned by Mrs. Blanche Warren, Casa Gatos Cattery, Idyllwild, California: *jacket and facing page 127*

Persian, Grand and Double Champion Leilani's Petitepointe, owned by Mrs. Walker Johnston, Azulita Cattery, San Diego, California: *jacket and facing page 127*

Index

A-P-L hormone, 108
Abortifacients, 107, 163
Abscesses, opening, 144
Abyssinian cats, 24, 251
Acceptance period in bitches, *see* Mating cycle
Accidental mating, remedies for, 107, 163
  telegony, 246
Accidents, automobile, first-aid treatment for, 127–28
Acetanilid, 102
Acetophenatidin, 102
Acetylsalicylic acid, 101–2
Acidophilus bacteria, 64
Acids taken internally, antidotes for, 137
Acriflavin, 117
Adrenal glands, 43
Adrenalin, 43
  in combination with other anesthetic, 100–1
  as heart stimulant, 105–6
Afterbirth, *see* Placenta
Ailments (*see also* Diseases)
  bites, animal and insect, 130–31
  bladder, 213
  convulsions, 228–29
  cuts, 129–30
  digestive tract, 215
  ear, 235–36
  eye, 232–35
  foreign bodies, removal of, 131–33
  fractures, *see* Fractures
  gullet, 216–17
  heat strokes, 127
  hernias, 147
  intestinal, 220
  kidney, 212–13
  liver, 220–21
  mouth, 215–16
  nutritional deficiencies, 229–30
  poisoning, 136–38
  stomach, 217–20
  uterine, 213–14
Albino cats, 254
Albumin, in food, 61
  in urine, in kidney disease, 37
Alcohol, benzyl, 101
  effect on pets, 100
  ethyl, 100
Alfalfa, and laxation, 68
Alimentary tract, nature of, 39–40
Alkalies taken internally, antidotes for, 137
Allergies, food, 56
Altering of cats, 214
American Veterinary Medical Association, 27

Amino acids, conversion of proteins into, 40–41
  as diet essential, 60–61
Aminopyrene, 102
Ammonia, conversion into urea, 41
  spirits of, 103
  in urine, 37
Ammonium bromide, 102
Amniotin (trade name of follicular hormone), 44
Amytal, 100
Anal glands, accumulation in, 240
  odor from, 171–72
Anaplasmosis, 92
Anatomy, 29–52
  circulatory system, 34–36
  definition of, 29
  digestive system, 37–42
  excretory system, 36–37
  glandular system, 42–45
  nervous system, 45–49
  reproductive system, 50–52
  respiratory system, 36
  skeletal structure, 31–33
  skin, 30–31
Anemia, 94–95, 229
  from parasites, 86, 94
Anesthesia, administering of, 139–40
Anesthetics, general, 98–101
  local, 100–1
  topical, 101
Angora cats, 24
Animal bites, treatment of, 130–31
Animal starch (glycogen), 41, 64
Anterior nares of nose, 49
Anthelmintics, 108
Antibiotics, 120
Antibodies against disease, 78
  in serums, 123
Antidotes, household, for poisoning, 137–38
Antifebrine, 102
Antipyrene, 102
Antiseptics, 117
Antiserum, 123

Antitoxin, danger of second dosage, 105–6
Anus, 39, 52
Apomorphine, as emetic, 120–21
Arecolene hydrobromide, 122–23
  antidote for, 106
  for tapeworms, 108–10
Arsenic, antidote for, 137
Arteries, 34–35
  tying off or stretching of, 142
Arterioles, 34
Aspirin, 101–2
Atropine, 106
Aureomycin, see Antibiotics

Bacilli form of bacteria, 75
Back, broken, 136
Bacteria, 75–76
  destruction in body of, 36, 41
  in feces, 42
Bacterial diseases, 75–76, 209–11
Bacteriocides, definition of, 117
Bacteriostatics, definition of, 117
Baker virus, 207
Bandages, applying of, 156–58
  pressure, 142, 157
Barbiturates, 98–100
Bathing, 173–75
Beds and bedding, 176–77
  for kittens, 200
Bee stings, treatment for, 136
Behavior patterns, inherited, 259
Belladonna, 106
"Bench" legs, 33
Benign growths, 93 (see also Growths)
Benzene hexachloride, 112
Benzyl alcohol, 101
Bile, in digestion, 40, 55
Bile duct obstruction, 220
Birth of kittens, 163–64, 198–200
  drugs, effect of, 107
Birthmarking, misconceptions about, 246
Bites, animal and insect, treatment of, 130–31
  from rabid cats, 129

Black cats, 23, 251
Bladder, ailments of, 213
  capacity, 37
Bloat, tapping for, 144
Blood, absorption of food products
      by, 40–41
  circulation of, 34–35
  composition of, 35
  purification of, 35–36
Blood sugar (glucose), 40
  control by pancreas of, 42
  maintaining level of, 41
Blood vessels, 34–35
  tying off, 142
Blooded inheritance, 246–47
Blue cats, 251–54
Blue-eyed white cats, 23, 254
Boarding pets, 181–85
Body, functions of (see Circulatory
      system; Digestive system;
      Excretory system; Glandu-
      lar system; Nervous system;
      Reproductive system; Re-
      spiratory system)
  skeletal structure of, 31–34
Bones, of body skeleton, 31–33
  callus of, in healing, 33–34
  digestion of, 55
  formation of, 31–32
  healing process of, 33–34
  long, 32
  setting, 33
Boric acid, 115
"Boxing gloves" to prevent scratch-
      ing, 143
Brain, 45–47
  inflammation of, see Encephalitis
Brain cells, 30
Breastbone, 32
Breasts, caked, 107
  function of, 50
  infections of, 164
Breeding, 159–66, 197–98 (see also
      Heredity)
  accidental, 107, 163
  care of mother, 197–200
  diagnosing pregnancy, 198

Brilliant green, 117
Broken bones, see Fractures
Bromine and bromides, 102
Bronchial tubes, 36 (see also Bron-
      chitis)
Bronchioles of lungs, 36
Bronchitis, 36
Bruises, 135
Burial or cremation, 188–89
Burmese cats, 23–24, 254
Burns, first-aid treatment for, 134
  remedies for, 116–17
Butyn, 100–1

"Cabbits," 246
Cade, oil of, 114
Caffeine, as diuretic, 105
  as stimulant, 103
Calamine lotion, 115
Calcium, in body, regulation of, 43
  deficiency, 95
  functions and sources, 58
Calcium bromide, 102
Callus formation after bone frac-
      tures, 33–34
Calomel, as diuretic, 105
Calories, 56–57
  computing, 66–67
Camphor, 103
Cancer, 92–94 (see also Growths)
Canker, 235–36
Canned food, 194
  caloric content of, 66
  starches in, 63
Capillaries, 34
Capsules, administering, 155–56
Carbohydrate metabolism, regula-
      tion of, 43
Carbohydrates, as diet essential,
      63–64
  digestion of, 40, 63–64
Carbolic acid, 116
Carcinoma, 93–94 (see also
      Growths)
Carnivores (flesh eaters), 53
Cartilage, epiphyseal, 32
  in skeletal structure, 32–33

Casein, sources and properties, 62
Castor oil, 121
Castration, advisability of, 167–68
    operation, 147
Cat scratch fever, 242–43
Cat shows, see Shows
Cathartics, 121–23
Catnip, 196
Catteries, boarding pet at, 181–85
Cellular structure of animal, 29–30
Cereals, in diet, 56, 59, 61, 227
Cerebellum, 46
Cerebrum, 46
Cervix, 50, 51
Chambers of heart, 35
Chastek paralysis, 95
Chiggers, 84
Chloral hydrate, 98
Chloramine, 118
Chlordane, 112
Chlorine, functions and sources, 59
Chloroform, 98
Chondrin, sources and properties,
    62
Choosing a cat, 22–25
Choosing a veterinarian, 25–28
Chromosomes, 247–50
    sex determination by, 250–51
Circulatory system, 34–36
Cirrhosis of liver, 221
Clitoris, function of, 50
Clostridia, 75
Coal tar in medications, 114
Coat, care of, 170–72
    color of, 23–25, 247–57
    removal of tar or paint from, 174
    shedding, 172–73
Cocaine, 100
Coccal bacteria, 75
Coccidia, 91–92
Coccidiosis, 225–27
Cocoa as stimulant, 103
Coffee, see Caffeine
Collars, to prevent self-injury, 144
    types of, 176
Color of coat, classification of, 251–
    55

genetic symbols for, 255–56
hereditary determination of, 247–
    50, 256–57
for show standards, 23–25
Color perception in cats, 48
Combing coat, 170–71
Compound fractures, 34, 148
Cone collars for preventing self-
    injury, 144
Convulsions, 228–29
    treatment of, 134–35
Coon cats, 25
Copper, functions and sources, 60
Copper sulfate as emetic, 121
Copulation, 161
Cord, spinal, 45–46
Corn, nutritional value of, 61
Cornea of eye, 47
    diseases of, 233–34
Corpuscles, blood, 35
Coryza, 209
Cream cats, 251–54
Cremaster muscle, 52
Cremation, 188–89
Cretinism and iodine deficiency, 43
Cross eyes, 235
Cryptorchidism, 147, 214
Cube root for flea control, 175
Cuts, drugs for, 117–19
    first-aid treatment of, 129–30
    suturing, 146
Cyclochlorohexane, 112
Cysts, liberating fluids from, 144
    on ovaries, as cause of sterility,
    162

Dandruff, 239–40
DDT, 112
    antidote for, 138
Deafness, 258
Death of pets, 186–89
Deficiency diseases, 94–95
Dehydrated food, caloric content
    of, 66
Demodectic mange, 83
Depressants, secretory gland, 106
Dermis, 30

Derris root for flea control, 175
Deworming, 108–11, 201, 222–23
Dextrin, conversion of starch into, 40, 64
Diabetes, *mellitus,* 42
Diarrhea, 217
Diet, *see* Food and feeding
Digestion, 55–56 (*see also* Digestive system)
Digestive system, 37–42
    ailments of, 215–21
    intestines, 40–41
    liver, 41
    mouth and teeth, 38–39
    pancreas, 41–42
    peristalsis, 39–40
    stomach, 40
    throat, 39
    tongue, 39
Digitalis, 105
Diseases, 74–95, 203–11 (*see also* Ailments)
    bacterial, 75–76, 209–11
    coryza, 209
    deficiency, 94–95
    distemper, 203–5
    fungi, 76
    growths, 92–94, 240 (*see also* Growths)
    heart, 230–31
    immunity to, 78
    kidney, 37
    leptospirosis, 209–10
    parasitic, 79–91, 222–28
    pneumonia, 207–8, 211
    protozoan, 91–92
    psittacosis-ornithosis, 208
    rabies, 205–7
    respiratory, 231–32
    rickettsiae, 76
    skin, 56–57, 236–40
    tetanus (lockjaw), 210
    transmission of, 77–78
    tuberculosis, 211
    virus, 76–77, 203–8
Disinfectants, 179
    definition of, 117

Dislocations, 149
    of hip joint, 151
    of shoulder, 151–52
    of wrist and hock, 152
Distemper, feline, 203–5
Diuretics, 104–5
Domestic Short-Haired cats, 22–23, 252–53
Dominant characteristics in heredity, 247–50
Dried food, *see* Dry foods
Dropsy, 230–31
    diuretics for, 104–5
    tapping in, 144
Drowning, first aid for, 134
Drugs, 96–124 (*see also* Parasitic diseases)
    abortifacients, 107
    action of, 97–98
    anesthetics, 98–101
    antibiotics, 120
    cathartics, 121–23
    depressants, 106
    diuretics, 104–5
    emetics, 120–21
    heart stimulants, 105–6
    painkillers, 101–2
    for parasites, external, 111–12
        internal, 108–11
    for reproduction cycle, 107–8
    sedatives, 98–100
    for skin, 113–19
    stimulants, 103–4, 105–6
    sulfa, 119–20
    vaccines and serums, 123–24
Dry foods, 66, 194
Ductless glands, 42
Duodenum, 40
Dyes in medications, 119

Ear hematomas, liberating fluid from, 145–46
Ear mange mites, 83–84, 227–28, 235–36
Eardrum, broken, detection of, 49
Ears, ailments of, 235–36
    care of, 176

Ears—(Cont'd)
    flaps, injuries to, 146
    structure and function of, 48–49
Eclampsia, 43, 95, 230
Eczema, 237–38
    in relation to food, 56
Edema, of lungs, 231
Electric shock, treatment for, 134
Elizabethan collars for preventing
    self-injury, 143–44
Emetics, 120–21
Emphysema, 211, 231–32
Encephalitis, 205–6
Enteritis, see Distemper
Enzyme (digestive ferments), 42
Ephedrine, 106
Epidermis, 30
Epididymis, 51
Epiglottis, 39
Epinephrine, 43, 100–1, 105–6
Epiphyseal cartilage, 32
Epsom salts, 122
    for euthanasia, 188
Erectile tissue, in nose, 49
Esophagus (gullet), 39
    ailments of, 216–17
Estrin, to prevent pregnancy, 107
Estrone, 44
Ether, 98
    as anesthesia, 139–40
Ethyl alcohol, 100
Eustachian tubes, 49
Euthanasia, 186–88
Excretory system, 36–37
External parasites, see Parasites
Eyes, ailments of, 232–35
    care of, 175
    color of, by inheritance, 257–58
    cross, 235
    injuries to, 48
    protruding, 234–35
    structure and function of, 47–48

Fallopian tubes, see Reproductive
    system
Fat, absorption by body, 41

    in diet, 64–66
    digestion of, 40
Fatty acids, 40–41
Feces, see Stools
Feeding, see Food and feeding
Fees, veterinary, 27
Feline agranulocytosis, see Dis-
    temper
Feline distemper, see Distemper
Female organs, 50–51
    ailments of, 213–14
    effect of drugs on, 107
Femur, fracture of, 150
Feral cats, 191–93
Fertility, see Breeding
Fever fits, see Convulsions
Fibrin in blood, 35
Fibrinogen, properties and sources,
    62
First aid, 125
    accidents, 127–28
    bee stings, 136
    bites, animal and insect, 130–31
    broken bones, 135–36
    bruises, 135
    burns, 134
    cuts, 129–30
    drowning, 134
    electric shock, 134
    fits, 134–35
    foreign bodies, removal of, 131–
        33
    heat stroke, 127
    poisoning, 136–37
    rabid cat, 128–29
    shock, 127
    skunk spraying, 133–34
Fish, in diet, 95, 194
Fish-host tapeworm, 90–91
Fistulas, liberating fluid from, 144–
    45
Fits, see Convulsions
Flea-host tapeworm, 88–89
Fleas, 79–80, 227
    sand, 84
Follicles, hair, 30
    of ovaries, 44

Follicular hormone, 44
Follicular mange, 83, 238–39
Food and Drug Administration, Federal, 97
Food and feeding, 53–73, 191–96
  allergies, 56
  calories in, 56–57, 66–67
  canned, 194
  carbohydrates in, 63–64, 194
  changing methods of, 70–71
  conditioning to, 71, 195
  essential, 56–57, 193–94
  fats in, 64–66, 194
  fish, 194
  of kittens, 71, 200–2
  laxation in, 67–68
  meats and by-products, 194
  milk, 195
  minerals in, 58–60
  of mother, 164
  in natural state, 53–54, 193
  of orphans, 165–66, 200–1
  overfeeding, 72
  proteins and amino acids, 60–63
  quantity required, 56–57, 71–73, 195
  reducing overweight pet, 72–73
  skin disease caused by, 56–57
  starch in, 55, 63–64, 194
  variety in, 192–93
  vitamins in, 68–71
  water in, 57–58
Food poisoning, antidote for, 138
Foreign bodies, 131–33
  in mouth, 131–32
  in rectum, 132–33
  in skin, 133
  in stomach, 132, 219–20
Foster mothers, 165–66
Fractures, 33–34, 148–49
  bandaging, emergency, 149–51
  of femur, 150
  of head, 150–51
  of pelvis, 149–50
  of tail, 150
  of toes, 150
  treatment of, 135–36

Fungi as cause of skin disease, 56, 76
Fungicides, definition of, 117

Gall bladder, 40, 41
Gelatine, sources and properties, 62
Genes and chromosomes, 247–50
Genetic symbols, 255–56
Gentian violet, 115, 117
Germ plasm, 247
Germicides, definition of, 117
Glands, adrenal, 43
  depressants for, 106
  ductless, 42
  oil, 31
  ovaries, 43–45
  parathyroid, 43
  pituitary, 42–43
  salivary, 39
  sebaceous, 31
  sweat, 31
  testicles, 45
  thyroid, 43
Glandular system, 42–45
Glaucoma, 234
Glucose (blood sugar), 40–41, 64
  as diuretic, 104–5
Glycerine in medication, 113
Glycogen (animal starch), 64
Goiter, 43
Green-eyed cats, 254
Greenstick fractures, 34, 148
Grooming, see Hygiene
Growths, 92–94, 240
  cysts, 146
  liver, 221
  lungs, 232
  removal of, 146
Gullet, see Esophagus
Gums, ailment of, 216

Hair (see also Coat)
  absence of, 258
  length of, by heredity, 257
  nature of, 30–31
Hair balls in stomach, 217–19
Hairless cats, 25, 258

Handling pets, *see* Restraint
Hard palate, 39
Harnesses, 176
Head, fracture of, 150–51
Health checkups for pets, 179
Health hazards of mingling pets, 181–85
Heart, diseases of, 230–31
    stimulants for, 105–6
    structure and function, 34–35
Heat period of female animals, *see* Mating cycle
Heat strokes, treatment of, 127
Hematomas, liberating fluid from, 145–46
Hemoglobin, 35
Hemorrhage, control of, 142
Herbivorous animals, 53
Hereditary anomalies, 229
Heredity, 245–60
    behavior patterns, 259
    color classification, 251–55
    color inheritance, 256–57
    deafness, 258
    eye color, 257–58
    genes and chromosomes, 247–50
    genetic symbols, 255–56
    germ plasm, 247
    hair length, 257
    hairlessness, 258
    inbreeding and line breeding, 259
    misconceptions about, 246–47
    polydactylism, 258
    selective breeding, 259–60
    sex linkage, 250–51
    taillessness, 257
Hernias, 147
Hexylresorcinol, 118
Hip joint dislocations, 151
Histidine, 60
Home surgery, *see* Operations
Hookworms, 85–87, 223–24
Hormone, female, 107
    follicular, 44
    male, 45, 108
Hospitalization, health hazards of, 181–85

Hydatid tapeworm, 90
Hydrocyanic acid, antidote for, 138
Hydrogen peroxide, as emetic, 120
    for wounds, 118
Hydrophobia, *see* Rabies
Hydrothorax, 232
Hygiene, 170
    bathing, 173–75
    beds and bedding, 176–77
    coat, 170–75
    collars and harnesses, 176
    ear, 176
    eye, 175
    health checkups, 179–80
    mouth and teeth, 175
    nail, 172
    outdoor accommodations, 178–79
    sanitary provisions, 177–78

Ichthyol, 116
Immunity to disease, 78
Inbreeding, 259
Incision to liberate fluids, 144–45
Infectious enteritis, gastroenteritis, or feline panleukopenia, *see* Distemper
Insulin, manufacture by pancreas of, 42
Internal parasites, *see* Parasites
Intestines, 40–41
    ailments of, 220 (*see also* **Parasites, internal**)
    digestion in, 55
Iodine, 116, 117–18
    functions and sources, 59
    importance in diet, 43, 95
Ipecac, 121
Iris of eye, 47
Iron, functions and sources, 59
Isoleucine, 60
Itching, food as cause of, 56

Jaundice, 41, 220–21
Jaws, fracture of, 151
Jiggers, 84

Joints, skeletal, 32–33
Juniper tar in medications, 114

Keratin, sources and properties, 63
Kidneys, 36–37
  ailments of, 212–13
    diet in, 212
    diuretic in, 105
  blood pressure in, 37
  purification of blood by, 36
Kinesthetic sense, 45–46
Kittens, assisting at birth of, 163–64, 198–200
  deworming, 201, 222–23
  feeding, 164–66, 200–2
  general care of, 164–66, 200–2
  lice, danger from, 81
  nest for, 199–200
  orphans, care of, 165–66, 200–1
  preparing for birth of, 197–98
  spaying of, 44, 166–67

Lactation, 50
Lactose, 64
Lard as base for skin drug, 113
Larynx, 39
Lauric acid, 65
Laxation, 67–68
Lead poisoning, antidote for, 138
Legs, bandy or "bench," 33
  fractured, treatment for, 135
Lens of eye, 47
Lentin, antidote for, 106
  as cathartic, 122–23
  as emetic, 121
  in poisoning, 138
Leptospirosis, 209–10, 244
Leucene, 60
Lice, 80–81, 227
  anemia from, 94
Life expectancy of cats, 186–89
Light, effect on shedding, 172
Lindane, 112
Line breeding, 259
Linoleic acid, 64
Lip-pocket method of medication, 154

Lips, 38
  sores on, 215
Liquid medicine, administering, 153–55
Litters, mixed, 162
Liver, ailments of, 220–21
  functions of, 41
  manufacture of bile in, 40
Local anesthetics, 100–1, 140
Lockjaw, see Tetanus
Long-Haired cats, 24–25
Louse, see Lice
Luminal, 98–99
Lungs, diseases of, 231–32
  excretion of gases by, 37
  function and structure, 34, 36
  growths in, 232
Luteal bodies in ovarian follicles, 44–45, 160
Lymph, flow of, 36
Lymph glands, 34, 42
Lymph vessels, 34
Lysine, 60

Mad cat, see Rabies
Magnesium, functions and sources, 60
Magnesium sulfate for euthanasia, 188
Maine coon cats, 25
Male fern, 108
Male fertility, drugs for, 108
Male sex organs, 51–52
Malignant growths, 93 (see also Growths)
Maltese cats, 24, 254
Mange, diet as cause of, 56
  ear, 83–84
  red (follicular demodectic), 83, 238–39
  sarcoptic, 83, 237, 243
  treatment of, 227
Manx cats, 24
  taillessness, inheritance of, 257
Mating cycle, 44–45, 159–61 (see also Breeding)

Meat, caloric content of, 66, 227
  digestibility of, 55–56
Medicine, giving of, 153–56
  kinds of, *see* Drugs
Mercurial salts, action of, 97
Mercuric compounds, 118
Mercurochrome, 118
Mercury, antidote for, 138
Merthiolate, 118
Metaphen, 118
Methionine, 60
Metropine, 106
Middle ear, 49
Milk, amino acids in, 61
  composition of, 165, 201
  in diet, 195
  for orphans, 165–66, 243–44
  production of, 50
Milk of magnesia, 122
Milk sugar, 64
Mineral oil, 122
Minerals, deficiency of, in diet, 95
  sources and functions, 58–60
Minor operations, *see* Operations
Mites, 83–84
  ear, 227–28
Molds, *see* Fungi
Mouth, ailments of, 215–16
  care of, 175
  foreign bodies, removal of, 131–32
  structure and function of, 38–39
Muscles, of digestive system, 39–40
  in hair follicles, 30
  kinds of, 34
Mustard as emetic, 121
Mutations, 247
Mycobacteria, 75
Myesin, sources and properties, 62

N butyl chloride, *see* Normal butyl chloride
Nails, trimming, 172
  of kittens, 202
Nembutal, 99
  as home anesthesia, 140
Nemural, 110

Nerves, functions of, 45
  structure of, 46
Nervous system, 45–49
  ailments of, 228–29
Neutering, 214
Nictitating membrane of eye, 47, 222, 232–33
Nitrogen, eliminated by kidneys, 37
Nits, 80–81
  control of, 175
Normal butyl chloride, 110–11
Nose, structure and function, 49
Novocaine, *see* Procaine
Nupercaine, 100–1
Nursing by cattas, 50
Nutritional deficiencies, 229–30
Nutritional wisdom in animals, experimental studies of, 70

Obesity in pets, 72–73
Odor, from glandular secretion of skin, 31, 171–72
  mouth, cause of, 175
  perception of, 49
  removal of, 174
Oil glands of skin, 31
Oils, penetration of skin by, 31
Ointments, *see* Drugs, for skin
Oleic acid, 65
Olfactory organs, 49
Omnivores, 53
Operations, minor, 139–52
  anesthesia, administering, 139–40
  castration, 147
  cleaning wound before, 140–41
  fractures and dislocations, setting, 148–52
  growths, removal of, 146
  hemorrhage, controlling, 142
  incising to liberate fluids, 144–46
  preparation for, 139
  self-injury, preventing, 143–44
  sutures, kinds of, 142
    materials for, 141
    performing, 146
  tapping fluids and gas, 144

teeth extractions, 147
tissue joining, 141
Orange cats, 251
Orphans, raising, 165–66, 243–45
Outdoor accommodations for pets, 178–79
Ovaries, 43–45 (see also Mating cycle)
    ailments of, 268–69
    as cause of sterility, 162
    changes during mating cycle, 44
    functions of, 50
    removal of, 44
    transplantation of, 45
Overfeeding, 72–73
Overweight in pets, reducing, 72–73
Ovulation, 44, 179 (see also Mating cycle)
Ovum, 44 (see also Mating cycle)
    fertilization and growth of, 50
Owning cats, obligations of, 19–22
Ox warble, 227

Painkillers, 101–2
Paint removal from coat, 174
Palate, hard, soft, 39
Palmitic acid, 65
Palpation, to determine completion of birth, 199
    to diagnose pregnancy, 198
Pancreas, functions of, 40, 41–42
    manufacture of insulin by, 42
Pancreatic juices in digestion, 55
Pans, sanitary, 177–78
Parasites, drugs for eradication of, 108–12
    external, 79–84
    internal, 84–91
    sanitary control of, 175
Parasitic diseases, 79–91 (see also Parasites)
Parathyroid glands, 43
Pathogenic bacteria, 75
Pelvis, fractured, 34, 149–50
    treatment for, 135–36
    restricted, in cattas, 199

Penicillin, see Antibiotics
Penis, 52, 161
Pentobarbital (Nembutal), 99
    for euthanasia, 188
    as home anesthesia, 140
Pentothal, 99
Peptone, sources and properties, 62
Perception, organs of, 45–49
Pericardium, 35
Periosteum, bone skin, 32
Peristalsis, 39–40
Peroxide of hydrogen, see Hydrogen peroxide
Persian cats, 24
Petrolatum, 113
Phantom pregnancy, 161, 197
Pharynx, 39
Phenacetine, 102
Phenobarbital (Luminal), 98–99
Phenol, 101, 116
    action of, 97
Phenolphthalein, 122
Phenylalanine, 60
Phosphorus, antidote for, 138
    functions and sources, 59
Physical checkups, periodic, 179
Physiology, 29–52
    of bones, 31–34
    cellular reproduction, 29–30
    circulatory system, 34–36
    definition of, 29
    digestive system, 37–42
    excretory system, 36–37
    glandular system, 42–45
    muscles, 34
    nervous system, 45–49
    reproductive system, 50–52
    respiratory system, 36
    skin, 30–31
Pills, administering, 155–56
Pine tar in medications, 114
Pink-eyed albino cats, 254
Piroplasmosis, 92
Pitocin, 107
Pituitary gland, 42–43, 45
Pituitrin, 107

Placenta (*see also* Birth)
  retained, 199
Plasma, blood, 35
Platelets, in blood, 35
Pleurisy, 211, 232
Pneumonia, bacterial, 211
  virus, 207–8, 242
Poisoning, symptoms of, 136
  treatment of, 136–37
Poisons, eliminated by kidneys, 36–
  37
  household antidotes for, 138
  jaundice caused by, 221
Polydactylism (extra toes), 258
Polyps, treatment of, 146
Post-mortem examinations, 189
Posterior nares of nose, 49
Potassium, functions and sources,
  59
Potassium bromide, 102
Potassium permanganate, 115
  for wounds, 118
Pregnancy, care of mother during,
  197–200
  diagnosis of, 198
  drugs, effect of, 107
  period of, 198
  pseudo, phantom, false, 161, 197
Prenatal influence, misconceptions
  about, 246
Pressure bandages, 142, 157
Procaine, 100–1
  as home anesthetic, 140
Prolapsed rectum, treatment of,
  146
Proteins, 60–63
  diet requirement, 61
  digestion of, 40
  sources and properties, 61–63
Protoplasm, in diet, 60
Protozoan diseases, 91–92
Pseudo-pregnancy, 161, 197
Psittacosis-ornithosis, 208
Ptyalin (salivary amylase), 55
Pupil of eye, 47
Pylorus, 40
Pyrethrum, 112

Quinine, 101
  and urea for local anesthesia,
  101

Rabbit-host tapeworm, 89–90
Rabbits, mating of cats with, 246
Rabies, 205–7, 242
  cause and dissemination, 205–6
  destruction of feeling by, 45
  encephalitis, 205–6
  first-aid treatment for, 128–29
  prevention and control, 206–7
  symptoms, 206
Radius, enlargement of, 33
Ranula, 144
Recessive characteristics in hered-
  ity, 247–50
Rectum, foreign bodies in, 132–33
  prolapsed, treatment of, 146
Red bugs, 84
Red corpuscles, 35
Red mange, 83, 238–39
Red Tabby cats, 23
Reducing overweight pets, 72–73
Reflexes, 46
Reproductive system, 50–52 (*see
    also* Mating cycle)
  ailments of, 212–14
  as cause of sterility, 161–63
  drugs, effect of, 107–8
Residue in animal food, 67–68
Resorption of fetuses, 107, 162–63
Respiratory system, 36
  diseases of, 231–32
Restraint of injured cats, 126–27
  surgical, 139
Retina of eye, 47–48
Rib cartilages, 32
Ribs, 32–33
Rickets, 95
  evidenced by joint swellings, 33
Rickettsiae, 76
Ringworm, 236–37, 243–44
Rodent-host tapeworm, 90
Roof of mouth, hard and soft pal-
  ates, 39
Rotenone, 111–12

Roundworms, 84–87, 222–23
Russian Blue cats, 24

Salicylic acid, 115
Saliva, in digestion, 39, 55
Salivary amylase, 55
Salivary glands, 42
Salmonella organisms, 75
Salt, as emetic, 121
    importance in diet, 95
Sand fleas, 84
Sanitation, 177–78 (see also Hygiene)
Sarcomas, 93–94
Sarcoptic mange, 83, 237, 243
Scabies, 83
Scalds, healing of, 31
    treatment of, 116–17
Scenting ability, 49
Sclera of eye, 47
Scratching at injuries, preventing, 143–44
Season of mating, see Mating cycle
Sebaceous glands, animal odor from, 31
Sebum, 31
Secretory gland depressants, 106
Sedatives, 98–100
    antidotes for, 138
Selective breeding, 247, 259–60
Self-injury after operation, prevention of, 143–44
Semicircular canal of ear, 49
Senses, 45–46
Sensory perception, 45–49
Septum of nose, 49
Serum, 123
    pockets, liberating fluid from, 145
Sex, determination of, 250–51
    distinguishing, 168–69
Sex cycle, see Mating cycle
Sex organs (see also Mating cycle)
    structure and functions, 50–52
Shampoos, dry, 174
Shedding, 172–73
Shigella, 75

Shock, treatment for, 127
Short-haired cats, 22–24
Shoulder, dislocations, 151–52
Shows, health hazards of, 181–82
Siamese cats, 23, 254
Siamese-colored cats, 254
Silver nitrate, 117
Silver preparations for skin, 118–19
Silver Tabby cats, 23, 254
Simple fractures, 148
Sixide, 112
Skeletal muscles, 34
Skeletal structure, 31–34
Skin, appendages of, 30
    care of, 170–71
    cuts, suturing, 146
    drugs applied to, 113–19
    excretion of waste by, 37
    foreign bodies in, 133
    healing, method of, 31
    nature of, 30–31
Skin diseases, 236–40 (see also Parasites, external)
    effect of food on, 56–57
    remedies, 113–16
Skunk odor, removing, 133–34
Small intestine, 40
    digestion in, 55
Smell, sense of, 49
Smoke cats, 23, 254
Smooth muscles, 34
    movement of food by, 39–40
Snake bites, treatment of, 131
Sodium, functions and sources, 59
Sodium bromide, 102
Sodium pentobarbital, see Pentobarbital
Soft palate, 39
Spaying, 147, 166–67
    advisability of, 214
    results of early, 44
Spergon, 116
Sperm, 45
    fertilization of ovum by, 50
Spider bites, treatment of, 131
Spinal cord, 45–46
Spirochetes, 76

Spleen, as ductless gland, 42
    functions of, 35–36
    rupture of, 36
Splints, in first aid, 135
Squill as diuretic, 105
Staphylococci, 75
Starch, animal (glycogen), 41
    digestion of, 39, 40, 55, 63–64
Starvation, of obese pets, 72–73
Stearic acid, 65
Sterility, 161–63
    and testosterone, 45
Sternum (breastbone), 32
Sticktight flea, 79–80
Stilbestrol, 107
Stimulants, 103–4
    heart, 105–6
Stomach, 40
    digestion in, 55
    foreign bodies in, 132, 219–20
    hair balls in, 217–19
    ulcers, 220
Stomach-tube method of dosing, 154–55
Stomatitis, 215–16
Stools, 42
    and fiber consumption, 68
Streptococci, 75
Strychnine, 103–4
    antidotes for, 138
Subcutaneous connective tissue, 30
Sugar, cane, 64
    as diuretic, 104–5
    milk, 64
    regulation by liver, 41
    in urine, 42
Sulfa drugs, 119–20
    for burns, 117
    and immunity, 78
Sulphur, in amino acids, 60–61
    functions and sources, 60
    for skin diseases, 114
Summer boarding, health hazards of, 181–85
Suprarenal glands, 43
Surgery, home, 139–52

administering anesthesia, 139–40
castration, 147
cleaning wound before, 140–41
fractures and dislocations, setting, 148–52
growth removal, 146
hemorrhage stopping, 142
incising to liberate fluids, 144–46
preparing pet for, 139
self-injury, preventing, 143–44
suturing, 141–42, 146
tapping fluids and gas, 144
teeth extraction, 147
tissue joining, 141
Sutures, kind, 142
    materials for, 141
    performing, 146
Sweat glands, 31
    excretion of impurities by, 37
Syntonin, properties and sources, 62

Tabby cats, 23
    types of, 251
Tables, I—Minerals: Their Functions and Sources, 58–60
    II—Some Common Proteins and Sources, 61–63
    III—Vitamins: Their Properties, Functions, and Sources, 69–70
    IV—Household Antidotes for Common Poisons, 138
    V—Composition of Milk in cows and cats, 165
    VI—Feeding of Orphans, 166
    VII—Life Expectancy by Breeds, 186
    VIII—Milk of Cattas and Other Species, Composition, 201
Tail, fracture of, 150
Taillessness, inheritance of, 257
Tannic acid, 115–16, 117
Tapeworms, 88–91, 224–25
Tapping fluids or gas, 144
Tar, in medications, 114
    removal from coat of, 174

Tartar on teeth, 38
  removal of, 216
Taste buds in tongue, 39
Tea as stimulant, 103
Teeth, 38–39, 55
  care of, 175, 216
  extractions, 147
  tartar, removing, 216
Telegony, 246
Temperature, external, adaptability
    to, 178–79
  effect on testicles, 52
Testicles, 45, 51–52
  undescended, 108, 162, 214
Testosterone, 45, 108
Tetanus, 210
Tetany from removal of parathy-
    roids, 43
Tetrachlorethylene, 109–11
Thallium, antidote for, 138
Theelin (trade name for follicular
    hormone), 44
Theobromine, 103
  antidote for, 138
Thermometer, using, 158
Third eyelid, see Nictitating mem-
    brane
Threonine, 60
Throat, 39
Thrombin in blood, 35
Thyroid gland, 43
Thyroxin, 43
Ticks, 81–82, 227
Tissue joining in home surgery, 141
Toes, extra, 258
  fractures of, 150
Tongue, cysts under, 144
  as organ of taste, 39
Topical anesthetics, 100
Tortoiseshell cats, 23, 251
Tourniquets, applying, 157
Trachea, see Windpipe
Training pets, 46
Tryptophane, 60
Tuberculosis, 211, 242
Tubes, bronchial and trachea (wind-
    pipe), 36

Tubules in kidneys, 37
Tumors, 92–94 (see also Growths)
Turbinate bones of nose, 49
Turpentine in medications, 114

Ulcers, 220
Urea, as diuretic, 104
  elimination by kidneys, 36–37
  manufacture by liver, 41
Urea-and-quinine as anesthetic, 101
Uremia, 213
Urinary incontinence, 213
Urinary system, ailments, 212–14
Urine, composition of, 37
  in diabetes, 42
  diuretics for flow of, 104–5
Uterus, ailments of, 213–14
  infection of, 164
  structure and function of, 50–51

Vaccines, 123–24
Vagina, 50
Valine, 60
Valves, of heart, 35
Vas deferens, 51–52
Vegetable proteins, sources and
    properties, 63
Veins, 34–35
Venules, 34
Vestibule of nose, 49
Veterinarian, choosing, 25–28
Veterinary hospitals, health hazards
    of, 181–85
Villi, hairlike projections of intes-
    tines, 40–41
Viricides, 117
Virus diseases, 76–77, 203–8
Virus vaccines, 124
Vitamins, 57, 68–70
  deficiency in, 95
Vulva, 50 (see also Mating cycle)

Water, content, in body organs, 57
  as diet essential, 57–58
  as diuretic, 104
Whipworms, 87, 224

White cats, 254–55
White corpuscles, 35
White-spotted cats, 254–55
Windpipe, 39
Wool fat, 113
Worms (*see also* Deworming; Skin
    diseases)
  convulsions from, 228
  intestinal, 84–91, 222–25
  in kittens, 201

Wounds, cleaning for operation,
    140–41
  drugs for, 117–19
Wrist dislocation, 152

Yale virus, 207–8
Yellow cats, 251
Yellowing tissue, *see* Jaundice

Zein, 61